PHYSICS
Principles and Problems

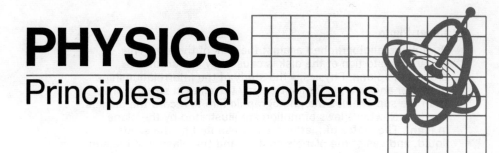

JAMES T. MURPHY

ROBERT C. SMOOT, Consultant

CHARLES E. MERRILL PUBLISHING CO.
A Division of Bell & Howell Company   Columbus, Ohio

A Merrill Science Text

Physics: Principles and Problems
Physics: Principles and Problems, Teacher's Guide and Solutions
    Manual
Laboratory Physics
Laboratory Physics, Teacher's Annotated Edition
Evaluation Program (Spirit Duplicating Masters)
    for Physics: Principles and Problems
Graphic Physics Chart

Cover Photo

A jet plane photographed against the disk of the sun. The
apparent distortion of the disk is caused by air turbulence
around the plane. Physics is the study of the interrelationships
of matter and energy. Radiant energy traveling in straight lines
from the sun enables the photographic film to record the plane's
shadow. Newton's laws of motion are illustrated by the plane
in flight. The states of matter are represented by the solid,
liquid, and gas of the plane's contrail and the plasma of the sun.

Knowledge of physics principles will help citizens evaluate and
make decisions concerning problems which affect their environment.
*Photo courtesy of Walter A. Feibelman, originally published in
Physics Today.*

Chapter Opening Photo Descriptions and Credits

1   Slide rule   *Ashland Oil Co.*
2   Analytical balance   *United Nations*
3   Car at raceway   *American Motors Corp.*
4   Plotting of a graph   *Ashland Oil Co.*
5   Sailboat   *Ashland Oil Co.*
6   Pool table   *Bruce Charlton*
7   Apollo 10 liftoff   *NASA*
8   Pole-vaulter   *Pflaum Photo by Paul Tucker*
9   Sky jumper   *Official U.S. Navy Photo*
10   Crane loading logs   *Mead Paper Co.*
11   Waterfall in Oregon   *USDA Photo*
12   Winter scene in New Hampshire   *American Airlines*
13   Pouring molten metal at Cleveland Foundry   *Ashland Oil Co.*
14   Splash of a milk drop   *H. E. Edgerton of M.I.T.*
15   Cleaving a crystal   *Optovac, Inc.*
16   Launching a balloon   *Official U.S. Air Force Photo*

17   Bug making waves in water   *Vance A. Tucker*
18   Solar eclipse   *NASA*
19   Glass stirring rod illustrating refraction   *Ashland Oil Co.*
20   Optical engineer cleaning lens   *Wild Heerbrugg Limited*
21   X-ray diffraction pattern of a crystal   *Courtesy Sargent-Welch
        Scientific Co.*
22   Whirlpool Galaxy   *Lick Observatory*
23   Van de Graff generator   *Courtesy of M.I.T.*
24   Overhead wires and poles   *USDA Photo*
25   Circuit board in a computer   *Control Data Corp.*
26   Iron filings in a magnetic field   *Bell Telephone Laboratories*
27   Electromagnet lifting scrap iron
28   Radiotelescope antenna   *British Information Services*
29   Arthur H. Compton   *Brown Brothers*
30   Field ion emission pattern   *Courtesy Dr. Erwin Muller,
        Pennsylvania State University*
31   Bubble chamber photo   *Brookhaven National Laboratory*

ISBN 0–675–07461–4

Copyright 1972 by
CHARLES E. MERRILL PUBLISHING CO.
A Division of Bell & Howell Company
Columbus, Ohio 43216

PREFACE

Physics: Principles and Problems is a clear, straightforward exposition of the basic concepts of physics. The central theme, the interrelationship between matter and energy, is applicable to all sciences. To present a unified, logical sequence each concept of physics is developed rather than merely inserted in the thirty-one chapters. Detail has been omitted where it would obscure or confuse the main idea and memorization has been minimized.

Mechanics, needed to interpret most phenomena, is presented first. Once this foundation is laid, each form of energy — heat, light, electricity, nuclear — and the basic structure of matter are intertwined. As these interrelationships are developed, each topic demonstrates the conservation laws which current trends emphasize.

Before the student can solve specific problems, he must understand the principles. With this in mind, the authors have written this text to bridge the gap between understanding a general statement, theory, or law and the application of principles to solution of numerical problems. *Physics: Principles and Problems* presents each principle clearly before introducing related problems. Reasoning based on experience and experiment leads the student to an awareness of these principles and how they interrelate with physical phenomena.

Often, it is necessary to apply more than one principle to solve a problem. *Physics: Principles and Problems* helps the student understand the application of several principles to arrive at a solution. When he understands both the problem and the principles to be applied, he can solve any problem. Complex problems are developed as combinations of fundamental concepts and each problem emphasizes the thinking involved in setting up a logical solution.

Because mathematics is the language of science, a basic background in this subject is necessary to understand physics. Hence, a brief review of algebra and trigonometry is provided in Chapter 1. Enough mathematics content is presented so that the text is self-sustaining. There is no need to employ outside resources for basic problem-solving skills.

Physics and its practical applications are basic and vital to all students whatever their educational goals. Conscious of both the science-oriented student and the nonscience-oriented student, the authors of *Physics: Principles and Problems* have designed this text with unlimited appeal to a wide spectrum of students. Within this wide range, the text can be used equally well for both classroom and individual study.

Special thanks are due to Mr. John W. Slauter, Physics Instructor, Lakeland Community College, Mentor, Ohio, and to Mr. Gordon A. Yount, Instructor, Department of Physics and Mathematics, Catawba Valley Technical Institute, Hickory, North Carolina, who have read the manuscript and have offered invaluable assistance with their helpful comments and suggestions.

CONTENTS

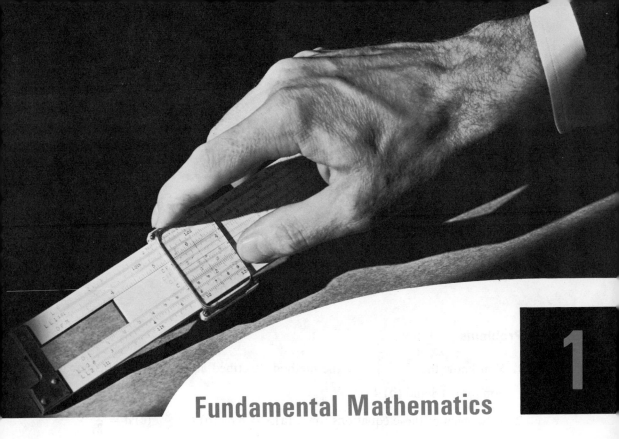

Fundamental Mathematics

Physics is often defined as the study of matter and energy. Mathematics is fundamental in expressing relationships in physics. It enables one not only to express general relationships among units but also to solve specific numerical problems. The slide rule pictured above is a time-saving device used to facilitate computations. With it you can multiply, divide, find squares and square roots of numbers. Why is the slide rule not used for addition and subtraction?

1:1   Solving Equations Algebraically

Frequently, it is necessary to solve an equation for an unknown. For example, in the equation $F = ma$ what is the value of a? To determine this, solve the equation for a. Remember that *both sides of any equation may be multiplied or divided by the same factor*. You can isolate a by dividing both sides of the equation by m.

$$F = ma$$

$$\frac{F}{m} = a$$

It is customary to place the unknown on the left side of an equation. So this should be rewritten as:

$$a = \frac{F}{m}$$

If an equation contains several factors, the same process is followed until the unknown is isolated.

Sample Problem 1

Solve this equation for x: $\dfrac{ay}{x} = \dfrac{cb}{s}$

Solution:

(Multiply both sides by x) $ay = \dfrac{cbx}{s}$

(Multiply both sides by s) $ays = cbx$

(Divide both sides by $c\,b$) $\dfrac{ays}{cb} = x$

$$x = \dfrac{ays}{cb}$$

Problems

1. You know that $2 = \dfrac{8}{4}$. Use the method described above to solve this equation for (a) 8 and (b) 4

2. Solve each of these equations for v. (a) $s = v\,t$ (b) $t = \dfrac{s}{v}$ (c) $a = \dfrac{v^2}{2s}$

3. Solve the equation $s = \dfrac{at^2}{2}$ for (a) t^2 (b) a (c) 2

4. Solve each of these equations for x. (a) $\dfrac{x}{a} = \dfrac{b}{c}$ (b) $\dfrac{a}{x} = \dfrac{f}{b}$ (c) $g = \dfrac{2y}{x}$

5. Solve each of these equations for E. (a) $f = \dfrac{E}{s}$ (b) $m = \dfrac{2E}{v^2}$ (c) $m = \dfrac{E}{c^2}$

6. Solve the equation $P = h\,D$ for (a) h and (b) D
7. Solve the equation $v^2 = 2\,a\,s$ for (a) s (b) a (c) v

1:2 Scientific Notation

The mass of the earth is about 6 000 000 000 000 000 000 000 000 kg. The mass of an electron is 0.000 000 000 000 000 000 000 000 000 000 911 kg. Large and small numbers constantly confront scientists. Such numbers, when written as above, occupy considerable space. They are also difficult to manipulate mathematically. To use such numbers more easily, they can be written in an abbreviated form with decimal places expressed in powers of ten. The power of ten is called the exponent. This method of expressing numerals is called scientific notation.

Suppose you want to express the number 4257 in scientific notation. Place the decimal point so that one digit is to the left of the decimal point and multiply this number by ten raised to some power: $4.257 \times 10^?$. To find the correct exponent for the ten, count the number of places you moved the decimal point to the left from its original position (in this case, three places). Use this number as the exponent for the ten: 4.257×10^3. The number is now expressed in scientific notation. If the decimal point is moved to the left, the exponent is positive. If the decimal point is moved to the right, the exponent is negative. If the exponent is positive, the number is greater than ten. If the exponent is negative, the number is less than one. If the exponent is zero, the number is equal to the number written before the power of ten. For example,

$$1\ 000\ 000 = 1 \times 10^6$$
$$95\ 000\ 000 = 9.5 \times 10^7$$
$$96\ 000 = 9.6 \times 10^4$$

- -

$$0.00063 = 6.3 \times 10^{-4}$$
$$0.007 = 7 \times 10^{-3}$$
$$0.000\ 000\ 95 = 9.5 \times 10^{-7}$$

- -

$$5.6 = 5.6 \times 10^0$$

Problems

Express the following numbers in scientific notation.
8. (a) 5800   (b) 450 000   (c) 60 000   (d) 86 000 000 000
9. (a) 0.00058   (b) 0.000 000 45   (c) 0.0036   (d) 0.004
10. (a) 300 000 000   (b) 186 000 (c) 93 000 000
    (d) 5 000 000 000 000 000 000 000 000
11. (a) 0.0073   (b) 0.00087   (c) 0.0032
    (d) 0.000 000 000 000 000 000 166

1:3   Addition and Subtraction

When numbers are expressed in scientific notation, they can be added or subtracted only if the exponents of ten are equal. If the powers of ten are not equal, they must be made equal before the numbers may be added or subtracted. When this is done the numbers are simply added or subtracted and the same power of ten is retained.

$$4 \times 10^8 + 3 \times 10^8 = 7 \times 10^8$$
$$4 \times 10^{-8} + 3 \times 10^{-8} = 7 \times 10^{-8}$$
$$8 \times 10^6 - 4 \times 10^6 = 4 \times 10^6$$
$$8 \times 10^{-6} - 4 \times 10^{-6} = 4 \times 10^{-6}$$
$$4.0 \times 10^6 + 3 \times 10^5 = 4.0 \times 10^6 + 0.3 \times 10^6 = 4.3 \times 10^6$$
$$4.0 \times 10^6 - 3 \times 10^5 = 4.0 \times 10^6 - 0.3 \times 10^6 = 3.7 \times 10^6$$
$$4.0 \times 10^{-6} - 3 \times 10^{-7} = 4.0 \times 10^{-6} - 0.3 \times 10^{-6} = 3.7 \times 10^{-6}$$

Problems

Find the value of each of the following:

12. (a) $5 \times 10^7 + 3 \times 10^7$ (b) $6 \times 10^8 + 2 \times 10^8$ (c) $4.2 \times 10^4 +$ 3.6×10^4 (d) $1.8 \times 10^9 + 2.5 \times 10^9$

13. (a) $5 \times 10^{-7} + 3 \times 10^{-7}$ (b) $4 \times 10^{-3} + 3 \times 10^{-3}$ (c) $1.66 \times 10^{-19} +$ 2.30×10^{-19} (d) $7.2 \times 10^{-12} + 2.6 \times 10^{-12}$

14. (a) $6 \times 10^8 - 4 \times 10^8$ (b) $3.8 \times 10^{12} - 1.9 \times 10^{12}$ (c) $5.8 \times 10^9 -$ 2.8×10^9

15. (a) $6 \times 10^{-8} - 4 \times 10^{-8}$ (b) $3.8 \times 10^{-12} - 1.9 \times 10^{-12}$ (c) $5.8 \times 10^{-9} - 2.8 \times 10^{-9}$

16. (a) $6.0 \times 10^8 + 4 \times 10^7$ (b) $7.0 \times 10^4 + 2 \times 10^3$ (c) $4 \times 10^4 +$ 3.0×10^5

17. (a) $5.0 \times 10^{-7} + 4 \times 10^{-8}$ (b) $6.0 \times 10^{-3} + 2 \times 10^{-4}$ (c) $3.0 \times 10^{-14} +$ 2×10^{-15}

18. (a) $5.0 \times 10^{-7} - 4 \times 10^{-8}$ (b) $6.0 \times 10^{-3} - 2 \times 10^{-4}$ (c) $3.0 \times 10^{-14} - 2 \times 10^{-15}$

1:4   Multiplication and Division in Scientific Notation

To multiply two numbers which are in scientific notation:
1. Multiply the numbers preceding the powers of ten.
2. Add the exponents of ten to obtain the correct power of ten for the product.

Sample Problem 2

$$(3 \times 10^6)(2 \times 10^3) = 6 \times 10^9$$
$$(2 \times 10^{-5})(4 \times 10^9) = 8 \times 10^4$$
$$(4 \times 10^3)(5 \times 10^{11}) = 20 \times 10^{14} = 2 \times 10^{15}$$

To divide numbers expressed in scientific notation:
1. Divide the numbers preceding the powers of ten as usual.
2. Subtract the exponent of the power of ten in the denominator from the exponent of the power of ten in the numerator. The result is the power of ten for the answer.

Sample Problem 3

$$\frac{8 \times 10^6}{2 \times 10^3} = 4 \times 10^{6-3} = 4 \times 10^3$$

$$\frac{8 \times 10^6}{2 \times 10^{-2}} = 4 \times 10^{6-(-2)} = 4 \times 10^8$$

Problems

Find the value of each of the following:

19. (a) $(2 \times 10^4)(4 \times 10^8)$ (b) $(3 \times 10^4)(2 \times 10^6)$ (c) $(6 \times 10^{-4})(5 \times 10^8)$

 (d) $(6 \times 10^{-4})(5 \times 10^{-8})$ (e) $(2.5 \times 10^{-7})(2.5 \times 10^{16})$

20. (a) $\dfrac{6 \times 10^8}{2 \times 10^4}$ (b) $\dfrac{6 \times 10^8}{2 \times 10^{-4}}$ (c) $\dfrac{6 \times 10^{-8}}{2 \times 10^4}$ (d) $\dfrac{6 \times 10^{-8}}{2 \times 10^{-4}}$

21. (a) $\dfrac{(3 \times 10^4)(4 \times 10^4)}{6 \times 10^4}$ (b) $\dfrac{(3 \times 10^4)(4 \times 10^4)}{6 \times 10^{-4}}$

 (c) $\dfrac{(2.5 \times 10^6)(6 \times 10^4)}{5 \times 10^2}$ (d) $\dfrac{(6 \times 10^{12})(6 \times 10^{-6})}{1.2 \times 10^6}$

1:5   Trigonometry of Right Triangles

 A right triangle is a triangle which contains a 90° angle as one of the included angles. Trigonometry is useful because the ratios of corresponding sides of similar triangles are equal. Given the right triangle in Figure 1-1, three functions of angle A are called sine (sin), cosine (cos), and tangent (tan).

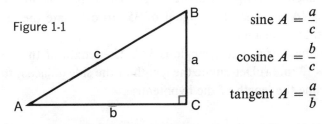

Figure 1-1

$$\text{sine } A = \frac{a}{c}$$

$$\text{cosine } A = \frac{b}{c}$$

$$\text{tangent } A = \frac{a}{b}$$

These functions are often expressed as,

$$\text{sine } A = \frac{\text{opposite side}}{\text{hypotenuse}}$$

$$\text{cosine } A = \frac{\text{adjacent side}}{\text{hypotenuse}}$$

$$\text{tangent } A = \frac{\text{opposite side}}{\text{adjacent side}}$$

Sample Problem 4

 If angle A in Figure 1-1 is 30° and the hypotenuse is 8 inches, what is the length of side a and of side b?

Solution: (a) $\sin A = \dfrac{a}{c}$ (b) $\cos A = \dfrac{b}{c}$

$a = c \sin A$ $b = c \cos A$

$a = 8 \text{ in.} \times 0.50$ $b = 8 \text{ in.} \times 0.866$

$a = 4 \text{ in.}$ $b = 7 \text{ in.}$

Problems

22. Use Table A- 2 of the Appendix, to find the number of degrees in the angles associated with each trigonometric function. The Greek letter theta, θ, is used to designate the angle. (a) $\sin \theta = 0.358$ (b) $\sin \theta = 0.259$ (c) $\sin \theta = 0.682$ (d) $\cos \theta = 0.866$ (e) $\cos \theta = 0.500$ (f) $\cos \theta = 0.174$

23. Find the number of degrees associated with each trigonometric function. (a) $\sin \theta = 0.500$ (b) $\sin \theta = 0.985$ (c) $\cos \theta = 0.707$ (d) $\sin \theta = 0.707$ (e) $\tan \theta = 1.00$ (f) $\tan \theta = 0.364$ (g) $\tan \theta = 2.050$

24. One acute angle of a right triangle is 20°. The length of the hypotenuse is 6 in. (a) Construct the triangle graphically and measure the lengths of the other two sides. (b) Use trigonometry to calculate the lengths of the two sides.

25. One acute angle of a right triangle is 40°. The length of the hypotenuse is 12 cm. (a) Construct the triangle and measure the length of the other two sides. (b) Use trigonometry to calculate the lengths of the other two sides.

26. One angle of a right triangle is 60°. The length of the hypotenuse is 15 cm. Calculate the lengths of the other two sides.

27. One acute angle of a right triangle is 35°. The length of the side opposite the angle is 14 cm. Use the tangent of 35° to calculate the length of the side adjacent to the angle.

28. One acute angle of a right triangle is 37°. The length of the side opposite the angle is 12 in. (a) Determine the length of the side adjacent to the angle. (b) Determine the length of the hypotenuse.

1:6   The Law of Cosines

To use the trigonometry of the right triangle, two of the three sides of a triangle must be perpendicular. The law of cosines applies to *all* triangles. Consider

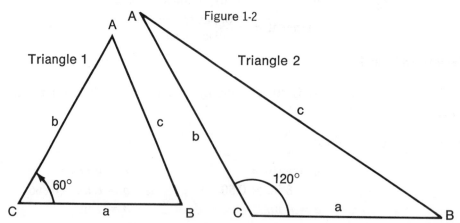

Figure 1-2

the two triangles shown in Figure 1-2. They are not right triangles. When angle C is known, the lengths of the sides obey the following relationship:

$$c^2 = a^2 + b^2 - 2ab \cos C$$

When the angle C is larger than 90°, its cosine is negative and is numerically equal to the cosine of its supplement. In Figure 1-2, triangle 2 , angle C is 120°. Therefore, its cosine is the negative of the cosine of (180° − 120°) or 60°. The cosine of 60° is 0.500 so the cosine of 120° is −0.500.

Problems

29. In triangle 1, Figure 1-2 let the length of side a be 7 cm, the length of side b be 8 cm, and the angle C be 60°. (a) Construct this triangle graphically and measure side c. Record the value. (b) Use the law of cosines to calculate the length of side c. Compare the measured and calculated values.
30. In triangle 2 of Figure 1-2, let the length of side a be 8 cm, the length of side b be 10 cm, and angle C be 120°. (a) Construct this triangle graphically and measure the length of side c. (b) Use the law of cosines to calculate the length of side c. Compare this solution with your graphical solution.

1:7   The Law of Sines

Just as the law of cosines applies to all triangles, the law of sines applies to all triangles. The relationship is:

$$\frac{a}{\sin A} = \frac{b}{\sin B} = \frac{c}{\sin C}$$

Problems

31. In triangle 1 of Figure 1-2 the length of side a is 7 cm, the length of side b is 8 cm. If angle A is 53° calculate the value of angle B.
32. In triangle 2 of Figure 1-2 the length of side b is 10 cm and the length of side a is 8 cm. Angle A is 26°. Calculate the value of angle B. (For the sine of 120°, use the sine of its supplement 60°.)
33. The three included angles of a triangle are angle $A = 55°$, angle $B = 55°$ and angle $C = 70°$. If the length of side c is 20 cm, what is the length of side a? What is the length of side b?

1:8   The Slide Rule

In reality, a slide rule is a logarithmic analog computer. It is an invaluable aid for computation. The accuracy of a slide rule is limited to three digits, but this is sufficient for the majority of calculations in physics. Obtain a slide rule and practice until you become confident of your ability to use it. No amount of explanation can equal a few hours of actual practice with this instrument.

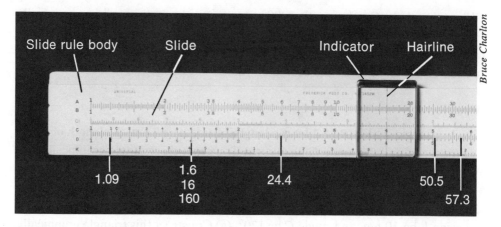

Figure 1-3.   Reading the slide rule. Determine the value of each division on the slide rule by counting the number of divisions in each of the major divisions.

As shown in Figure 1-3, a slide rule contains four principal scales identified as *A*, *B*, *C*, and *D*. Concentrate first on the *C* and *D* scales. Notice that they are identical. Also notice that there is a number "1" at each end of the *C* scale. These "1's" are called the *indexes* (indices).

1:9   Reading the Scales

Figure 1-3 also points out a few sample readings. Notice that the numbers are given the values that you want to give them. The value 1.09 shown in the diagram could as easily be 10.9 or 109. Likewise, the 6.65 could be 0.665 or 66.5 or 665. The value depends upon the original number in a problem.

Some numbers on the scale require interpolation; that is, their exact position must be estimated. The 57.3 shown in Figure 1-3 is such a number. Notice that the 57.0 and 57.5 are marked on the scale. To find 57.3 it is necessary to estimate the position of the hairline between these two points.

Problems

34. Locate these readings on scale *D* of a slide rule. (a) 12   (b) 17   (c) 2.0 (d) 24   (e) 57   (f) 6.55   (g) 84.5   (h) 20.8   (i) 306   (j) 42.3   (k) 27.3 (1) 98.5   (m) 57.3   (n) 57.8   (o) 96.6

1:10   Multiplication on a Slide Rule

To multiply two factors on a slide rule perform the following steps:

1. Locate one of the factors on the D scale. Set the hairline over the number.
2. Move the left-hand index (the "1") of the C scale to the right until it is exactly under the hairline.
3. Move the hairline along the C scale until it is exactly over the second number of the C scale.
4. Read the product of the two factors on the D scale under the hairline.

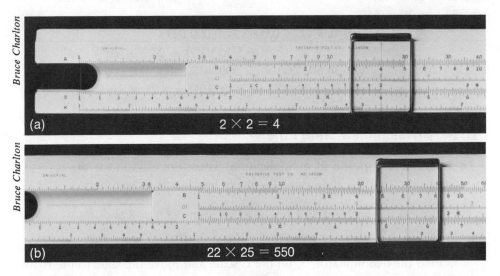

Figure 1-4. Multiplying two factors on the slide rule. Practice multiplication by imitating the settings shown.

Next try to multiply 2×6 on your rule. You will find that when the left index is placed on the 2 on the D scale, the 6 is beyond the end of the D scale. Therefore, you cannot place the hairline over it. Whenever this happens use the right-hand index (1) instead of the left-hand index and proceed as before.

Figure 1-5.   Multiplying 2×6 on a slide rule.

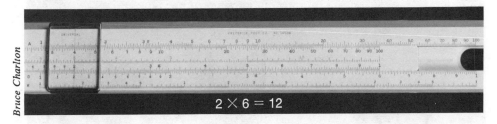

Problems

35. *Perform these multiplication operations on a slide rule. The correct answers are given to each problem.*

(a) $2 \times 4 = 8$

(b) $2 \times 12 = 24$

(c) $2 \times 32 = 64$

(d) $8 \times 5 = 40$

(e) $5 \times 5.4 = 27$

(f) $18 \times 16 = 288$

(g) $25 \times 25 = 625$

(h) $32.5 \times 20 = 650$

(i) $8.2 \times 4 = 32.8$

(j) $75 \times 32 = 2400$

(k) $6.45 \times 5.9 = 38$

(l) $55.5 \times 73.5 = 4080$

(m) $3.33 \times 8.2 = 27.3$

(n) $126 \times 52 = 6550$

(o) $96.5 \times 85 = 8200$

(p) $0.0042 \times 0.0065 = 0.000\ 0273$

$$(4.2 \times 10^{-3})(6.5 \times 10^{-3}) = 27.3 \times 10^{-6}$$

(q) $36\ 500\ 000 \times 22\ 500 = 821\ 000\ 000\ 000$

$$(3.65 \times 10^{7})(2.25 \times 10^{4}) = 8.21 \times 10^{11}$$

1:11 Division on a Slide Rule

Division is the opposite of multiplication. Therefore, division is the reverse of multiplication on the slide rule. To divide one factor by another:

1. Express the problem as a fraction, for example $6 \div 3$ is $\frac{6}{3}$.

2. Locate the hairline directly over the numerator, 6, on the *D* scale.

3. Find the denominator, 3, on the *C* scale and move the slide to the right or left until the 3 is directly under the hairline.

4. Read the answer under the 1 index of the *C* scale.

Figure 1-6. Dividing two factors on a slide rule.

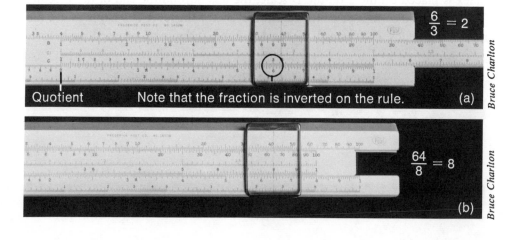

Quotient   Note that the fraction is inverted on the rule.   (a)

$\frac{6}{3} = 2$

$\frac{64}{8} = 8$

(b)

Bruce Charlton

Bruce Charlton

Think of the four steps in this way: Arrange the problem as a fraction in your mind. Place the fraction on the *C* and *D* scales upside-down. Then read the answer under the index.

Problems

36. *Use a slide rule to find these quotients. Correct answers are provided.*

(a) $8 \div 4 = 2$

(b) $16 \div 4 = 4$

(c) $27 \div 9 = 3$

(d) $28.4 \div 4 = 7.1$

(e) $308 \div 4.6 = 67$

(f) $58 \div 4.4 = 13.2$

(g) $109 \div 12 = 9.1$

(h) $164 \div 8.2 = 20$

(i) $225 \div 9 = 25$

(j) $25 \div 4 = 6.25$

(k) $22 \div 65 = 0.338$

(l) $680 \div 350 = 1.94$

(m) $35 \div 6.2 = 5.65$

(n) $0.00063 \div 0.025 = 0.0252$

$$\frac{6.3 \times 10^{-4}}{2.5 \times 10^{-2}} = 2.52 \times 10^{-2}$$

1:12 Finding the Square Root of a Number

To find the square root of a number on a slide rule, use the *A* and *D* scales. Place the hairline over the number on the *A* scale. The square root of the number is located under the hairline on the *D* scale.

Note that the *A* scale consists of two identical scales, side-by-side. To find the square roots of numbers containing an odd number of digits ahead of the decimal point, use the left-hand scale. To find the square roots of numbers containing an even number of digits ahead of the decimal point, use the right-hand scale. For example, this is how to find the square root of 4 on the rule. The number 4 contains one digit. Thus it has an odd number of digits. Find the 4 on the left-hand *A* scale. Its square root, 2, will appear under the hairline on the *D* scale. The number 40 contains an even number of digits. The square root of 40 is found by placing the hairline over the number on the right-hand *A* scale. The square root of 40 is 6.32.

To find the square root of a very large or a very small number, that number must first be expressed in scientific notation. The square root of the number preceding the power of ten then is found. The power of ten assigned to the square root is half of the power of ten of the original number. This means that when the number is written in scientific notation, it must be so written with an even power of ten. For instance, suppose you must find the square root of

0.000064. This number would usually be written in scientific notation as 6.4×10^{-5}. Instead the number is written as 64×10^{-6}. The square root of 64 found on the slide rule is 8. The power of ten assigned to it is 10^{-3}. Hence the answer is 8×10^{-3}.

Problems

37. *Find the square roots of each of these numbers. Correct answers are provided.*

(a) 2 *ans* 1.41
(b) 25 *ans* 5
(c) 640 *ans* 25.3
(d) 4.3 *ans* 2.07
(e) 360 *ans* 19

(f) 3600 *ans* 60
(g) 67 *ans* 8.2
(h) 840 *ans* 29
(i) 8400 *ans* 91.5
(j) 0.00000366 *ans* 0.00192 or 1.92×10^{-3}

PROBLEMS

1. Solve each of these equations for x. (a) $W = fx$ (b) $s = kx$ (c) $F = mx$ (d) $q = \dfrac{f}{x}$ (e) $m = \dfrac{x}{y}$

2. Solve these equations for k. (a) $d = \dfrac{k}{m}$ (b) $W = kx$ (c) $F = \dfrac{kqq'}{r^2}$ (d) $s = \dfrac{ak^2}{2}$

3. Express these numbers in scientific notation. (a) 650 000 (b) 5 000 000 (c) 22 000 (d) 226 (e) 4500

4. Write these numbers in scientific notation. (a) 0.025 (b) 0.000 25 (c) 0.000 004 26 (d) 0.0006 (e) 0.000 000 000 000 19

5. Find the value of: (a) $6 \times 10^8 + 3 \times 10^8$ (b) $2.2 \times 10^4 + 3.6 \times 10^4$ (c) $4.3 \times 10^{16} + 5.2 \times 10^{16}$ (d) $5.0 \times 10^8 + 6.0 \times 10^7$ (e) $9.8 \times 10^5 + 2.0 \times 10^4$

6. Subtract: (a) $8.4 \times 10^{-8} - 3.2 \times 10^{-8}$ (b) $5.4 \times 10^7 - 3.4 \times 10^7$ (c) $6.0 \times 10^{-8} - 6.0 \times 10^{-9}$ (d) $2.2 \times 10^{12} - 8.0 \times 10^{11}$ (e) $7.0 \times 10^{-18} - 4.0 \times 10^{19}$

7. Multiply: (a) $(3 \times 10^4)(2 \times 10^4)$ (b) $(4 \times 10^6)(6 \times 10^4)$ (c) $(2.2 \times 10^{12})(3.6 \times 10^{20})$ (d) $(9.5 \times 10^{14})(6.0 \times 10^8)$ (e) $(2.5 \times 10^5)(2.5 \times 10^4)$

8. Divide: (a) $(6 \times 10^{14}) \div (3 \times 10^7)$ (b) $(9.9 \times 10^{12}) \div (4.5 \times 10^{-6})$ (c) $(2.6 \times 10^{-8}) \div (4.0 \times 10^{-4})$ (d) $(5.8 \times 10^3) \div (6.0 \times 10^{-2})$ (e) $(7.6 \times 10^{16}) \div (2.4 \times 10^8)$

9. Consult Table A-2 of the Appendix to find the number of degrees associated with these trigonometric functions. (a) $\sin \theta = 0.0848$ (b) $\sin \theta = 0.5150$ (c) $\sin \theta = 0.3090$ (d) $\cos \theta = 0.9816$ (e) $\cos \theta = 0.7771$ (f) $\cos \theta = 0.2588$ (g) $\tan \theta = 0.3640$ (h) $\tan \theta = 1.000$ (i) $\tan \theta = 3.0777$

10. One acute angle of a right triangle is 26° and the hypotenuse is 10 cm. Calculate the lengths of the other two sides.

11. One angle of a right triangle is 50°. The length of the side opposite the 50° angle is 8.5 cm. Calculate the length of the adjacent side and the hypotenuse.

12. The three included angles of a triangle are, angle $A = 39°$, angle $B = 31°$ and angle $C = 110°$. If the length of side c is 14.7 in., what is the length of side a and of side b?

13. Use a slide rule to perform these multiplication operations.
   (a) 6×7.5 (b) 18×12 (c) 72×12 (d) 220×48 (e) 60×26
   (f) 24×28 (g) 4.9×6.3 (h) 65×35 (i) 8.7×7.2 (j) 2.96×568

14. Use a slide rule to find these quotients. (a) $\dfrac{28}{7}$ (b) $\dfrac{16}{5}$ (c) $\dfrac{97}{12}$ (d) $\dfrac{220}{48}$
   (e) $\dfrac{25}{4}$ (f) $\dfrac{176}{5.2}$ (g) $\dfrac{18}{4.3}$ (h) $\dfrac{386}{122}$ (i) $\dfrac{8.43}{2.8}$ (j) $\dfrac{48.8}{14.2}$

15. Find the square root of each number. (a) 4.5   (b) 400   (c) 625   (d) 2680
   (e) 8.8

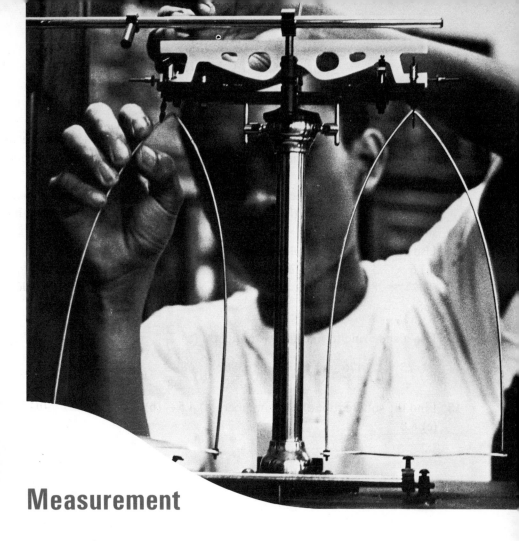

2

Measurement

Measuring devices which provide accurate and reproducible experimental results are essential to modern science. Until units of measurements were defined internationally, and until precision equipment was available, numerical observations were of little value. With the analytical balance pictured above a sample can be weighed accurately to the fourth decimal place. What instruments are used to measure very short distances and time intervals?

2:1   Fundamental and Derived Units

In mechanics, three fundamental units are used to measure quantities. These are the units of mass, length, and time. All other units are derived from these three fundamental units. They are called *derived units*. Speed, for example, is measured in miles per hour. The mile, a unit of length, is divided by the hour, a unit of time. Area is found by multiplying length by length. Volume is found by multiplying length by length by length. Similarly, density is mass per unit volume or mass divided by length times length times length. Other than the three fundamental units, all units are composites of the fundamental units.

In the English system of measurement, the fundamental unit for length is the foot, the unit for mass is the slug, and the unit for time is the second. In the metric system of measurement, the basic units for length, mass, and time are meter, kilogram, and second, respectively (MKS). The MKS system of measurement is the system most commonly used by physicists.

2:2 The MKS System

Internationally, physicists use the MKS system of measurement. The standard unit of length in the metric system is the *meter*. Originally it was supposed to be one ten-millionth (10^{-7}) of the distance from the north pole to the equator as measured along the meridian passing through Paris. Once this length was decided upon, it was marked off on a platinum-iridium bar by carefully making two scratches on the bar. The distance between these two scratches when the bar is at a temperature of $0°$ Celsius is the standard meter. Because metals expand and contract with temperature variations, the temperature qualification is necessary.

National Bureau of Standards

Figure 2-1. The United States Bureau of Standards maintains prototype metric mass, volume, and length standards.

Actually, the meter is not exactly one ten-millionth of the distance from the north pole to the equator. The first determination of this distance was slightly in error. What is important is that the meter is accepted as the standard of length the world over. Recently, the meter has been redefined to accommodate the more precise measurements being made today. It is now defined as 1 650 763.73 times the wavelength of orange light emitted by the gas krypton 86.

The advantage of the metric system over the English system is that it is a decimal system. Each fraction or multiple of metric units is a power of ten. Thus, a tenth of a meter is a decimeter, a hundredth of a meter is a centimeter, and a thousandth of a meter is a millimeter. If you look at a meterstick, you will see these divisions carefully marked off. The decimeter (tenth of a meter) is rarely used. It is common practice to express a length as 53 centimeters rather than as 5 decimeters and 3 centimeters. It is similar to saying 53 cents rather than 5 dimes and 3 cents.

The mass of an object is the quantity of matter it contains. The standard of mass is the kilogram. This is the mass of a platinum-iridium cylinder kept near Paris. One thousandth of this mass is called a *gram*.

In all systems of measurement, the standard unit of time is the second. The second was defined as 1/86 400 of the mean solar day. A mean solar day is the average length of the day over a period of one year.

From time to time, it will be necessary also to use the English system of measurement. Currently in the United States and other English-speaking countries, a strong effort is under way to introduce the metric system of measurement into general use. It is hoped that eventually there will be only one system of measurement — the metric system.

2:3   Errors in Measurement

Scientists are constantly measuring quantities and then comparing the data obtained through these measurements. Thus, they determine if any specific relationships become apparent. If relationships are found and are confirmed through a great deal of experimentation, these relationships become accepted scientific theories. Our understanding of the universe and our ability to cope with our surroundings increases through these theories.

Whenever you make measurements, remember that the accuracy of measurements is subject to error. The length of a ruler can change with temperature variations. An electric measuring device is affected by any magnetic fields near it. All instruments are, in one way or another, subject to external influence. Errors in measurement are to be expected.

In addition to the possibility of error due to external agents, accuracy of measurement depends on the person taking the reading. In an automobile, the passenger's reading of the gas gauge and the driver's reading of the same gauge can be quite different. From the passenger's position, the gauge may read empty. From the driver's more direct view, the gauge may read one-quarter full. The driver's reading is the more correct one. Meters must be read by looking at them straight on. Otherwise an error due to *parallax* is possible. Parallax is the apparent shift in the position of an object when it is viewed from different angles. An object does not shift its position when it is looked at from various

Figure 2-2. An example of parallax. (a) Voltage meter as seen from straight-on; (b) as seen from an angle. Notice the difference in readings

angles. Rather, it is the reference points behind the object that are different. The object looks as if it has moved. When sitting next to the driver in the automobile, you line up the gauge needle on the *E* (for empty). But if you moved to the driver's position, you would line the needle up on the one-quarter full mark.

2:4 Accuracy

All measuring devices are accurate only within specific limits. Scales used on any instrument are marked off into finer and finer divisions. The finest division used on the instrument limits the accuracy of that instrument. A meterstick found in laboratories is marked in millimeters as the finest division. This limits the stick as a measuring device. Other devices can measure certain lengths to a hundredth of a ten millionth of a millimeter, but again accuracy is limited.

2:5 Significant Digits

Because the accuracy of all measuring devices is limited, the number of digits that can be assumed for any measurement is also limited. When making a measurement, you read the instrument to its finest division and then estimate to within a part of that finest division. The figures that you write down for the measurement are called *significant digits*. Suppose you want to measure a length of a strip of metal with a metric ruler. You try to determine its length as accurately as possible.

As shown in Figure 2-3, you might say that the metal strip is 5.6 cm long. A closer examination reveals that the strip is somewhat longer. Looking closely at the rule, you estimate that the end of the metal strip is four-tenths of the way between 5.6 cm and 5.7 cm. Therefore, the length of the strip is 5.64 cm. The last digit is an estimate, but certainly it is better to estimate in this case. Either 5.6 cm or 5.7 cm as the length of the strip would be more in error than the 5.64 cm. Both the 5.6 cm and 5.7 cm are at least 0.03 cm and probably 0.04 cm in error. It is not likely that the 5.64 cm is more than 0.01 cm in error.

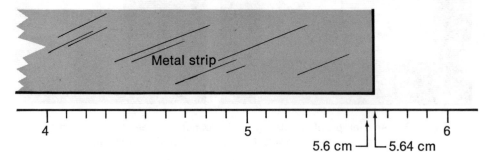

Figure 2-3. The accuracy of any measurement depends upon the instrument which is used and upon the observer. After a calculation, keep only those digits which truly imply the accuracy of the original measurement.

It is possible that the end of the metal strip could have been right on the 5.6 cm mark. In that case, you would write the measurement as 5.60 cm. The zero would indicate that, as well as you can tell, the metal is not 0.01 cm more or less than 5.6 cm. Therefore the zero is a significant digit for it has meaning. It is the doubtful or uncertain digit because you are still guessing. The last digit written down for any measurement is the uncertain digit. All nonzero digits in a measurement are significant.

Zeroes are often a problem. The zero mentioned in 5.60 cm is significant. However, a zero that only serves to locate the decimal point is not necessarily significant. Thus the value 0.0026 kg contains two significant digits. A measurement of 0.00206 kg contains three significant digits. The measurement 0.002060 kg contains four significant digits, the final zero indicating a probable value.

There is no way to tell how many of the zeroes in the number 186 000 are significant. The 6 may have been the estimated digit, and the three zeroes are needed only to place the decimal point. On the other hand, all three zeroes may be significant. To avoid this difficulty, it is customary to express such measurements in scientific notation including in the number that appears before the power of ten all the significant digits. Thus 1.86×10^5 has three significant digits, 1.860×10^5 has four.

Problems

1. State the number of significant digits in each of these measurements:
(a) 2804 m   (b) 2.84 m   (c) 0.0029 m   (d) 0.003068 m   (e) 4.6 $\times$ 10^5 m   (f) 4.06 $\times$ 10^5 m

2. Determine the number of significant digits in these measurements:
(a) 75 m   (b) 75.00 cm   (c) 0.00840 g   (d) 0.007060 kg   (e) 1.87 $\times$ 10^6 m   (f) 1.008 $\times$ 10^8 m   (g) 1.20 $\times$ 10^{-4} m

2:6   Operations With Significant Digits

Results of any mathematical operation with measured quantities cannot be more accurate than the least accurate of the quantities involved. Assume that you must add the lengths 6.48 m and 18.2 m. The length 18.2 m is accurate only to a tenth of a meter. Therefore, the sum of the two lengths only can be accurate to a tenth of a meter. To add the two lengths, round off 6.48 m to 6.5 m. Then add 6.5 m to 18.2 m giving the sum of 24.7 m. Subtraction operations, the reverse of addition operations, are handled in the same way. To add or subtract measured quantities, first round off all values to correspond in accuracy to the least accurate value involved.

Sample Problem 1

Add: 24.686 m + 2.34 m + 3.2 m

Solution:

$$
\begin{array}{r}
24.7 \text{ m} \\
2.3 \text{ m} \\
3.2 \text{ m} \\
\hline
30.2 \text{ m}
\end{array}
$$

Whenever two measured quantities are to be multiplied or divided, retain in the product or quotient only as many significant digits as are contained in the least accurate measured quantity. Suppose you want to multiply 3.22 in. by 2.1 in. to find the area of a small rectangle.

$$
\begin{array}{r}
3.2② \text{ in.} \\
2.① \text{ in.} \\
\hline
③②② \\
64④ \\
\hline
6.⑦⑥② \text{ in.}^2
\end{array}
$$

Note that each digit circled in the problem is either a doubtful digit or was obtained by using a doubtful digit. A doubtful digit when multiplied is even more doubtful. Since the 7 in the product is doubtful, the 6 and 2 which represent even finer divisions are certainly invalid. The solution is best stated as 6.8 square inches.

Problems

3. Add: 6.201 cm + 7.4 cm + 0.68 cm + 12.0 cm
4. Add: 28.662 m + 32.34 m + 17.5 m
5. Add: 26.38 kg + 14.531 kg + 30.8 kg
6. The sides of a rectangular plot of land are measured and their lengths found to be 132.68 ft, 48.3 ft, 132.736 ft and 48.37 ft. What is the perimeter of the plot of land as can best be determined with these measurements?
7. Subtract: 8.264 g from 10.8 g
8. Subtract: 26.082 l from 44.12 l
9. A beaker weighs 3.64 oz when empty and 51.8 oz when filled to a certain level with water. What does the water in the beaker weigh?
10. Multiply: (a) 1.31 cm × 2.3 cm   (b) 6.87 cm × 2.2 cm   (c) 3.2145 mi × 4.23 mi
11. Multiply: (a) 20.2 in. × 7.41 in.   (b) 3.1416 × 12.4 cm   (c) 64.39 m × 13.6 m
12. Measurements of the length and width of a rectangular floor give 15.72 m and 4.40 m. Calculate the area of the floor to the best possible value using these measurements.

2:7   Graphs

Quantitative experiments are performed to learn what relationships exist between measured quantities. During the course of the experiment, one quantity called the independent variable is carefully varied. The value of another quantity called the dependent variable is recorded for each variation of the independent variable. Both values are then recorded in a table with the independent variable in the first column and the dependent variable in the second column. A graph can then be plotted from the table. *The values of the independent variable are plotted horizontally (x axis). The values of the dependent variable are plotted vertically (y axis).* The curve that best fits the plotted points then is drawn. Frequently the shape of the resulting curve clearly indicates the mathematical relationship that exists. When the graph is a straight line passing through the origin, the dependent variable y varies directly as the independent variable x. A *hyperbola* indicates that the dependent variable varies inversely as the independent variable. A *parabola* indicates that the dependent variable varies as the square of the independent variable.

2:8   Linear and Direct Variation

The general equation for a linear equation is $y = kx + b$, where k and b are constants. The graph of a linear relationship is a straight line. For example, the graph of the equation $y = 3x + 2$ is shown in Figure 2-4.

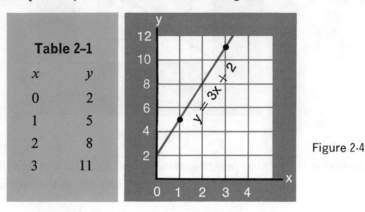

Table 2–1

x	y
0	2
1	5
2	8
3	11

Figure 2-4

When one quantity varies directly as another, it increases or decreases in proportion to the amount the other quantity increases or decreases. The general equation for direct variation is $y = kx$ where k is a constant. The graph of direct variation is always a straight line passing through the origin. A good example of direct variation is provided by a law discovered by Sir Robert Hooke and is known as Hooke's law. Hooke discovered that the elongation (e) of a spring varies directly as the force (F) that produces it. Thus, if a force of 1 newton (nt) causes a spring to stretch 1.5 cm, a force of 2 nt will cause it to stretch 3.0 cm, a force of 3 nt will cause it to stretch 4.5 cm, and so on. The results of an experiment during which the force acting on a spring was varied and the resulting elongations measured is shown in Table 2-2.

Table 2–2

Force (nt)	Elongation (cm)
0	0.0
1	0.7
2	1.5
3	2.1
4	2.7
5	3.5

Plotting the independent variable (the force) horizontally, and the dependent variable (the elongation) vertically, the graph in Figure 2-5 is drawn.

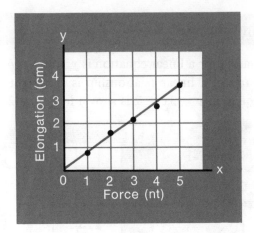

Figure 2-5

Note that the plotted points are suited best to a straight line passing through the origin. The elongation is shown to vary directly as the applied force.

2:9 Inverse Variation

When one quantity varies inversely as another quantity, the second quantity will decrease as the first increases; or the second will increase as the first decreases. The general equation for inverse variation is $y = \dfrac{k}{x}$ where k is a constant.

Behavior of a gas under varying pressures illustrates inverse variation. When the pressure on a gas is doubled, its volume is reduced to one-half its original volume. When the pressure on the gas is tripled, the volume of the gas is reduced to one-third its original volume. Conversely, if the pressure acting on the gas were reduced to one-half the original pressure, the volume of the gas would

Table 2–3	
Pressure (atmospheres)	Volume (liters)
0.1	225
0.2	110
0.3	74.9
0.5	44.6
0.7	32.0
1.0	22.4

double. Further reductions in pressure would bring about corresponding volume increases. Table 2-3 lists a set of values that might be collected during an experiment with a gas.

Notice the shape of the curve that results when the data of Table 2-3 are plotted. This shape is typical of the hyperbola which always indicates that the quantities plotted vary inversely as one another.

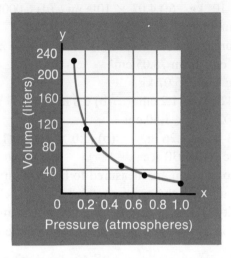

Figure 2-6. A pressure-volume graph illustrating inverse variation.

QUESTIONS

1. Distinguish between a fundamental and a derived unit.
2. What are the fundamental units in (a) the metric MKS system of measurement and (b) the English system of measurement?
3. Show how speed can be expressed in terms of fundamental units.
4. Give the proper name for each multiple of the meter listed: (a) 1/100 m (b) 1/1000 m (c) 1000 m
5. (a) What is mass? (b) What is the standard of mass in the metric system?
6. (a) Which digit of any measured quantity is the doubtful digit? (b) Is this digit significant?
7. (a) Why is it difficult to tell how many significant digits are in a measured value such as 76 000? (b) How can the number of significant digits in such a number be made clear?
8. During a laboratory experiment one quantity is varied and the change in the other quantity is recorded. What are each of these quantities called?
9. When plotting a graph which quantity customarily is plotted (a) vertically and (b) horizontally?

PROBLEMS

1. How many significant digits are contained in these measurements? (a) 248 m
   (b) 64.01·m   (c) 0.00003 m   (d) 0.003 m   (e) 80.001 m
2. State the number of significant digits in these measurements. (a) 2.40×10^6 kg   (b) 6×10^8 kg   (c) 4.07×10^{16} mi   (d) 6.0008×10^3 j
3. Add these measurements: 16.2 ft, 5.008 ft, 13.48 ft
4. Add these measurements: 5.006 m, 12.0077 m, 8.0084 m
5. Subtract: 32.046 cm² from 78.05 cm²
6. Subtract: 12.0 kg from 15.07 kg
7. Multiply: (a) 1.42 cm $\times$ 1.2 cm   (b) 6.8 m $\times$ 3.145 m   (c) 74.0 in. $\times$ 2.54 in.   (d) 8.002 cm² $\times$ 1.50 cm
8. Multiply: (a) 4.3 in. $\times$ 8.26 in.   (b) $(2.0 \times 10^8$ m$)(1.6 \times 10^7$ m$)$
   (c) 0.00050 m/sec $\times$ 0.0030 sec
9. The dimensions of a room are measured to be 16.40 m $\times$ 4.5 m $\times$ 3.26 m. What volume of air does the room contain?
10. Gold has a density of 19.3 g/cm³. (a) A cube of gold measures 4.23 cm on each edge. What is its volume? (b) What should be the mass of the cube of gold?
11. One cm³ of silver has a mass of 10.5 g. (a) What should be the mass of 65 cm³ of silver? (b) If when placed on a beam balance the piece of silver is shown to have a mass of only 616 g, what portion of it is hollow?
12. During a laboratory experiment, a student measured the mass of 10 cm³ of water. Then he increased the sample of water to 20 cm³ and measured its mass again. Proceeding in this way he collected the data shown in Table 2-4.

Table 2–4

Volume (cm³)	Mass (g)
10	10.0
20	20.1
30	29.8
40	40.2
50	50.3

(a) Plot the values given in the table on a graph and draw the best line to fit all points.
(b) What is the graph?
(c) What relationship between volume of water and its mass does the graph indicate?

13. During a science demonstration, an instructor placed a 1 kg mass on a horizontal table that was nearly frictionless. He applied various horizontal forces to the mass. Then he measured the rate at which the mass gained speed (its acceleration) for each force applied to it. The results of the experiment are shown in Table 2-5.

Table 2-5

Force (nt)	Acceleration (m/sec²)
5.0	4.9
10.0	9.8
15.0	15.2
20.0	20.1
25.0	25.0
30.0	29.9

(a) Plot the values given in the table and draw the curve that best fits all points.
(b) What relationship between the force in newtons applied to a mass and the rate at which it gains speed does the graph indicate?

14. The instructor who performed the experiment in Problem 13 then changed his procedure. Using a constant force, he varied the mass on which the force acts. He recorded the rate at which each mass gained speed. His results are shown in Table 2-6.

Table 2-6

Mass (kg)	Acceleration (m/sec²)
1.0	12.0
2.0	5.9
3.0	4.1
4.0	3.0
5.0	2.5
6.0	2.0

(a) Plot the values given in the table and draw the curve that best fits all points.
(b) What is the resulting curve called?
(c) What relationship between mass and the acceleration produced upon it by a constant force does the curve indicate?

3

Motion in a Straight Line

Motion describes what movement, if any, an object is undergoing. The units used for motion describe speed, acceleration, time and distance. A racing car at the starting line is pictured above. Note the units on the official track record board. What can be learned about the performance of this car from these units?

3:1   Vector and Scalar Quantities

All measurable quantities are either vector or scalar in nature. *Scalar quantities have size (magnitude) but no direction.* For example, mass is a scalar quantity. You can measure the amount of a mass — one kilogram, ten kilograms, ten grams — but you cannot describe mass as having direction. Other examples of scalar quantities are volume, area, and time. *Vector quantities have both magnitude and direction.* Force is a vector quantity because any given force must not only have a given magnitude but must also act in a given direction. It is impossible to exert a force and not exert it in some direction. Likewise velocity, acceleration, and momentum have both size and direction; therefore, they are vector quantities.

3:2   Distance and Displacement

Distance and displacement are not the same. Distance is a scalar quantity; displacement is a vector quantity. To illustrate the distinction between the two quantities, suppose you leave your home one morning to take a walk. If you walk 2 mi due west then turn and walk 2 mi due north, you would have walked a total *distance* of 4 mi. You would not, however, be 4 mi from your home. Instead you would be a little over 2.8 mi from home in a northwest direction. This actual distance and direction from the point of origin of the trip is the *displacement* and is quite different from distance. Distances add-up arithmetically but do not tell you where you are. Hence, they are scalar quantities. On the other hand, displacements include directions as well as distances, so they are vector quantities. Vectors are dealt with in detail in Chapter 5.

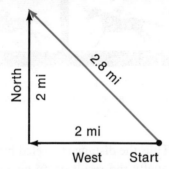

Figure 3-1. A hiker walks a distance of 4 miles. His displacement is 2.8 miles north of west.

3:3   Speed and Velocity

The speed of a moving body is the distance it travels per unit time. Speeds are stated in miles per hour, feet per second, kilometers per hour or meters per second. The speed of light is usually stated as 186 000 miles per second or 3.0×10^8 m per second. *Speed is a scalar quantity.*

To state the velocity of a body, it is necessary to designate both speed and direction. *Velocity is a vector quantity.* Speed is the magnitude of velocity and is a scalar quantity.

3:4   Motion in a Straight Line

When a body moves in a straight line, its velocity has only two directions along that line. If the directions do not change within a problem, you can neglect to specify direction. For simplicity you can consider velocity as speed only. For speed, use the symbol v. The symbol for velocity is the letter v also, but a small arrow is placed over it to signify that it is a vector quantity $(\vec{v})$.

3:5   Average and Instantaneous Speed

The instantaneous speed of a moving body is the actual speed at which it is moving at any given instant. For an automobile this is the reading of the speed-ometer at a particular instant. Often a moving body cannot maintain a constant speed. During even a short trip, an automobile intermittently slows down

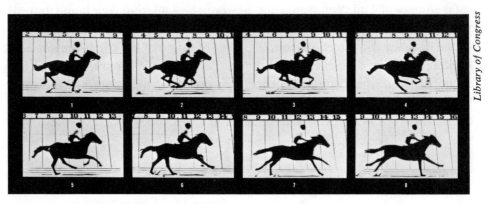

Library of Congress

Figure 3-2.   One of the first series of "high speed" photographs was taken in 1878. The vertical lines are 27 in. apart and the time between exposures is 1/25 sec. What is the average speed of the horse in the photo?

(decelerates) and speeds up (accelerates). Thus the distance traveled by a moving body at the end of a period of time is usually the result of an average speed. The *average* speed of a moving body during a period of time is determined by dividing the distance traveled by the period of time.

$$\bar{v} = \frac{s}{t}$$

Here $\bar{v}$ represents the average speed, s is the distance traveled, and t is the time spent traveling. If the speed is actually constant, the small bar over the v is dropped to signify uniform speed.

Sample Problem 1

An automobile travels a distance of 450 miles during a 10 hour period. What is its average speed?

$$\bar{v} = \frac{s}{t}$$
$$= \frac{450 \text{ mi}}{10 \text{ hr}}$$
$$= 45 \text{ mi/hr}$$

During some calculations it is necessary to change miles per hour to feet per second. This can be done quickly if you remember that 60 mi/hr is equivalent to 88 ft/sec. A proportion may be set up.

Sample Problem 2

Change 45 mi/hr to its equivalent in ft/sec.

Solution:

$$\frac{60 \text{ mi/hr}}{88 \text{ ft/sec}} = \frac{45 \text{ mi/hr}}{x}$$

$$x = \frac{(88 \text{ ft/sec})(45 \text{ mi/hr})}{60 \text{ mi/hr}}$$

$$x = 66 \text{ ft/sec}$$

Problems

1. A motorist travels a distance of 406 mi during a 7 hour period. What is his average speed (a) in mi/hr and (b) in ft/sec?
2. During a canoe race a boy paddles a distance of 406 m in 70 sec. What is his average speed?
3. A rocket launched into outer space travels a distance of 144 000 miles during the first 6 hr after the launching. What is the average speed of the rocket in (a) mi/hr and (b) ft/sec?
4. An electron traverses a vacuum tube 2 m long in 2×10^{-3} sec. What average speed does the electron have during this time in (a) m/sec and (b) cm/sec?
5. Light traveling at 3.0×10^8 m/sec requires 8.3 min to reach the earth. How far away is the sun in kilometers?
6. In the English system of measurement the sun is 9.3×10^7 miles away. If light travels at 186 000 mi/sec, how long does it take light originating in the sun to reach the earth? Determine the solution in (a) seconds and (b) minutes.
7. A bullet leaves the muzzle of a rifle and 5 sec later becomes embedded in the trunk of a tree 9000 ft away. What is the average speed of the bullet in (a) ft/sec and (b) mi/hr?

3:6 Uniform Acceleration

Acceleration is the rate at which velocity (or speed) is changing with time. If a body (moving in a straight line) is undergoing an increase in speed, the acceleration is positive. If the speed of the body is decreasing, the acceleration is negative.

The manner in which accelerations are expressed often seems confusing at first. Do not confuse accelerations with velocities — they are not the same at all. Acceleration is the rate of change in speed (or velocity). It is correctly expressed as feet per second per second. That is the number of feet per second added to or taken away from a moving body's speed each second of the acceleration period. Similarly, accelerations might be designated as meters per second per second or miles per hour per second. These expressions are usually written as ft/sec², m/sec², and mi/hr-sec respectively.

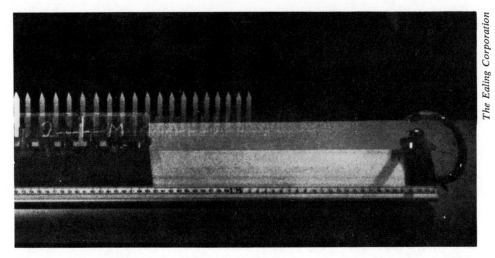

Figure 3-3. A multiple exposure photograph of an object moving along a track. Notice that as the object moves to the right the distance traveled between exposures becomes less. Is the object speeding up or slowing down?

It is better to think through acceleration equations than to memorize them. If you attempt to memorize equations without regard to their meaning, the result usually is confusion. Consider the equation for acceleration. Acceleration is the rate of change of speed. Therefore, to determine acceleration you divide the change in speed of a moving body by the time required to make the change. As an equation,

$$a = \frac{\Delta v}{t}$$

where a represents the acceleration, Δv (read "delta-vee") is the change in speed, and t is the time lapse required to make the speed change. In the strictest sense the change in speed of a body, and therefore, the acceleration of a body, need not be uniform but can occur in spurts. However, in this chapter, we will consider all accelerations to be uniform, and the symbol a will denote constant acceleration.

The change in speed of any moving body is the difference between its final speed v_f and the original speed v_o. Thus, Δv is simply $v_f - v_o$. By substitution,

$$a = \frac{v_f - v_o}{t}$$

You can use this equation because you understand what acceleration is and not because you memorized it.

Sample Problem 3

Over an 11-sec period, the driver of an automobile increases his speed from 44 ft/sec to 88 ft/sec. What is the acceleration?

Solution:

$$a = \frac{v_f - v_o}{t}$$

$$= \frac{88 \text{ ft/sec} - 44 \text{ ft/sec}}{11 \text{ sec}}$$

$$= \frac{44 \text{ ft/sec}}{11 \text{ sec}}$$

$$= 4 \text{ ft/sec}^2$$

Consider what would happen if the auto were slowing down uniformly from 88 ft/sec to 44 ft/sec during the 11 seconds. *The equation does not change.* Subtracting the original speed from the final speed will give a negative value for Δv and so the acceleration will be negative.

Sample Problem 4

Over an 11 sec period, the driver of an automobile uniformly decreases his speed from 88 ft/sec to 44 ft/sec. What is the acceleration?

Solution:

$$a = \frac{v_f - v_o}{t}$$

$$= \frac{44 \text{ ft/sec} - 88 \text{ ft/sec}}{11 \text{ sec}}$$

$$= \frac{-44 \text{ ft/sec}}{11 \text{ sec}}$$

$$= -4 \text{ ft/sec}^2$$

Problems

8. What is the acceleration of an auto if its speed is increased uniformly from 44 ft/sec to 66 ft/sec over an 11 sec period of time?
9. What is the acceleration of an auto if its speed is decreased uniformly from 66 ft/sec to 44 ft/sec over an 11 sec period of time?
10. A train traveling at a speed of 15 m/sec is accelerated uniformly to 45 m/sec over a 12 sec period. What is its acceleration?
11. A plane starting from rest ($v_o = 0$) accelerates uniformly to its takeoff speed of 72 ft/sec during a 5 sec time interval. What is the plane's acceleration?
12. A bullet leaves the muzzle of a rifle in a direction straight up with a speed of 700 m/sec. Ten seconds later its speed straight up is only 602 m/sec. At what rate does the earth's gravitational field decelerate the bullet?
13. An arrow is shot straight up with an initial speed of 320 ft/sec. Nine seconds later its speed straight up is only 32 ft/sec. At what rate is the arrow decelerated by the pull of the earth's gravitational field?

14. Upon passing through a vacuum tube, an electron is accelerated uniformly from rest to a speed of 2.6×10^5 m/sec during a time period of 6.5×10^{-2} sec. Calculate the acceleration of the electron.

In some cases where the uniform acceleration is known, it may be desirable to calculate the final speed that a body will have at the end of an acceleration period. Solving the equation

$$a = \frac{v_f - v_o}{t} \text{ for } v_f,$$

$$v_f - v_o = at$$

and so,

$$v_f = v_o + at$$

Sample Problem 5

A ball rolling down an incline undergoes a uniform acceleration of 4 m/sec² for 5 sec. If the ball has an initial speed of 2 m/sec² when it starts down the incline, what is its final speed?

Solution:

$$v_f = v_o + at$$
$$= 2 \text{ m/sec} + (4 \text{ m/sec}^2 \times 5 \text{ sec})$$
$$= 22 \text{ m/sec}$$

Problems

15. An automobile uniformly accelerates at the rate of 2 ft/sec² for 12 sec. If the original speed of the car is 36 ft/sec, what is its final speed?

16. An airplane flying at 90 m/sec accelerates uniformly at the rate of 0.5 m/sec² for ten seconds. What is its final speed in (a) m/sec and (b) km/hr?

17. An automobile traveling at 60 mi/hr slows down uniformly at the rate of 2.2 ft/sec² for ten seconds. What is its final speed in (a) ft/sec and (b) mi/hr?

18. A spacecraft traveling at 1200 m/sec uniformly accelerates at the rate of 150 m/sec² by burning its second-stage rocket. If the rocket burns for 18 sec, what is the final speed of the craft?

3:7   Distance Traveled During Uniform Acceleration

The distance traveled by any moving body during any given time interval can be calculated if the average speed of the body during that time interval is known. The distance then is simply the average speed times the time ($s = \bar{v}t$). For a body undergoing uniform acceleration, the average speed is not difficult to determine.

Consider a car that accelerates uniformly from 40 ft/sec to 60 ft/sec over a 10-sec period. The car progresses smoothly through the entire set of speeds between 40 ft/sec and 60 ft/sec. Half of these speeds are sequentially less than 50 ft/sec. Half are sequentially greater than 50 ft/sec. Thus, all the speeds average out to be the middle speed or 50 ft/sec.

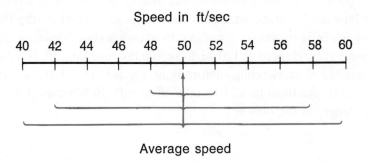

Figure 3-4.   The average speed of a uniformly accelerated body is the middle speed.

The middle speed of the car is found by adding the final speed and the original speed and dividing by two. That is $\dfrac{40 \text{ ft/sec} + 60 \text{ ft/sec}}{2} = 50$ ft/sec. Hence the expression for the average speed of an accelerating body ($\bar{v}$) is $\dfrac{v_o + v_f}{2}$. To find the distance traveled by the body during the acceleration period, this expression is substituted into the equation $s = \bar{v}t$.

$$s = \frac{v_o + v_f}{2} t$$

Sample Problem 6

What distance is traveled by a train as it accelerates uniformly from 44 ft/sec to 88 ft/sec over a 20-sec period?

Solution:

$$s = \frac{v_o + v_f}{2} t$$

$$= \frac{44 \text{ ft/sec} + 88 \text{ ft/sec}}{2} \times 20 \text{ sec}$$

$$= 66 \text{ ft} \times 20$$

$$= 1320 \text{ ft}$$

Problems

19. An auto traveling at 88 ft/sec uniformly decelerates to a speed of 44 ft/sec over an 11 sec period. What distance does it travel during this time?

20. A racing car starts from rest ($v_o = 0$) and accelerates uniformly to 40 m/sec in 8 sec. What distance does the car travel during this time?

21. A plane flying at the speed of 150 m/sec accelerates uniformly at a rate of 5 m/sec². (a) What is the plane's speed at the end of 10 sec? (b) What distance has it traveled during the 10 sec?

22. A car traveling at 60 mi/hr accelerates uniformly to 90 mi/hr over a 15-sec time interval. What distance in feet does the car travel during this time?

23. An engineer is to design a runway to accommodate airplanes that must achieve a ground speed of 120 mi/hr before they can take off. If these planes are capable of accelerating uniformly at the rate of 4.4 ft/sec², (a) How long will it take them to achieve take-off speed? (b) What must be the minimum length of the runway?

3:8 Starting and Stopping

In the special case of a body accelerating uniformly from rest, $v_o = 0$, and the equation $v_f = v_o + at$ becomes simply $v_f = at$.

Now the equation for the distance traveled by a uniformly accelerating body is,

$$s = \frac{v_o + v_f}{2} t$$

But $v_o = 0$ and $v_f = at$, so the above equation becomes,

$$s = \frac{at}{2} t \text{ or } s = 1/2 \, at^2$$

This means that for a body starting from rest, the distance it will travel in any given time can be calculated if its acceleration is known. The same distance will be traveled whether a body starts at 0 ft/sec and accelerates to 88 ft/sec in 10 sec or starts at 88 ft/sec and decelerates to 0 ft/sec in 10 sec. The equation works equally well in either case, starting from rest or going to rest.

Sample Problem 7

A car starting from rest accelerates at a constant rate of 6.2 m/sec². What distance does the car travel during the first 7 sec of acceleration?

Solution:

$$s = 1/2 \, at^2$$
$$= 1/2 \, (6.2 \text{ m/sec}^2) \, (7 \text{ sec})^2$$
$$= 152 \text{ m}$$

Problems

24. An airplane starts from rest and undergoes a uniform acceleration of 6 ft/sec² for 30 sec before leaving the ground. What distance does it travel?

25. A car traveling at 60 mi/hr decelerates uniformly to rest in 11 sec. Calculate (a) its deceleration in ft/sec² and (b) the distance it travels.

26. A train accelerates from rest at a constant rate of 1 ft/sec² for 1 min. What distance does it travel during this time?

27. Starting from rest, a racing car travels a distance of 200 m in the first 5 sec of uniform acceleration. At what rate is it being accelerated?

28. In an emergency, a driver brings his car to a full stop in 5 sec. If the car is traveling at a rate of 38 m/sec when braking begins (a) at what rate is the car decelerated and (b) what distance does it travel before stopping?

29. A stone is dropped from an airplane at a height of 1600 ft. It requires 10 sec to reach the ground. At what rate does gravity accelerate the stone?

By combining the equations $v_f = v_o + at$ and $s = \dfrac{v_f + v_o}{2} t$ an equation can be derived. This equation gives the final velocity of a body starting from rest in terms of the distance traveled and the uniform acceleration. When v_o is zero, the two equations may be written as,

$$v_f = at \text{ and } s = \frac{v_f}{2} t$$

Solving for t:
$$t = \frac{v_f}{a} \text{ and } t = \frac{2s}{v_f}$$

Therefore
$$\frac{v_f}{a} = \frac{2s}{v_f}$$

and,
$$v_f{}^2 = 2as \text{ or } v_f = \sqrt{2as}$$

The initial velocity of an object coming to rest in terms of its deceleration and distance traveled is $v_o{}^2 = 2as$ or $v_o = \sqrt{2as}$.

Sample Problem 8

An airplane flying at 63 m/sec touches down on a runway and travels 1000 m before stopping. At what rate is the plane decelerated? (Note: Let a represent deceleration.)

Solution:

$$\text{Since } v_o{}^2 = 2as, \quad a = \frac{v_o{}^2}{2s}$$

$$a = \frac{(63 \text{ m/sec})^2}{2 \times 1000 \text{ m}}$$

$$= 2.0 \text{ m/sec}^2$$

Problems

30. A plane accelerates from rest at the constant rate of 3.0 m/sec² over a distance of 500 m. What is its speed after traveling this distance?

31. Decelerating his car at the uniform rate of 8 ft/sec², a driver brings it to a halt in 484 ft. How fast was he going before braking?

32. A box falls off the tailgate of a truck and slides along the street for a distance of 62.5 ft. If friction decelerates the box at 5.0 ft/sec², at what speed was the truck moving when the box fell?

33. A light plane flying at 40 m/sec touches down on a runway and travels 100 m before stopping. At what rate is the plane decelerated?

34. If you are driving along a highway at 90 mi/hr. and the best deceleration your brakes can produce is 20 ft/sec², what minimum distance will your car travel during an emergency stop?

3:9   Acceleration of Gravity

Any falling body that is close to the surface of the earth gains speed towards the earth at the same rate as any other body, if both are allowed to fall freely (neglecting any frictional effects of air on light bodies such as feathers, etc.). Since this uniform rate of acceleration is common to all falling bodies, it is worthwhile to remember the value of gravitational acceleration. In English units, *the acceleration of gravity is 32 ft/sec². In the MKS system, it is 9.8 m/sec².* All the equations discussed so far in this chapter apply to gravitational acceleration. However, it is customary to replace the a used in acceleration equations with g when using these special values. Hence $v_f = v_o + gt$, $v_f^2 = 2gs$, etc.

Sample Problem 9

(a) What is the speed in ft/sec of a brick that drops from a high scaffold after 4 sec of free fall? (b) What distance does the brick fall during the 4 sec? (Being dropped, the brick starts from rest.)

Solution:

$$(a) \ v_f = v_o + gt$$
$$= 0 \text{ ft/sec} + (32 \text{ ft/sec} \times 4 \text{ sec})$$
$$= 128 \text{ ft/sec}$$

$$(b) \ s = \frac{gt^2}{2}$$
$$= \frac{32 \text{ ft/sec}^2 \ (4 \text{ sec})^2}{2}$$
$$= 16 \text{ ft} \times 16$$
$$= 256 \text{ ft}$$

The acceleration of gravity exists whether an object is moving up or down. An object shot straight up decelerates at the same rate of 32 ft/sec² until it comes to rest. It then accelerates down at the same rate of 32 ft/sec² or 9.8 m/sec². Suppose an arrow leaves an archer's bow with a speed of 160 ft/sec straight up. Gravity removes 32 ft/sec from its speed each second for 5 seconds. The arrow then has a speed of 0 ft/sec or is instantaneously at rest. The arrow then accelerates downwards by gravity, just the same as any falling body starting from rest. It falls for just 5 sec and travels at the rate of 5 sec × 32 ft/sec² or 160 ft/sec when it falls to the point from which it left the bow. It follows from this that the arrow spends just 10 sec in the air and rises to the same height during the 5 sec of rise that an object falls from rest in 5 sec. To find out how high an object will rise when shot straight up, first find the time it takes gravity to bring the body to rest. Then calculate how far the body would fall starting from rest during this same time.

Sample Problem 10

A mortar shell is shot straight up with an initial speed of 98 m/sec. (a) How long does the shell remain in the air? (b) How high does the shell rise:

Solution:

(a) Starting from rest, an object takes 10 sec to reach a speed of 98 m/sec when it falls freely.

$$v_f = gt \text{ and } t = \frac{v_f}{g}$$

$$t = \frac{98 \text{ m/sec}}{9.8 \text{ m/sec}^2}$$

$$= 10 \text{ sec}$$

Gravity takes 10 sec to bring the shell to a halt and another 10 sec to bring it back to earth. The time spent in the air by the shell is 20 sec.

(b) Since the shell rises for 10 sec, the height it reaches equals the distance an object falls, starting from rest in 10 sec. Hence,

$$s = \frac{gt^2}{2}$$

$$= \frac{9.8 \text{ m/sec}^2 (10 \text{ sec})^2}{2}$$

$$= 4.9 \text{ m} \times 100$$

$$= 490 \text{ m}$$

Problems

35. A stone drops straight downwards from a high cliff. What is its speed (m/sec) after 5 sec of free-fall?

36. Suppose that a stone is thrown straight downwards from a high cliff. If its speed prior to release is 40 ft/sec, what is its speed after 4 sec of free-fall?

37. A stone falls from rest for four sec. What distance in meters does it fall?

38. A stone is dropped from a high tower and 3 sec later hits the ground. How high is the tower in (a) feet and (b) meters?

39. While flying his plane parallel to the ground, a fighter pilot releases a fuel tank in order to reduce the plane's weight. What is the tank's vertical speed after falling (a) 10 ft and (b) 1000 ft?

40. A boy throws a stone straight down from a high cliff with an initial speed of 20 ft/sec downwards. (a) What is the stone's speed after 3 sec? (b) How far does the stone travel after 3 sec?

41. What is the final speed of an object that starts from rest and falls freely for a distance of 64 ft?

42. A mortar shell accidentally is shot straight up with an initial speed of 147 m/sec. (a) How long does it take the acceleration of gravity to reduce its vertical speed to zero? (b) How high does the shell rise?

QUESTIONS

1. How does distance differ from displacement?

2. If 60 mi/hr is the same thing as 88 ft/sec, what speed in ft/sec is (a) 120 mi/hr, (b) 90 mi/hr, (c) 45 mi/hr, (d) 30 mi/hr and (e) 15 mi/hr?

3. Write the equations for (a) acceleration (b) the final velocity of an accelerating body and (c) the distance traveled by a moving body during an acceleration period. You should be able to reason these out.

4. A piece of string is 9.8 m long. How long is the string in ft?

5. Starting from rest, car A accelerates at 6 ft/sec², car B accelerates at 5.4 ft/sec², car C at 8.0 ft/sec², and car D at 12 ft/sec². In the first column of a table, show the speed of each car at the end of 2 sec starting from rest. In a second column, show the distance each travels during the same two seconds. What conclusion do you reach regarding the speed attained and the distance traveled by a body starting from rest during the first two seconds of acceleration?

6. A body shot straight up rises for 7 sec before gravity brings it to a halt. A second body falling from rest takes 7 sec to reach the ground. What do the two bodies have in common?

PROBLEMS

1. An automobile increases its speed at a constant rate. If the speed increases by 42 m/sec over a 7 sec period, what is the acceleration?

2. Determine the uniform acceleration of a body that changes its speed uniformly from 32 ft/sec to 96 ft/sec in an 8-sec period.

3. An electron, initially at rest, leaves a cathode and uniformly accelerates toward an anode. It reaches the anode in 0.01 sec traveling with a speed of 2000 m/sec. What is its acceleration?

4. An automobile slows down at a constant rate from 86 ft/sec to 20 ft/sec in 8 sec. What is its deceleration?

5. A plane flying at 220 ft/sec touches down and comes to a halt along the runway after 5.5 sec. What is its deceleration?

6. A car traveling at a speed of 20 m/sec accelerates uniformly at the rate of 1.6 m/sec² for 6.8 sec. What is its final speed?

7. Determine the final speed of a racing car that has a speed of 264 ft/sec and then decelerates uniformly at the rate of 16 ft/sec² for 15 sec.

8. A supersonic jet flying at 200 m/sec accelerates uniformly at the rate of 23.1 m/sec² for 20 sec. (a) Determine the final speed. (b) If the speed of sound is 331 m/sec in air, how many times the speed of sound is the plane's final speed?

9. Determine the distance traveled during constant acceleration by an auto that accelerates from 66 ft/sec to 88 ft/sec over a 12 sec time period.

10. How far does a plane fly while decelerating uniformly from 140 m/sec to 70 m/sec in 15 sec?

11. Starting from rest, a car accelerates at the uniform rate of 18 ft/sec² for 5 sec. What distance does it travel during this time?

12. A plane flying at 220 ft/sec touches down and travels 605 ft before coming to rest. At what rate is the plane decelerated?

13. If a bullet leaves the muzzle of a rifle with a speed of 600 m/sec and the barrel of the rifle is 0.9 m long, at what rate is the bullet accelerated while in the barrel?

14. A car comes to a halt by decelerating uniformly at the rate of 12 ft/sec² for 8 sec. What distance does it travel during this time?

15. A plane travels a distance of 500 m while accelerating uniformly from rest at the rate of 5 m/sec². What final speed does it attain?

16. A stone falls freely from rest for 8 sec. (a) Calculate the final speed. (b) What distance does the stone fall during this time?

17. A pack of instruments is dropped from a weather balloon and hits the ground with a speed of 240 ft/sec. (a) How high is the balloon when the instruments are released? (b) How long do the instruments fall?

18. A diver executes a vertical dive from a high board and strikes the water at a speed of 14.7 m/sec. (a) What is the height of the diving board? (b) How long is he in the air?

19. During a baseball game, a batter hits a long fly ball. If the ball remains in the air for 6 sec, how high does it rise?

20. A boy drops a rock from a bridge 120 m high. With what speed does the stone strike the water below?

Graphical Analysis of Motion

Graphs are used extensively in science not only to illustrate relationships between quantities but also to determine relationships which were not previously recognized. These plots may have a variety of shapes. You must learn to graph data accurately and to recognize general relationships from the shapes of the graphs. Glance at the plots included in this chapter. What do their shapes indicate?

4:1 Distance-Time Graph for Motion at a Constant Speed

A body moving in a straight line at constant speed is traveling the same distance during each second of motion. Therefore for a body moving at uniform speed the total distance traveled varies directly as the elapsed time. A graph of its motion would show a straight line passing through the origin. Table 4-1 illustrates the distance traveled by an airplane flying at a constant 60 m/sec for a 5-sec interval. In Figure 4-1 the distances traveled by the plane are plotted against the time of travel. The result is a straight-line graph passing through the origin.

Table 4-1	
Time (seconds)	Distance (meters)
0	0
1	60
2	120
3	180
4	240
5	300

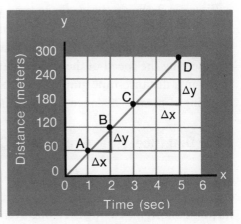

Figure 4-1

4:2   Slope of a Distance-Time Graph

The steepness of a graph is called the slope of the graph. Slope is the vertical interval or rise (Δy) divided by the corresponding horizontal interval or run (Δx) between any two points on the graph. For example, between points A and B in Figure 4-1, the rise is 120 m − 60 m or 60 m. The run is 2 sec − 1 sec or 1 sec. Using these two points to determine the slope,

$$\text{slope} = \frac{\text{rise}}{\text{run}} = \frac{\Delta y}{\Delta x} = \frac{60 \text{ m}}{1 \text{ sec}} = 60 \text{ m/sec}$$

Between points C and D,

$$\text{slope} = \frac{\text{rise}}{\text{run}} = \frac{300 \text{ m} - 180 \text{ m}}{5 \text{ sec} - 3 \text{ sec}} = \frac{120 \text{ m}}{2 \text{ sec}} = 60 \text{ m/sec}$$

Thus, the slope of a distance-time graph yields the speed of the moving object. When the curve of a graph is straight, its slope is the same all along its length.

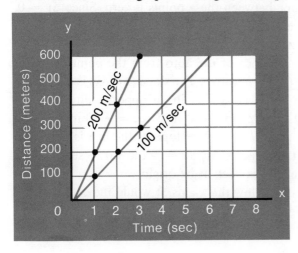

Figure 4-2. The steeper the slope of a distance-time graph the higher the speed.

Figure 4-2 shows the distance-time graph for two planes. One is traveling at 100 m/sec while the other is traveling at 200 m/sec. The slope of the line representing the speed of the faster plane is steeper than the slope of the line representing the speed of the slower plane. The steeper the slope, the higher the speed in a distance-time graph. A steeper slope indicates that a moving body is covering a greater distance in less time. This is what a higher speed means.

4:3 Distance-Time Graph for a Complete Trip at Constant Speed

The distance-time graph (Figure 4-3), represents a short automobile trip. During the first 10 sec, the automobile travels a total distance of 200 m from its point of origin. Taking the slope over the entire 10 sec period, gives $\Delta y/\Delta x = 200 \text{ m}/10 \text{ sec}$ or 20 m/sec. This is the speed of the automobile during the first 10 sec of travel.

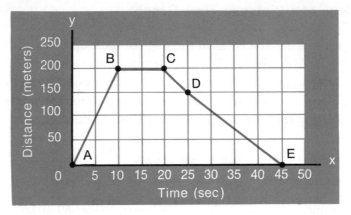

Figure 4-3

Between points B and C the auto is at rest. Its distance from the point of origin does not change. The slope between these points is zero. Since $\Delta y = 0$, $\Delta y/\Delta x$ must also be zero. Therefore, the speed of the auto between the tenth and twentieth sec of the trip is zero.

Between points C and D the distance of the auto from the point of origin decreases. Thus the change in y (Δy) is negative. The slope ($\Delta y/\Delta x$) is also negative. This means that the auto is now traveling in an opposite direction. Its speed between points C and D is $\Delta y/\Delta x$ or $-50 \text{ m}/5 \text{ sec} = -10$ m/sec. The speed of the auto decreases at point D, and the slope of the line is less steep thereafter. Between D and E the slope is $\Delta y/\Delta x = -150 \text{ m}/20 \text{ sec} = -7.5$ m/sec. Note that at point E the auto is back at its origin.

If the line of the graph extended below the x-axis, it would indicate that the auto had passed its point of origin and was continuing to travel in a direction opposite to that which it traveled during the first 10 sec of the trip.

4:4   Speed-Time Graph for Constant Speed

Figure 4-4 plots the speed of an airplane flying at a constant 60 m/sec against the time of travel for a 5-sec period. Since the speed is constant, every point along the line has the same ordinate (vertical position). Therefore, the line through these points is parallel with the horizontal axis.

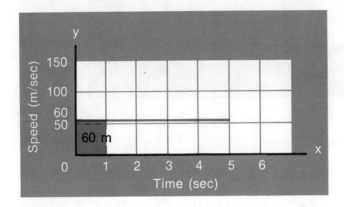

Figure 4-4. The speed-time graph of a body moving with constant speed.

A speed-time graph is useful because the area between the line of the graph and the horizontal axis represents the distance traveled by the body. The vertical side of the first shaded block is the speed, $v = 60$ m/sec. The horizontal side is the time, $t = 1$ sec. Therefore, its area is $v \times t$ or vt. This is 60 m/sec $\times$ 1 sec or 60 m, the distance the plane travels in 1 sec. The same is true for each block under the line. The total distance a moving body travels at the end of any number of seconds is determined by counting the number of blocks up to that time position on the graph. For example, at the end of 4 sec of travel, the count is four blocks of area under the line. Since each block has a value of 60 m, the four blocks represent 240 m as the distance the plane travels in 4 sec. For a plane flying in a straight line at a constant 60 m/sec, this is the correct distance it travels.

Problems

1. An airplane flies in a straight line with a constant speed of 50 m/sec for 20 sec. (a) Construct a table showing the total distance the plane travels at the end of each second over the entire 20-sec period. (b) Use the data from the table to plot a distance-time graph. (c) Show that the slope of the line gives the speed of the airplane. Use at least two different sets of points along the graph. (d) Plot a speed-time graph of the airplane's motion for the first 12 sec of the 20-sec interval. (e) Find the distance the plane travels between the eighth and eleventh sec.

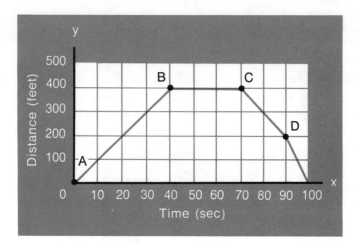

Figure 4-5.   Use this graph for Problems 2, 3, 4, and 5.

2. Use the distance-time graph in Figure 4-5 to determine (a) the distance the body travels between $t = 0$ sec and $t = 40$ sec, (b) the distance it travels between $t = 40$ sec and $t = 70$ sec, and (c) the distance it travels between $t = 90$ sec and $t = 100$ sec.

3. Use Figure 4-5 to find (a) the speed of the body during the first 40 sec, (b) the speed of the body between $t = 40$ sec and $t = 70$ sec, (c) the speed of the body between $t = 70$ sec and $t = 90$ sec, and (d) the speed of the body between $t = 90$ sec and $t = 100$ sec.

4. If the slope of the line between points A and B in Figure 4-5 is positive, what must be true of the slope of the line between points C and D?

5. Use the distance-time graph of Figure 4-5 to construct a table showing the speed of the plane for each 10-sec interval over the entire 100 sec.

6. As a solution to Problem 5, plot a speed-time graph using the table you constructed.

7. A car moves along a straight road at a constant speed of 40 ft/sec. (a) Plot its distance-time graph for a 10-sec interval. (b) Find the slope of the graph at two different places along the line. (c) Plot a speed-time graph for the car. What does the area under the line of the graph represent? (d) Calculate the area under the line of the graph between the fifth and sixth sec. What does this area represent?

4:5   Speed-Time Graph for Uniformly Accelerated Motion

Table 4-2 shows the speeds of a race car. The car starts from rest and accelerates uniformly at the rate of 20 ft/sec² over a 5-sec period.

Table 4–2	
Time (sec)	Speed (ft/sec)
0	0
1	20
2	40
3	60
4	80
5	100

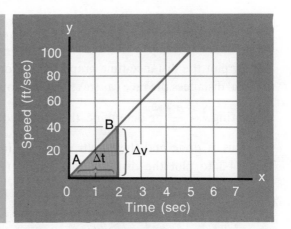

Figure 4-6

Figure 4-6 plots the speeds of the racing car against time. The speed-time graph for uniformly accelerated motion is a straight line passing through the origin. This indicates that during uniform acceleration the speed varies directly as time.

For uniform acceleration, the slope of the line in a speed-time graph is constant along its entire length and is equal to the acceleration. Between points A and B the slope is,

$$\frac{\text{rise}}{\text{run}} = \frac{\Delta v}{\Delta t} = \frac{40 \text{ ft/sec}}{2 \text{ sec}} = 20 \text{ ft/sec}^2$$

This agrees with the stated acceleration of the car.

Section 4:4 deals with the speed-time graph for a body moving with constant speed. The area under the speed-time line gives the distance the moving body travels. This section also deals with speed-time graphs, but for a body that undergoes uniform acceleration rather than constant speed. Notice that the area under the speed-time line still yields the distance the accelerating body travels. In fact, the area under a speed-time line always yields distance regardless of the type-of motion.

Examine the shaded area under the line between points A and B. Consider the entire rectangle of which the shaded area is half. The vertical limit of the rectangle is the speed of 40 ft/sec. This speed is attained by the race car when the driver accelerates at the rate of 20 ft/sec² for 2 sec. So v can be expressed as acceleration times time, or $v = at$. Thus, the vertical side of the rectangle equals at. The horizontal limit of the rectangle is the time, 2 sec. The area of the rectangle is its vertical side at multiplied by its horizontal side t, $at \times t = at^2$. But the area under the line is half this or $\frac{at^2}{2}$. This is the distance an accelerating body covers when starting from rest. (Section 3:8.)

4:6   Distance-Time Graph for Uniformly Accelerated Motion

Now plot the distance-time graph for uniformly accelerated motion. Obtain the total distances the race car travels in Section 4:5 at the end of each second by calculating $s = \dfrac{at^2}{2}$ or determine the area under the speed-time line of Figure 4-6. This is done and the results are given in Table 4-3. Use the data from Table 4-3 to plot the distance-time graph. (Figure 4-7.)

Table 4–3	
Time (seconds)	*Distance* (ft)
0	0
1	10
2	40
3	90
4	160
5	250

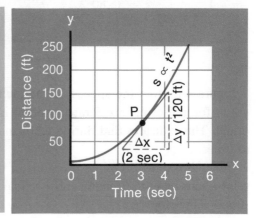

Figure 4-7. The distance-time graph for a uniformly accelerated body.

The curve in the distance-time graph is half a parabola. A parabola always indicates that one quantity varies directly as the square of the other. In this case, the distance the accelerating body travels varies directly as the square of the time.

The slope of a distance-time graph yields the speed. When the speed is uniform, the distance-time graph is a straight line. Figure 4-1 shows how to determine the slope of the line. However, when a body such as a race car accelerates, it travels a greater distance each second than it does the second before. The steepness of the curve changes constantly and results in a smooth distinctive parabola. (Figure 4-7.) The slope of a curve is more difficult to determine than the slope of a straight line. Usually it is done by constructing a tangent to the curve at the point where the slope is wanted. The slope of the tangent yields the instantaneous speed at the particular point on the curve that it touches. The tangent on the graph in Figure 4-7 at point P coincides with the end of 3 sec of travel. The slope of the tangent at this point is,

$$\frac{\Delta y}{\Delta x} = \frac{150 \text{ ft} - 30 \text{ ft}}{4 \text{ sec} - 2 \text{ sec}} = \frac{120 \text{ ft}}{2 \text{ sec}} = 60 \text{ ft/sec}$$

This is the speed to expect at the end of 3 sec for a body which accelerates at the rate of 20 ft/sec² from rest. Note also that it is the speed shown on the speed-time graph for the same body at the end of 3 sec.

4:7   Acceleration-Time Graph for Uniform Acceleration

Acceleration that is constant and does not change with time is called uniform acceleration. Because the acceleration is constant, an acceleration-time graph (*a-t*) is a line parallel to the horizontal axis.

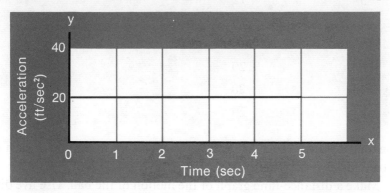

Figure 4-8.   The acceleration-time graph for a uniformly accelerated body.

In Figure 4-8 the acceleration of the race car in Table 4-2 is plotted against time. As expected, the acceleration-time line is a straight line parallel with the horizontal axis. The graph also shows that the area under the line is representative of the speed of the moving body. The vertical side of the first block represents acceleration *a*. The horizontal side of the same block represents time *t*. Therefore, the area of the block is $a \times t$ or *at*. Since $v = at$, the area of the block gives the speed. Each successive block has the same speed value. So to find the speed of the race car at the end of any period of time on the graph, count the number of blocks. At the end of 3 sec on the graph, there are three blocks of area under the line. This means the speed of the car is 3×20 ft/sec or 60 ft/sec at the end of that time period.

PROBLEMS

1. The speed of an automobile changes over an 8-sec time period as shown in Table 4-4.
   (a) Plot the speed-time graph of the motion. (b) Determine the distance the car travels during the first 2 sec. (c) Determine the distance the car travels during the first 4 sec. (d) What distance does the car travel during the entire 8 sec? (e) Find the slope of the line between $t = 0$ sec and

$t = 4$ sec. What does this slope represent? (f) Find the slope of the line
between $t = 5$ sec and $t = 7$ sec. What does this slope represent?

Table 4–4		Table 4–5	
Time (seconds)	Speed (m/sec)	Time (sec)	Distance (ft)
0	0	0	0
1	4	1	2
2	8	2	8
3	12	3	18
4	16	4	32
5	20	5	50
6	20		
7	20		
8	20		

2. The total distance a steel ball rolls down an incline at the end of each second
   of travel is given in Table 4-5.
   (a) Make a distance-time graph of the motion of the ball. Use five divisions
       for each 10 ft of travel on the vertical axis. Use five divisions for each
       second of time on the horizontal axis. (b) What type of curve is the
       line of the graph? (c) What distance has the ball rolled at the end of 2.2
       sec? (d) Find the slope of the line at $t = 3$ sec. What does this slope
       represent?

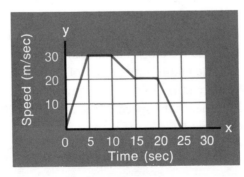

Figure 4-9.   Use this graph with Problems 3 and 4.

3. Use Figure 4-9 to find the acceleration of the moving body during (a) the
   first 5 sec of travel, (b) during the second 5 sec of travel, (c) between the
   tenth and the fifteenth sec of travel, and (d) between the twentieth and the
   twenty-fifth sec of travel.

4. Refer to Figure 4-9 to find the distance the moving body travels (a) between $t = 0$ and $t = 5$ sec, (b) between $t = 5$ sec and $t = 10$ sec, (c) between $t = 10$ sec and $t = 15$ sec and (d) between $t = 0$ and $t = 25$ sec.

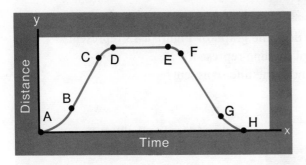

Figure 4-10.   Use this graph
with Problem 5.

5. Use intervals marked on the graph in Figure 4-10 to describe the entire trip of the moving body.
6. Make a table of the speeds of a body (ft/sec) at the end of each second for the first 5 sec of free-fall from rest. (a) Use the data in your table to plot a speed-time graph. (b) What does the total area under the graph represent?
7. (a) Compute the total distance the body in Problem 6 travels at the end of each second for the first 5 sec of the free-fall. (b) Use the distances calculated in Part (a) to plot a distance-time graph. (c) Find the slope of the curve at the end of 2 and 4 sec. What are the approximate slopes? Do these values agree with the table of speeds in Problem 6?
8. Use the data prepared in Problem 7 to plot the distance versus time squared. (a) What kind of curve is obtained? (b) Does this agree with the equation $s = \dfrac{at^2}{2}$? (c) Find the slope of the curve at any point. Explain the significance of the value you obtain.

9.

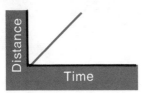

Figure 4-11.   For Problem 9.

(a) What kind of motion does the graph in Figure 4-11 represent?
(b) What does the slope of the graph represent?

10.

Figure 4-12.   For Problem 10.

(a) What kind of motion does the graph in Figure 4-12 represent?
(b) What does the area under the line of the graph represent?

11.

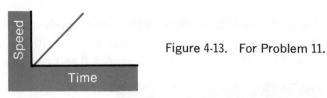

Figure 4-13. For Problem 11.

(a) What kind of motion does the graph of Figure 4-13 represent?
(b) What does the slope of the line represent?
(c) What does the area under the line represent?

12.

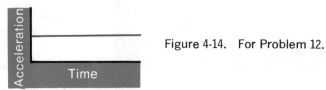

Figure 4-14. For Problem 12.

What does the area under the line of the graph of Figure 4-14 represent?

13.

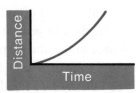

Figure 4-15. For Problem 13.

(a) What type of curve does the graph in Figure 4-15 represent?
(b) What does the slope of the line taken at any point represent?
(c) How would slopes taken at higher points on the line differ from those taken at lower points?

Vectors

Vectors are quantities which have both magnitude and direction. Velocity and acceleration are vector quantities which have already been introduced. Force and weight are also examples of vectors. In this chapter you will learn to draw vector diagrams and to solve vector problems both graphically and mathematically. After studying this chapter can you draw a vector diagram for the sailing situation pictured above?

5:1   Vector Quantities

A vector quantity is different from a scalar quantity. Scalar quantities have magnitude only. Examples of scalar quantities are mass, volume, and distance. Vector quantities require a description of both magnitude and direction. Force, velocity, and displacement are examples of vector quantities.

Scalar quantities add algebraically. Two liters of water plus two liters of water yield four liters of water. The sum of two vector quantities is determined by their directions and by their magnitudes. An airplane flies due east at 90 mi/hr. At the same time, the wind blows it due south at 50 mi/hr. The plane is not flying with a velocity of 140 mi/hr. Nor is its direction east or south. The magnitudes and directions of the two velocities produce a vector sum determined by vector addition.

5:2 Vector Addition by the Graphical Method

Two vector quantities are added graphically by representing each quantity as an arrow-tipped line segment. The length of the line is drawn in proportion to the magnitude of the quantity. The direction of the arrow represents the direction of the quantity. These arrow-tipped line segments are called vectors. Figure 5-1 shows some typical vectors.

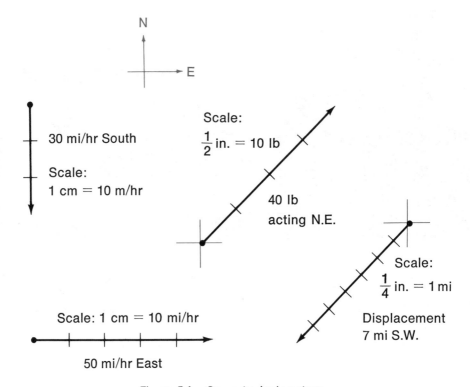

Figure 5-1. Some typical vectors.

Let us add the two velocities of the plane flying east at 90 mi/hr and being blown south by the wind at 50 mi/hr. In Figure 5-2 vectors $\vec{a}$ and $\vec{b}$ represent the two velocities. The vectors are added by placing the tail of one vector at the head of the second vector. Neither the direction nor the length of either vector is changed. A third vector connecting the tail of the first vector to the head of the second vector represents the sum of the two vectors. This third vector is called the resultant of $\vec{a}$ and $\vec{b}$. *The resultant is always drawn from the tail of the first vector to the head of the second vector.* To find the magnitude of the resultant, measure its length and evaluate it according to the same scale used to draw vectors $\vec{a}$ and $\vec{b}$. Its direction is found by using a protractor. Thus in terms of the scale used in Figure 5-2, the resultant vector indicates a velocity of 103 mi/hr in the direction 29° south of east.

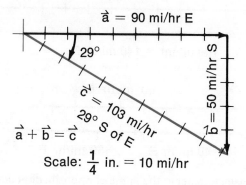

Figure 5-2.   Vector addition

In algebraic addition, the order of addition is of no consequence. This is also true of vector addition. The tail of vector $\vec{a}$ could have been placed at the head of vector $\vec{b}$. Figure 5-3 illustrates that the same sum would result.

Scale: $\frac{1}{4}$ in. = 10 mi/hr

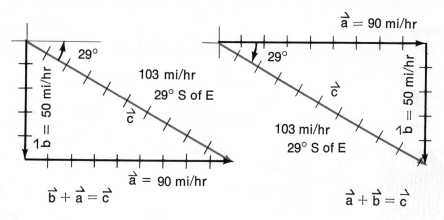

Figure 5-3.   The vector sum of $\vec{b} + \vec{a}$ is the same as the vector sum of $\vec{a} + \vec{b}$.

When two vector quantities act in the same or opposite directions, the numeric sum is the algebraic sum of the two. That is, if an airplane flies at 90 mi/hr due east and the wind blows it 50 mi/hr due east, its velocity is 140 mi/hr east. If the wind is blowing due west and the plane has to fly directly into it, the plane's velocity is 90 mi/hr − 50 mi/hr = 40 mi/hr east.

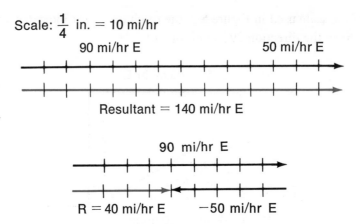

Scale: $\frac{1}{4}$ in. = 10 mi/hr

90 mi/hr E   50 mi/hr E

Resultant = 140 mi/hr E

90 mi/hr E

R = 40 mi/hr E   −50 mi/hr E

Figure 5-4. When two vectors act in the same or opposite directions, their resultant is numerically just the algebraic sum of the two.

5:3   Vector Addition of Two Forces

Add other kinds of vectors in the same way as adding two velocities vectorially. Concurrent forces are two forces acting on the same point simultaneously. In the English system of measurement, the unit of force is the pound. In the MKS system of measurement, the unit of force is the newton (nt).

Sample Problem 1

In Figure 5-5, two concurrent forces are acting at point P. The angle between the forces is 60°.

Solution:

Figure 5-5

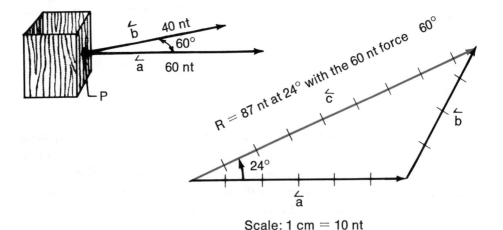

$\angle b$ 40 nt

60°

$\angle a$ 60 nt

P

R = 87 nt at 24° with the 60 nt force $\angle c$ 60°

$\angle b$

24°

$\angle a$

Scale: 1 cm = 10 nt

The sum of the two forces is found in the diagram by moving vector $\vec{b}$ parallel to itself until it is added to vector $\vec{a}$. The resultant is drawn and interpreted in terms of the scale used.

Problems

Draw vector diagrams to solve each problem. Use a protractor, a sharp pencil, and a metric ruler.

1. An airplane flying due north at 100 mi/hr is blown due west at 50 mi/hr by a strong wind. Determine the plane's resultant velocity (speed and direction).

2. A hiker leaves his camp and walks 10 km due north. His displacement at this point is 10 km north. The hiker then walks 10 km due east. This adds a second displacement of 10 km east to his first displacement. (a) What is the total distance walked by the hiker? (b) Determine the total displacement from the starting point.

3. A motorboat heads due east at 16 m/sec across a river that flows due south at 9 m/sec. (a) What is the resultant velocity (speed and direction) of the boat? (b) If the river is 136 m wide, how long does it take the motorboat to reach the other side? (c) How far downstream is the boat when it reaches the other side of the river?

4. An airplane flies due west at 120 mi/hr. At the same time, the wind blows it due north at 40 mi/hr. What is the plane's resultant velocity?

5. A man leaves his hometown and drives 26 km due north along a very straight highway. He turns onto a highway that leads in a direction 30° north of east. He continues along this highway for a distance of 62 km and then stops. What is his total displacement from his hometown?

6. Two boys kick a soccer-ball at exactly the same time. One boy's foot exerts a force of 30 lb north. The other boy's foot exerts a force of 40 lb east. What is the magnitude and direction of the resultant force on the ball?

7. Two forces of 60 nt each act concurrently on a point P. Determine the magnitude of the resultant force acting on point P when the angle between the forces is (a) 0° (b) 30° (c) 60° (d) 90° (e) 180°.

8. In Problem 7, what happens to the resultant of two forces as the angle between them increases?

9. A weather team releases a weather balloon. The balloon's buoyancy accelerates it straight up at 15 ft/sec². A wind accelerates it horizontally at 6.5 ft/sec². What is the magnitude and direction (with reference to the horizontal) of the resultant acceleration?

10. A meteoroid passes between the moon and the earth. A gravitational force of 600 nt pulls the meteoroid toward the moon. At the same time, a gravitational force of 480 nt pulls it toward the earth. The angle between the

two forces is 130°. The moon's force acts perpendicularly to the meteoroid's original path. What is the resultant magnitude and direction of the force acting on the meteoroid? State the direction in reference to the meteoroid's original path.

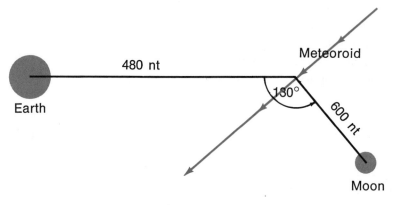

480 nt

Earth

Meteoroid

130°

600 nt

Moon

Figure 5-6

5:4 Mathematical Determination of the Resultant

The vector sum of any two vectors can be determined mathematically as well as graphically. If two vectors act perpendicularly, a right triangle is formed. The magnitude of their resultant is found by using the Pythagorean theorem.

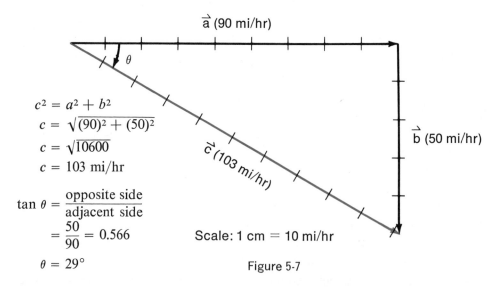

$\vec{a}$ (90 mi/hr)

θ

$c^2 = a^2 + b^2$

$c = \sqrt{(90)^2 + (50)^2}$

$c = \sqrt{10600}$

$c = 103$ mi/hr

$\vec{c}$ (103 mi/hr)

$\vec{b}$ (50 mi/hr)

$\tan \theta = \dfrac{\text{opposite side}}{\text{adjacent side}}$

$= \dfrac{50}{90} = 0.566$

Scale: 1 cm = 10 mi/hr

$\theta = 29°$

Figure 5-7

An airplane flies east at 90 mi/hr. A wind from the north blows at 50 mi/hr. What direction and speed is the airplane actually flying? To find the direction of the resultant, find the tangent of the angle θ. The tangent of an angle is the side opposite the angle divided by the side adjacent to the angle. Since these two sides are known, the tangent of θ is $\dfrac{50 \text{ mi/hr}}{90 \text{ mi/hr}}$ or 0.556. Table A-2 of trigonometric functions in the Appendix indicates 0.556 is the tangent of 29°. Therefore, the angle θ is 29°. The resultant is described as 103 mi/hr at 29° south of east.

When two vectors do not act at a right angle, the magnitude and direction of the resultant is determined by use of the law of cosines or the law of sines. (Sections 1:6 and 1:7.)

Sample Problem 2

A force of 40 nt and a force of 60 nt act concurrently on a point P. The 60-nt force acts in the direction due east. The 40-nt force acts in the direction 30° east of north. What is the magnitude and direction of their resultant?

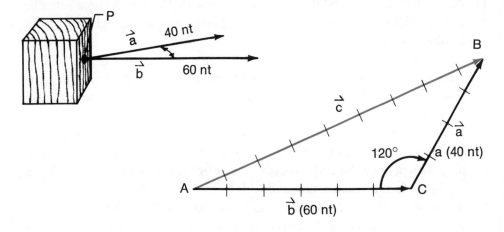

Scale: 1 cm = 10 nt

Figure 5-8

Solution:

To determine the magnitude of $\vec{c}$, use the law of cosines.

$$c^2 = a^2 + b^2 - 2ab \cos C$$
$$c^2 = (40)^2 + (60)^2 - [2 \ (40)(60) \ (-0.50)]$$
$$c^2 = 1600 + 3600 + 2400$$
$$c = \sqrt{7600}$$
$$c = 87 \text{ nt}$$

To determine the direction of $\vec{c}$, use the law of sines to find angle A.

$$\frac{a}{\sin A} = \frac{c}{\sin C}$$

$$\frac{40}{\sin A} = \frac{87}{\sin 120°}$$

$$\frac{40}{\sin A} = \frac{87}{0.866}$$

$$\sin A = \frac{40 \times 0.866}{87}$$

$$\sin A = 0.398$$

$$A = 23°$$

The direction of c is $90 - 23° = 67°$ east of north.

Problems

11. A 100 lb force and a 50 lb force act on point P. The 100 lb force acts due north. The 50 lb force acts due east. What is the magnitude and direction of resultant force?

12. A motorboat travels at 40 m/sec. It heads straight across a river 320 m wide. (a) If the water flows at the rate of 8 m/sec, what is the boat's velocity with respect to the water? (b) How long does it take the boat to reach the opposite shore?

13. A boat heads directly across a river 40 m wide at 8 m/sec. The current is flowing at 3.8 m/sec. (a) What is the resultant velocity of the boat? (b) How long does it take the boat to cross the river? (c) How far downstream is the boat when it reaches the other side?

14. An airplane flies at 150 mi/hr and heads 30° south of east. A 50 mi/hr wind blows the plane in the direction 25° west of south. What is its resultant velocity with respect to the earth?

15. Two 10 nt forces act concurrently on point P. Determine the magnitude of their resultant when the angle between them is (a) 0°   (b) 30°   (c) 90° (d) 120°   (e) 180°.

5:5   Addition of Several Vectors

Frequently three or more forces act concurrently on the same point. To determine the resultant of three or more vectors, follow the same procedure used to add two vectors. Add the vectors head-to-tail. The order of addition is not important. In Figure 5-9 the three forces $\vec{a}$, $\vec{b}$, and $\vec{c}$ are concurrent forces. Parts 1 and 2 of the diagram show that the vectors are added graphically. In placing the vectors head-to-tail, their directions are maintained carefully. Note that the resultant is the same although two different orders of addition are used.

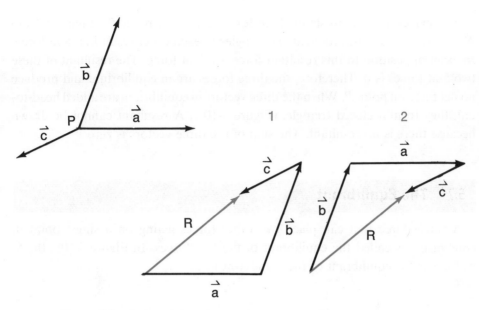

Figure 5-9. Determining the resultant of three concurrent forces.

5:6   Equilibrium

When two or more forces act concurrently on a body and their vector sum is zero, the body is in equilibrium. An example of this is the case of two equal forces acting in exactly opposite directions. (Figure 5-10a.)

Figure 5-10.   Vectors in equilibrium give a resultant of zero.

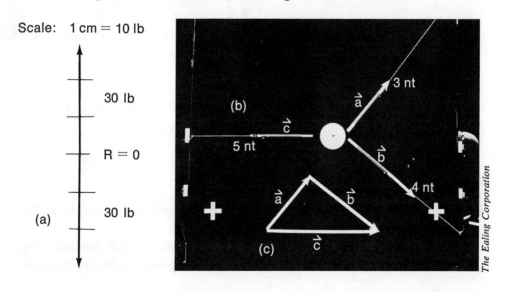

Another example consists of three forces acting on point *P*. (Figure 5-10b.) A 3-nt force and a 4-nt force at right angles to each other result in a 5-nt force. In exact opposition to this resultant force is a 5-nt force. The resultant of these two 5-nt forces is 0. Therefore, the three forces are in equilibrium and produce no net force on point *P*. When the three vectors in equilibrium are added head-to-tail, they form a closed triangle. (Figure 5-10c.) A resultant cannot be drawn because there is no resultant. The sum of the three vectors is zero.

5:7   The Equilibrant

A single force that can place two other forces acting on a single point in equilibrium is called the equilibrant of the two forces. In Figure 5-10b, the 5-nt force is the equilibrant of the 3 and 4-nt forces.

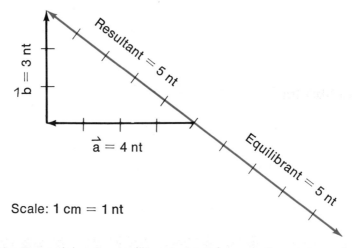

Scale: 1 cm = 1 nt

Figure 5-11.   Determining the equilibrant of two forces acting at an angle of 90° with each other.

To find the equilibrant of any two concurrent forces, first find the resultant of the two forces by vector addition. The equilibrant will be a force equal in magnitude to the resultant force but opposite in direction.

Problems

16. A force of 50-nt acts due west. What single force places this force in equilibrium?

17. Two forces act concurrently on a point *P*. One force is 60 lb due east. The second force is 80 lb due north. (a) Determine the magnitude and direction of their resultant. (b) Determine the magnitude and direction of their equilibrant.

18. A 60-nt force acting at 30° east of north and a second 60-nt force acting in the direction 60° east of north are concurrent forces. (a) Determine the resultant force. (b) Determine the magnitude and direction of their equilibrant.

19. A 60-lb force acts 45° west of south. An 80-lb force acts 45° north of west. The two forces are acting on the same point. What is the magnitude and direction of their equilibrant?

20. A 30-lb force acting due north and a 40-lb force acting 30° east of north both are acting concurrently on point *P*. What is the magnitude and direction of a third force that places the two in equilibrium?

5:8   Resolving Vectors into Components

Often it is necessary to apply a force in a direction other than that in which the force is to act. Consider a boy pulling a sled. (Figure 5-12a.) The boy exerts a 50-lb force on a rope held at an angle of 30° with the horizontal. The purpose of the 50-lb force is to pull the sled forward. However, not all of the 50-lb force the boy exerts does this. The only force that does pull the sled forward is the horizontal component of the force ($\vec{F}_h$).

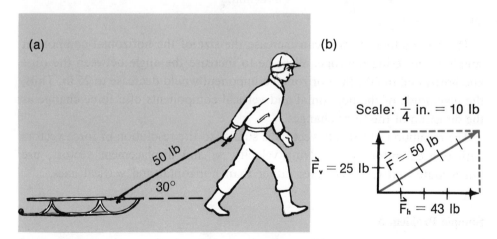

Figure 5-12.   Resolving a force into its vertical and horizontal components.

The horizontal and vertical directions always are perpendicular to one another. Therefore, the components of $\vec{F}$ are perpendicular components. The values of these components are determined either graphically or by mathematical calculation. To solve the problem graphically, an axis to represent the horizontal direction is drawn perpendicular to a second axis to represent the vertical direction. (Figure 5-12b.) The vector to represent the force ($\vec{F}$) in the rope is then drawn at the proper angle with the horizontal axis. To resolve that force into the components $\vec{F}_v$ and $\vec{F}_h$, draw lines perpendicularly from each axis to the tip of the force vector. The magnitudes of the two components are then interpreted in terms of the scale used for $\vec{F}$.

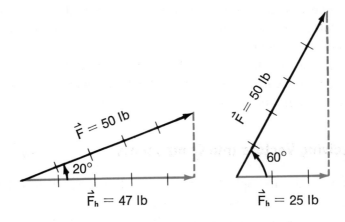

Scale: 1cm = 10 lb

Figure 5-13.   The horizontal and vertical components of a force depend upon its direction.

The boy pulling the sled can increase the size of the horizontal component simply by lowering the rope. Were he to increase the angle between the rope and horizontal to 60°, the horizontal component would decrease to 25 lb. Thus, the magnitude of the horizontal and vertical components of a force change as the direction of the force changes.

The resolution of velocity vectors is similar to the resolution of force vectors with one exception. In resolving velocity, $\vec{v}$, and displacement vectors, use north-south and east-west axes rather than horizontal and vertical axes.

Sample Problem 3

A 40 mi/hr wind blows 30° north of east. What is the north component of the wind's velocity? What is the east component of the wind's velocity?

Solution:

The solution is determined graphically as well as mathematically. For the north component of the wind, v_N

$$\sin 30° = \frac{v_N}{v}$$

$$v_N = v \sin 30°$$
$$= 40 \text{ mi/hr} \times 0.50$$
$$= 20 \text{ mi/hr}$$

For the east component of the wind,

$$\cos 30° = \frac{v_E}{v}$$

$$v_E = v \cos 30°$$
$$= 40 \text{ mi/hr} \times 0.87$$
$$= 34.8 \text{ mi/hr}$$

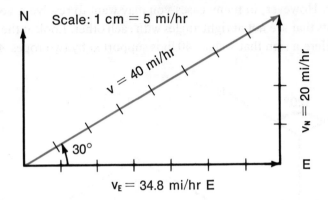

Figure 5-14. Resolving *v* into north and east components.

Problems

21. A boy pulls a heavy box across a wooden floor with a rope. The rope forms an angle of 60° with the floor. The boy maintains a tension of 80 lb on the rope. What force actually is pulling the box across the floor?

22. The boy in Problem 21 lowers the rope until it forms an angle of 30° with the floor. He still maintains a force of 80 lb on the rope. What force pulls the box across the floor?

23. An airplane flies 30° north of west at 500 mi/hr. At what rate is the plane moving (a) north (b) west?

24. A ship sails from Norfolk harbor. It maintains a direction of 45° north of east for a distance of 100 miles. How many miles has the ship progressed from Norfolk (a) north (b) east?

25. A man pushes a lawnmower by applying a force of 70 nt to the handle. Find the horizontal component of his force when he holds the handle at an angle with the lawn of (a) 60° (b) 40° (c) 30°.

26. A guy wire helps to hold a television tower in place. The wire forms an angle of 40° with the tower. It is under a tension of 4000 nt. (a) What force tends to support the tower? (b) What force tends to pull the tower over?

27. A water skier is towed by a speedboat. The skier moves to one side of the boat in such a way that the towrope forms an angle of 55° with the wake of the boat. The tension on the rope is 72 lb. What would be the tension on the rope if the skier were directly behind the boat?

5:9   Resolution into Non-perpendicular Components

In Section 5:8 two single vectors were resolved into two perpendicular components. The single vector was resolved into two components at right angles with each other. However, in many cases you may want to resolve a vector into two components that are not at right angles with each other. Look at the vector in Figure 5-15. Here a sign that weighs 40 lb is supported by two ropes A and B which

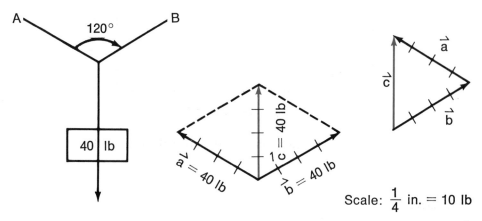

Scale: $\frac{1}{4}$ in. = 10 lb

Figure 5-15.   Resolving the force $\vec{c}$ into the non-perpendicular components $\vec{a}$ and $\vec{b}$.

form an angle of 120°. To keep the sign from falling, the two ropes must produce a net upward force of 40 lb. This force is represented by the vector $\vec{c}$. To find the tension needed in each rope, draw a line with the same direction as rope B from the tail end of vector $\vec{c}$. Then draw a line with the same direction as rope A from the head end of vector $\vec{c}$. The vectors $\vec{a}$ and $\vec{b}$ are limited by the points of intersection of these two lines. By interpreting $\vec{a}$ and $\vec{b}$ in terms of the same scale used for $\vec{c}$, the tension in each rope is determined. In this case, there is a tension of 40 lb in each rope. If the vectors $\vec{a}$, $\vec{b}$, and $\vec{c}$ are added, they form a closed triangle indicating that the sign is in equilibrium.

QUESTIONS

1. Distinguish between vector quantities and scalar quantities.
2. How are vectors always added?

3. When two vectors are added, what is the rule for drawing the resultant vector?

4. A boat travels at 10 m/sec. It heads straight across a river which flows at 3 m/sec. What is its velocity across the river?

5. What is meant by concurrent forces?

6. How does the resultant of two vectors change as the angle between the two vectors increases?

7. A man pushes a lawnmower. How can he increase the horizontal component of the force he applies to the handle of the mower?

8. What is the sum of three vectors that form a closed triangle? Assume that the vectors are force vectors. What does this imply about the object upon which the vector quantities act?

9. How is the equilibrant of two concurrent forces found?

PROBLEMS

1. What is the vector sum of a 65-lb force acting due east and a 30-lb force acting due west?

2. A plane flies due north at 200 km/hr. A wind blows it due east at 50 km/hr. What is the magnitude and direction of the plane's resultant velocity?

3. A boat travels at 8 m/sec and heads straight across a river 240 m wide. The river flows at 4 m/sec. (a) What is the boat's resultant speed with respect to the water? (b) How long does it take the boat to cross the river? (c) How far downstream is the boat when it reaches the other side?

4. Determine the magnitude of the resultant of a 40-lb force and a 70-lb force acting concurrently when the angle between them is (a) 0° (b) 30° (c) 60° (d) 90° (e) 180°.

5. Three men attempt to haul a heavy sign to the roof of a building by means of three ropes attached to the sign. Man A stands directly above the sign and pulls straight up on his rope. Man B and man C stand on either side of man A. Their ropes form 30° angles with man A's rope. Each man applies a force of 100 lb on his rope. What is the net upward force acting on the sign?

6. An electron in the picture tube of a television set is subjected to a magnetic force of 2.6×10^{-24} nt acting horizontally and an electric force of 3.0×10^{-24} nt acting vertically. (a) What is the magnitude of the resultant force acting on the electron? (b) What angle does this force make with the horizontal?

7. A plane travels 40° north of east for a distance of 300 mi. How far north and how far east does the plane travel?

8. A descent vehicle landing on the moon has a vertical velocity toward the surface of the moon of 30 m/sec. At the same time it has a horizontal velocity of 55 m/sec. (a) At what speed does the vehicle move along its descent path? (b) At what angle with the vertical is this path?

9. A boy pushes a lawnmower across a lawn by applying a force of 20 lb to the handle of the mower. The handle makes an angle of 60° with the horizontal. (a) What are the horizontal and vertical components of the force? (b) The boy lowers the handle so that it makes an angle of 30° with the horizontal. He continues to apply a 20-lb force to it. What are the horizontal and vertical components of the force?

10. A man exerts a force of 90 lb on a heavy box by means of a rope. He holds the rope at an angle of 45° with the horizontal. What are the vertical and horizontal components of the 90-lb force?

11. A river flows due south. A riverboat pilot heads his boat 27° north of west and is able to go straight across the river at 6 mi/hr. (a) What is the speed of the current? (b) What is the speed of the boat?

12. A street lamp weighs 30 lb. It is supported by two wires making an angle of 120° with each other. What is the tension of each of these wires.

13. If the angle between the wires in Problem 12 is reduced to 60°, what is the tension of each of the wires?

14. Three forces act concurrently on point P. Force $\vec{a}$ has a magnitude of 80 lb and is directed 30° east of north. Force $\vec{b}$ has a magnitude of 70 lb and is directed due east. Force $\vec{c}$ has a magnitude of 40 lb and is directed 45° south of east. (a) By graphical construction, add these three forces in the order $\vec{a} + \vec{b} + \vec{c}$. (b) By graphical construction, add these three forces in the order $\vec{c} + \vec{b} + \vec{a}$. (c) What is noted about the solutions in each case?

Dynamics

6

Dynamics explains the relationships between forces and motions of bodies. In this chapter you will study Newton's first two laws of motion which deal with inertia and acceleration. Billiard balls, because of their nearly uniform mass and shape and because of their relatively elastic collisions are ideally suited for use in demonstrating these laws. Can you apply Newton's laws in explaining the motions of the billiard balls pictured above?

6:1 Newton's First Law

Kinematics is the study of motion only without regard to the forces that govern motion. However, the science of dynamics explains how forces control the motions of bodies. Most of our knowledge of kinematics was developed by the scientist Galileo (1564–1642). The science of dynamics was investigated by Sir Isaac Newton (1642–1727), who was born in the year of Galileo's death.

Newton based his work on the studies made by Galileo. Newton explained the motions of the many bodies on earth and in the heavens by formulating three laws. They are known today as Newton's laws of motion. This chapter concentrates on the first two of these three laws of motion. Chapter 7 introduces Newton's third law of motion.

In a study of acceleration, Galileo rolled metal balls down smooth inclines. He was impressed by the distance a ball would roll across the floor after leaving his ramps. It occurred to Galileo that if the floor were frictionless and endless, the ball would roll on and on and never stop. This observation by Galileo required a remarkable amount of perception. No bodies on the surface of the earth do behave in this way. Friction is an ever-present force. Friction always causes a moving body to come to rest unless a propelling force constantly is applied to the body. This creates the misleading impression that it is the "natural tendency" for a body in motion to come to rest.

Galileo did not pursue his idea that a body in motion should remain in motion. Newton refined this principle in his first law of motion. *A body at rest or in uniform motion will remain at rest or in uniform motion in a straight line unless acted upon by a net external force.* This law makes it clear that it is the natural tendency of a body to retain whatever motion it has and that it will resist any change in that state of motion. This is a property of all matter. It is called the property of inertia.

The first law also makes the function of forces very clear. *A force is that which is capable of bringing about a change in the state of motion (acceleration) of a material body.*

6:2 Newton's Second Law

Newton's first law of motion implies that there is no fundamental difference between a body at rest and one that is moving with uniform velocity. The two automobiles in Figure 6-1 illustrate this fact. One automobile is at rest while the other one moves along a highway in a straight line at a constant 60 mi/hr.

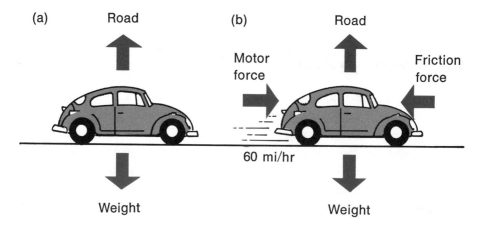

Figure 6-1. When forces are in equilibrium, there is no acceleration.

The automobile at rest is acted upon by two forces. The force of gravity pulls it downward. The force of the parking lot surface pushes it upward. The two forces are equal and opposite. Therefore, their vector sum is zero. The auto-mobile is in equilibrium.

Four forces act upon the automobile that moves along the highway in a straight line at a constant 60 mi/hr. The same two forces are present that act on the auto at rest. They are equal and opposite. The third force is the motor driving the auto forward. The fourth force is the friction opposing the forward motion. These must be equal and opposite because the velocity is constant. By Newton's first law, any unbalanced force would cause the car to accelerate and its speed would not be constant. Therefore, the motor force and the frictional force are equal and opposite. The vector sum of all the forces is zero. The moving auto and the auto at rest are both in equilibrium.

The moving auto illustrates Newton's first law of motion very clearly. As long as the driver keeps the forward force of the motor constant, the speed of the auto does not change. However, if the driver lets up on the accelerator, the motor force decreases and the frictional force is the larger of the two. The auto then is acted upon by a net force and decelerates. If the driver increases the motor force by depressing the accelerator, the motor force becomes larger than the frictional force. Then the car gains speed (accelerates). Just as Newton's first law of motion states, any unbalanced force causes acceleration.

Newton was the first to recognize that a net force always causes acceleration and not just motion. Newton then formulated his second law of motion. *When an unbalanced force acts on a body, the body will be accelerated. The acceleration will vary directly as the applied force, will be in the same direction as the applied force, and will vary inversely as the mass of the body.* The mathematical expression of Newton's second law is,

$$a = \frac{F}{m}$$

More often, Newton's second law of motion is remembered in this form,

$$F = ma$$

6:3   Units of Force

Forces accelerate masses and so are measured in terms of the acceleration they give to standard masses. Suppose a 1-kg mass is located on a completely friction-less, horizontal surface. The force that will accelerate this 1-kg mass at the rate of 1 m/sec² is called one newton.

$$F = ma$$

$$1 \text{ nt} = 1 \text{ kg} \times 1 \text{ m/sec}^2$$

Thus, the newton (nt) is the MKS unit of force.

The pound (lb) is the unit of force in the English system of measurement. It is that force which will accelerate a 1-slug mass at a rate of 1 ft/sec².

$$F = ma$$

$$1 \text{ lb} = 1 \text{ slug} \times 1 \text{ ft/sec}^2$$

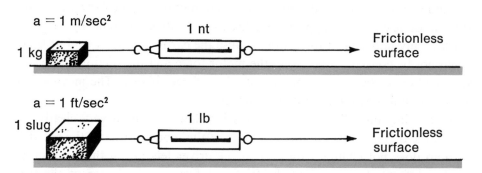

Figure 6-2. Units of force are defined in terms of the acceleration they give standard masses.

Sample Problem 1

A force gives a mass of 2 kg an acceleration of 5 m/sec². What is the magnitude of the force?

Solution:

$$F = ma$$

$$= 2 \text{ kg} \times 5 \text{ m/sec}^2$$

$$= 10 \text{ kg-m/sec}^2 = 10 \text{ nt}$$

Note that in the equation $F = ma$, we have the units nt = kg-m/sec². The equals sign means that the units on either side of the equation can be exchanged. The first sample problem did this when 10 kg-m/sec² was rewritten as 10 nt. By the same equivalence, lb can be exchanged for slug-ft/sec².

Sample Problem 2

A force of 20 lb gives a stone an acceleration of 4 ft/sec². What is the mass of the stone?

Solution:

$$F = ma$$

$$m = \frac{F}{a} = \frac{20 \text{ lb}}{4 \text{ ft/sec}^2}$$

$$= 20 \frac{\text{slug-ft/sec}^2}{4 \text{ ft/sec}^2} = 5 \text{ slugs}$$

Problems

1. A net force of 25 nt is applied to a 10-kg mass. What is the acceleration given to the mass?

2. A 16-lb net force is applied to a 2-slug mass. What is the acceleration of the mass?

3. An athlete exerts a force of 30 lb on a shot-put giving it an acceleration of 60 ft/sec². What is the mass of the shot-put?

4. A 1.5-kg mass accelerates across a smooth table at 15 m/sec². What is the net force applied to it?

5. What acceleration does a net force of 20 nt impart to a mass of (a) 5 kg (b) 10 kg (c) 20 kg (d) 40 kg (e) 100 kg?

6. What force gives a 1-slug mass an acceleration of 32 ft/sec²?

7. What force gives a 1-kg mass an acceleration of 9.8 m/sec²?

8. An artillery shell has a mass of 8 kg. The shell is fired from the muzzle of a gun with a speed of 700 m/sec. The gun barrel is 3.5 m long. What is the average force on the shell while it is in the gun barrel? (Hint: use $v^2 = 2as$)

9. A racing car has a mass of 50 slugs. It starts from rest and travels 352 ft in 2 sec. The car undergoes uniform acceleration during the entire 2 sec. What force is applied to it? $\left(\text{Ignore friction; use } s = \dfrac{at^2}{2} \right)$

6:4   Weight and Mass

It is important to understand clearly the distinction between weight and mass. Mass depends upon the amount of matter in a body. It is related to

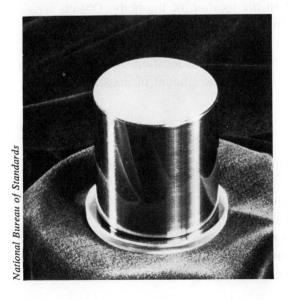

Figure 6-3. The international standard of mass is a platinum-iridium cylinder to which is assigned the value of exactly 1 kilogram.

the actual number of protons, neutrons, and electrons that make up the body. Weight refers to the gravitational force exerted on a given mass by the earth. It is a special name for gravitational force. Weight is measured in pounds or newtons, as are other forces. Mass, however, is measured in kilograms or slugs.

For example, consider the force that must act on a 1-kg mass allowed to fall freely from some point near the earth's surface. The kilogram mass accelerates at the rate of 9.8 m/sec². By Newton's second law of motion, the force needed to accelerate a 1-kg mass at the rate of 9.8 m/sec² is,

$$F = ma$$
$$= 1 \text{ kg} \times 9.8 \text{ m/sec}^2$$
$$= 9.8 \text{ kg-m/sec}^2$$
$$= 9.8 \text{ nt}$$

Thus, the earth's gravitational field must exert a force of 9.8 nt on the kilogram mass. Therefore, the kilogram mass weighs 9.8 nt.

Usually when Newton's second law is used to determine the weight of a mass, it is written in the form $W = mg$. The W represents the weight, the m represents the mass, and the g represents the acceleration of gravity. Using this method to determine the weight of a 1-slug mass:

$$W = mg$$
$$= 1 \text{ slug} \times 32 \text{ ft/sec}^2$$
$$= 32 \text{ slug-ft/sec}^2$$
$$= 32 \text{ lb}$$

Hence, a 1-slug mass weighs 32 lb.

The weight of a body varies with the location of the body. Objects weigh slightly less when on an airplane in flight than they do at sea level. An object on the moon weighs only one-sixth as much as it does on the earth. However, the mass of an object is the same regardless of its location. Moving an object from one place to another does not change the amount of mass in the object.

Problems

Use Newton's second law of motion expressed as $W = mg$ to solve these problems.

10. Determine the weight of a 4-slug mass.

11. A stone weighs 96 lb. What is its mass?

12. What is the weight in newtons of a 5-kg mass?

13. An object weighs 98 nt. What is its mass in kilograms?

14. What is the weight of a 20-kg mass?

15. What is the weight of a 20-slug mass?

16. An economy car has a mass of 50 slugs. What is the weight of the car?

17. An automobile has a mass of 1000 kg. What is its weight in newtons?

18. A small yacht weighs 4900 nt. What is its mass in kilograms?

19. An 8-kg mass weighs 78.4 nt. At what rate does the weight of the mass accelerate it?

20. (a) An automobile has a mass of 100 slugs. What is the weight of the car?
(b) Disregarding friction, what force does the car motor apply to accelerate the car along a level highway at the rate of 8 ft/sec²?

6:5   Net Forces and Acceleration

Newton's second law of motion ($F = ma$) requires that the force producing the acceleration of a mass be a net force. If a force of 100 lb is applied to a 10-slug mass located on a smooth, horizontal surface, the resulting acceleration is:

$$F = ma$$

$$a = \frac{F}{m} = \frac{100 \text{ lb}}{10 \text{ slug}} = \frac{100 \text{ slug-ft/sec}^2}{10 \text{ slug}} = 10 \text{ ft/sec}^2$$

If a frictional force is present, the actual net force must be known before the acceleration can be computed correctly. Suppose in this case the frictional force involved is 20 lb. The net force acting on the 10-slug mass is 100 lb − 20 lb or 80 lb. The acceleration amounts to 8 ft/sec² rather than 10 ft/sec².

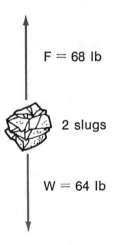

F = 68 lb

2 slugs

W = 64 lb

Figure 6-4.   A mass is accelerated upward if the total force exerted upward is greater than the weight.

Friction is not the only agent that prevents the total force applied to a body from being the net force acting on it. The stone in Figure 6-4 weighs 64 lb. This means that the earth pulls down on the stone with a force of 64 lb. If someone lifts up on the stone with a total force of 68 lb, the net force acting on it is only

4 lb. To find the acceleration the 4-lb net force produces on the stone, determine its mass first. Use,

$$W = mg$$

$$m = \frac{W}{g} = \frac{64 \text{ lb}}{32 \text{ ft/sec}^2} = \frac{64 \text{ slug-ft/sec}^2}{32 \text{ ft/sec}^2} = 2 \text{ slugs}$$

The acceleration given to the 2-slug stone by the net force of 4 lb must be in accord with Newton's second law,

$$F = ma$$

$$a = \frac{F}{m} = \frac{4 \text{ lb}}{2 \text{ slug}} = \frac{4 \text{ slug-ft/sec}^2}{2 \text{ slug}} = 2 \text{ ft/sec}^2$$

The 68-lb force applied to the stone accelerates it straight up at 2 ft/sec².

Problems

21. A stone weighs 96 lb. (a) What is its mass? (b) At what rate is the stone accelerated straight up if a 108-lb force is applied to it in that direction?
22. A stone weighs 4.9 nt. (a) What is its mass? (b) At what rate is the stone accelerated straight up if a 69-nt force is applied to it in that direction?
23. An automobile located on a level highway has a mass of 75 slugs. The frictional forces opposing the motion of the auto are 150 lb. What acceleration does a total force of 450 lb produce on it?
24. A small rocket weighs 14.7 nt. (a) What is its mass? (b) The rocket is fired from a high platform but its engine fails to burn properly. The rocket gains only a total up force of 10.2 nt. At what rate and in what direction is the rocket accelerated?
25. A boy exerts a force of 12 lb on an 8-lb stone in a direction straight up. Calculate (a) the mass of the stone (b) the net force acting on the stone (c) the acceleration of the stone.
26. The instruments attached to a weather balloon have a mass of 5 kg. (a) What do the instruments weigh? (b) The balloon is released on a calm day and exerts a total up force of 98 nt on the instruments. At what rate does the balloon with instruments accelerate straight up? (c) After 10 seconds of acceleration, the weather instruments are released automatically. What is the magnitude and direction of their velocity at that instant? (d) What net force acts on the instruments after their release? (e) What time elapses before the instruments begin to fall straight down?
27. A rocket which weighs 1600 lb on the earth is fired. The net force of propulsion is 2400 lb. Determine (a) the mass of the rocket (b) the upward acceleration of the rocket (c) the velocity of the rocket at the end of 10 sec.

6:6 Two Ways of Measuring Mass

One method to determine the mass of a body is to use a beam-balance. By this method, an unknown mass is placed on one pan at the end of a beam. The known masses are added to the pan at the other end of the beam until the pans balance. Since the force of gravity then is the same on each pan, the masses must also be the same on each pan. The beam-balance method actually is one of comparison rather than of weighing. It has the advantage of eliminating all concern about the variations of gravitational force from place to place. The same result for a measurement by the beam-balance method is obtained anywhere. The mass of a body when measured by comparison with known masses on a beam-balance is called the gravitational mass of the body.

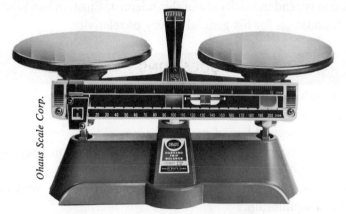

Ohaus Scale Corp.

Figure 6-5. A beam balance compares masses. The unknown mass is placed on the left and compared with known masses placed on the right. The masses are equal when the weights are equal causing the beam to be balanced.

The second method to determine the mass of a body is distinctly different. It uses the property of inertia. Suppose that a mass is placed on a completely frictionless, horizontal surface. Then a known force is applied to it. The magnitude of the mass is determined by carefully measuring the acceleration produced upon it by the known force. In accordance with Newton's second law of motion, $m = F/a$. Mass measured in this way is said to be the inertial mass of the body in question. This second method to determine the mass of a body seldom is used because it involves both a frictionless surface and a difficult measurement of acceleration. The gravitational method of mass measurement is much easier and more popular.

Gravitational and inertial mass measurements give exactly the same numerical value for mass. However, the fact that gravitational and inertial mass always have the same magnitude for a given mass is not to be accepted as "natural."

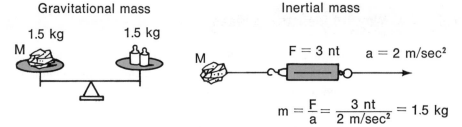

Figure 6-6. Measuring gravitational and inertial mass.

The two methods for the determination of the same quantity differ radically. For a long time this duality was taken to be one of nature's most remarkable coincidences. However, Albert Einstein did not think of this as a mere coincidence. As you may read in books about this scientist, Einstein used the phenomenon as the foundation for his general theory of relativity.

QUESTIONS

1. State Newton's first law of motion.
2. What do net forces produce?
3. State Newton's second law of motion.
4. Use Newton's second law of motion to explain why you may not be able to push a freight car down a track.
5. An automobile travels along a level highway at 50 mi/hr. Why is the auto said to be in equilibrium?
6. Define a newton.
7. Define a kilogram (use the newton and meter).
8. Define the pound.
9. An object on earth has a mass of 2 kg. What would be the mass of the object if it were taken to Jupiter where the pull of gravity is 10 times that of earth.
10. A boy stands on a bathroom scale in an elevator. He weighs 128 lb.
    (a) What does the scale read when the elevator is at rest?
    (b) The elevator starts to move up and accelerates the boy straight up at 4 ft/sec². What does the scale read now?
    (c) The elevator finally reaches a desirable speed and no longer accelerates. What is the boy's reading on the scale as the elevator rises uniformly?
    (d) The elevator begins to slow down as it reaches the proper floor. Do the scale readings increase or decrease?
    (e) The elevator starts to come down. Do the scale readings increase or decrease?
    (f) What does the scale read if the elevator comes down uniformly?
    (g) If the elevator cable snaps and the elevator assumes free-fall, what does the scale read?

1. Determine the acceleration that a force of 25 nt gives to a 4-kg mass. The frictional force to be overcome is 5 nt.
2. What net force gives an acceleration of 20 ft/sec² to a 1600-lb racing car?
3. Determine the weights of these masses. (a) 10 slugs (b) 22 slugs (c) 0.25 slug (d) 0.75 slug (e) 14 kg (f) 0.43 kg (g) 0.7 kg.
4. Determine the mass of these weights. (a) 320 lb (b) 16 lb (c) 48 lb (d) 4 lb (e) 98 nt (f) 80 nt (g) 0.98 nt.
5. What force keeps a 20-lb stone from falling?
6. What total force accelerates a 20-lb stone straight up at 10 ft/sec²?
7. A rocket weighs 9800 nt. (a) What is its mass? (b) What force gives it a vertical acceleration of 4 m/sec²?
8. An automobile travels at 80 ft/sec. The auto weighs 1600 lb. (a) What braking force brings it to rest in 320 ft? (b) in 32 ft?
9. A boy pulls a sled along level ground. The sled's rope makes an angle of 60° with the snow-covered ground. He pulls with a force of 36 lb. Determine the acceleration he gives to the sled if it weighs 48 lb and the frictional force to be overcome is 3 lb.
10. An elevator plus occupants weighs 3200 lb. The tension in the cable is 4000 lb. At what rate does the elevator accelerate upward?
11.

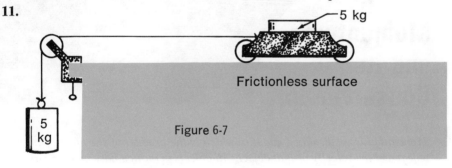

Figure 6-7

Determine the acceleration of the system.
12. A young woman plans to elope and wants to leave her room unnoticed. She makes a rope of nylon stockings that can support a maximum of 80 lb. The bride-to-be weighs 96 lb. (a) At what minimum rate must she allow herself to be accelerated downward if she is to descend without breaking the rope? (b) Her window is 50 ft above the ground. With what speed does she strike the ground?
13. An astronaut 100 m from his spaceship observes a 200-kg meteoroid drift past him toward the ship at 10 m/sec. If the astronaut can gain a hold on the meteoroid and the astronaut's rocket gun is capable of delivering a force of 100 nt, can he stop it before it hits the spaceship? (Neglect the mass of the astronaut.)

7 Momentum and its Conservation

Momentum is a calculated quantity which is the product of the mass of an object and the velocity of that object. All objects in motion have momentum. Do objects at rest have momentum? Can you apply Newton's third law, discussed in this chapter, to explain the liftoff process of the Apollo rocket pictured above?

7:1 Momentum

Momentum is the product of a body's mass and its velocity.

$$Momentum = Mass \times Velocity$$

Like velocity, momentum is a vector quantity. It has the same direction as the velocity. A body can have a large momentum if it has a large mass, or if it has a large velocity, or both.

The momentum of a mass changes whenever its velocity changes. Therefore, any acceleration produces a change in momentum. Accelerations are the result of net forces, so net forces must bring about momentum changes. Newton's second law of motion states this clearly.

$$F = ma$$

$$a = \frac{\Delta v}{t}$$

$$F = \frac{m\Delta v}{t}$$

$$Ft = m\Delta v$$

This is known as the momentum form of Newton's second law of motion. It says that when an unbalanced force acts on a body, it produces a change in the momentum of the body that is in the same direction as the applied force. It is proportional to the applied force and the time interval through which the force acts. The quantity Ft is called impulse. It is the impulse that produces the change in momentum $m\Delta v$. The statement above is read:

Impulse = Change in Momentum

Sample Problem 1

A force of 20 nt acts upon a 2-kg mass for 10 sec. Compute (a) the change in momentum (b) the resultant change in the speed of the mass.

Solution:

(a) $Ft = m\Delta v$

20 nt × 10 sec = 200 nt-sec

(b) $Ft = m\Delta v$

200 nt-sec = 2 kg (Δv)

$$\Delta v = \frac{200 \text{ kg-m/sec}^2 \text{ (sec)}}{2 \text{ kg}}$$

$$\Delta v = 100 \text{ m/sec}$$

Problems

1. An automobile weighs 1600 lb. (a) What is its mass? (b) The automobile's velocity is 40 ft/sec eastward. What is its momentum? (c) The auto was accelerated from rest to 40 ft/sec by a force of 100 lb. How long did the force act to give it this velocity?
2. A force of 6 nt acts on a body for 10 sec. (a) What is the body's change in momentum? (b) The mass of the body is 3 kg. What is its change in speed?
3. A car weighs 2400 lb and moves at 66 ft/sec. What braking force is needed to bring the car to a halt in 20 sec? (Neglect friction.)

4. A net force of 2000 nt acts on a rocket of mass 1000 kg. How long does it take this force to increase the rocket's speed from 0 m/sec to 200 m/sec?

5. A snow-scooter has a mass of 250 kg. A constant force acts upon it for 60 sec. The scooter's initial speed is 6 m/sec and its final speed is 28 m/sec. (a) What change in momentum does it undergo? (b) What is the magnitude of the force which acts upon it?

6. A car weighing 3520 lb and moving at 60 ft/sec is acted upon by a 220-lb force until it is brought to a halt. (a) What is the car's mass? (b) What is its initial momentum? (c) What change in the car's momentum does the force bring about? (d) How long does the braking force act on the car to bring it to a halt?

7. A constant force acts on a 600-kg mass for 68 sec. The speed of the mass before the application of the force is 10 m/sec. Its final speed is 44 m/sec. (a) What change in momentum does the force produce? (b) What is the magnitude of the force?

7:2   Newton's Third Law of Motion

Newton's first and second laws of motion were introduced in Chapter 6. Newton's third and final law of motion is called the law of action and reaction. This law states that every force is accompanied by an equal and opposite force. According to this law, there is no such thing as a single force. No body is capable of producing a force unless it has some other body to exert its force upon. Your hand pushes a ball; one magnet repels a second magnet; one charged body repels another charged body. There are always two bodies involved in any interaction.

Newton's second law of motion points out that when one body exerts a force on another, the second body accelerates. A fact often overlooked is that the body exerting the force also accelerates. For example, a golfer hits a ball with a golf club. The ball obviously is accelerated. But, so is the club. The club accelerates in a direction just opposite to the ball. After striking the ball, the club slows down (accelerates). The force produced on the ball by the club accelerates the ball, but so, too, the force exerted on the club by the ball accelerates the club. If body A produces a force on body B, then body B exerts an equal and opposite force on body A. Walking is an excellent example of Newton's third law of motion. As a person walks, he actually attempts to push the earth away from him. The reaction force of the earth on his feet propels him forward.

7:3   The Law of Conservation of Momentum

When two bodies interact, the third law of motion requires that exactly equal and opposite forces appear. These forces appear together and disappear together. Thus the time the force acts on each is the same. This means that the impulse (Ft) given to each body must be exactly the same though oppositely directed.

For Body A		For Body B
Ft	$=$	$-Ft$

and therefore $\qquad\qquad \Delta mv \quad = \quad -\Delta mv$

It follows from this that any gain in momentum by any body occurs only through the loss of a corresponding amount of momentum by another body. To understand the law of conservation of momentum, consider a system consisting of many bodies, such as the molecules in a small container of gas. Although the gas particles constantly are colliding and changing one another's momentum, each particle can only gain the momentum lost by another particle during a collision. Therefore, the total momentum of the system cannot change. In a system consisting of bodies upon which no outside force is acting, the total momentum of the system is constant.

When two particles collide, one particle can only gain the momentum lost by the other. Therefore, the momentum of the first particle plus the momentum of the second particle before the collision must equal the momentum of the first particle plus the momentum of the second particle after the collision.

$$m_1v_1 + m_2v_2 = m_1v_1' + m_2v_2'$$

Sample Problem 2

A glass ball of mass 5 g moves with a speed of 20 cm/sec. This ball collides with a second glass ball of mass 10 g which is moving along the same line with a speed of 10 cm/sec. After the collision, the 5 g mass still is moving along the same line, but it only has a speed of 8 cm/sec. What is the velocity (speed and direction) of the 10 g mass?

Solution:

$$m_1v_1 + m_2v_2 = m_1v_1' + m_2v_2'$$
$$(5 \times 20) + (10 \times 10) = (5 \times 8) + (10\ v_2')$$
$$200 = 40 + 10\ v_2'$$
$$160 = 10\ v_2'$$
$$v_2' = 16 \text{ cm/sec in its original direction}$$

Problems

8. A plastic ball of mass 200 g moves with a speed of 30 cm/sec. This plastic ball collides with a second plastic ball of mass 100 g which is moving along the same line with a speed of 10 cm/sec. After the collision, the velocity of

the 100 g mass is 18 cm/sec along the same line. What is the velocity (speed and direction) of the 200 g mass?

9. An ivory ball of mass 10 g moving with a speed of 20 cm/sec collides with a second ivory ball of mass 20 g moving along the same line in the same direction with a speed of 10 cm/sec. After the collision, the first ball is still moving in its original direction, but it has a speed of only 8 cm/sec. Determine the velocity (speed and direction) of the second ball after the collision.

10. A steel glider of mass 5 kg moves along an air-track with a speed of 15 m/sec. It overtakes and collides with a second steel glider of mass 10 kg moving in the same direction along the track with a speed of 7.5 m/sec. After the collision the first glider continues along the same line at 7 m/sec. (a) With what velocity (speed and direction) did the second steel glider leave the collision? (b) What is the change in momentum of the first glider? (c) What is the change in momentum of the second glider?

11. A car of mass 50 slugs travels at 20 ft/sec. The car collides with a stationary truck of mass 100 slugs. The two vehicles interlock as a result of the collision. What is the velocity (speed and direction) of the car-truck system?

12. A bullet of mass 50 g strikes a wooden block of mass 5 kg. The bullet becomes embedded in the block and the block with the bullet in it flies off at 10 m/sec. What was the original velocity of the bullet?

13. A billiard ball of mass 200 g travels at 40 cm/sec. This ball overtakes a second billiard ball of mass 150 g which is traveling along the same line at 15 cm/sec. After the collision, the 200 g ball moves along the same line at 20 cm/sec. What is the velocity of the second ball?

Figure 7-1. The momentum of the shell is equal to the momentum of the gun.

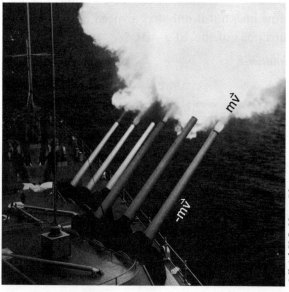

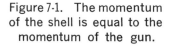

The law of conservation of momentum states that an outside force is needed to change the momentum of any system. This means that an *internal* force is incapable of changing the momentum of any system. Consider what happens when a shell is fired from a cannon. Before the firing, the cannon and shell are at rest. The total momentum of the cannon-shell system is zero. During the firing, the gases produced by the burning powder exert an internal force which cannot change the momentum of the system. Therefore, the momentum of the *system* must be zero after the firing just as it was before. This means that the forward momentum given to the shell must be equal and opposite to the backward momentum given to the cannon. Thus, if the momentum of the shell is considered to be positive, the momentum of the cannon is considered to be negative. Since the two momenta are equal in magnitude, their sum must be zero.

Sample Problem 3

A 20-kg shell leaves the muzzle of a 1200-kg cannon with a velocity of 600 m/sec forward. What is the recoil velocity of the cannon?

Solution:

Momentum before firing $=$ Momentum after firing

$$m_c v_c + m_s v_s = m_c v_c' + m_s v_s'$$
$$(1200 \times 0) + (20 \times 0) = (1200\ v_c') + (20 \times 600)$$
$$0 = 1200\ v_c' + 12000$$
$$v_c' = -10 \text{ m/sec}$$

The negative sign means that its direction is in the opposite direction from the shell.

Problems

14. A 40-kg shell leaves the muzzle of a 2000-kg cannon with a velocity of 800 m/sec forward. What is the recoil velocity (speed and direction) of the cannon?
15. A 40-slug cannon fires an 0.25 slug shell. The recoil velocity of the cannon is 10 ft/sec backward. What is the velocity (speed and direction) of the shell?
16. Use weights instead of mass to work problem 15. What solution is obtained? Why?
17. A bullet of mass 50 g is fired from a gun of mass 4 kg. The gun has a muzzle velocity of 600 m/sec. What is the gun's speed of recoil?
18. A young man succeeds in bringing his canoe alongside a dock and brings it to rest there. He then steps from the canoe to the dock. If the man weighs 180 lb and manages to propel himself forward at 12 ft/sec with what velocity

will his canoe plus lady friend weighing a total of 240 lb move away from the dock?

19. A locomotive with a rocket engine is being tested on a smooth, horizontal track. The mass of the locomotive is 12 000 kg. Starting from rest, the engines are fired for 20 sec. During this time they expel 500 kg of oxidized kerosene. The kerosene particles expel at an average speed of 1200 m/sec. Calculate the speed of the locomotive at the end of the 20-sec period.

20.

Figure 7-2

A light thread holds two carts together on a frictionless surface. As shown, a spring acts upon the carts. The thread burns and the 1.5-kg cart moves off with a velocity of 27 cm/sec to the right. What is the velocity of the 4.5-kg cart?

7:4   The Conservation of Momentum in General

So far, the treatment of the law of conservation of momentum has been confined to the interaction between two bodies that travel along the same line. However, the law of conservation of momentum is much more general in form. Momentum is always conserved. This is regardless of how many masses collide simultaneously and regardless of their directions prior to the collision.

Momentum is a vector quantity. The law of conservation of momentum states that *the vector sum of the momenta of all the bodies in a system remains constant in the absence of an external force.* Figure 7-3 illustrates how the vector sum of the momenta of a system remains constant when the collisions are glancing rather than head-on. Here a steel ball of mass 2 kg moves at 5 m/sec across a smooth surface toward a second stationary steel ball of mass 2 kg. The bodies collide and move off in the directions shown. Since the mass of each ball is 2 kg and the velocity of each can be measured, it is possible to calculate the momentum of each after the collision takes place. The vectors in part(b)of the diagram represent the momentum of each ball after the collision. The addition of these vectors in part(c)shows that their vector sum is equal to the momentum possessed by the original ball. Thus, the momentum of the system is the same after the collision as it was before the collision. If the collision had taken place between several steel balls simultaneously, the result would be no different. The vector sum of the momenta before the collision would be the same as the vector sum of the momenta after the collision.

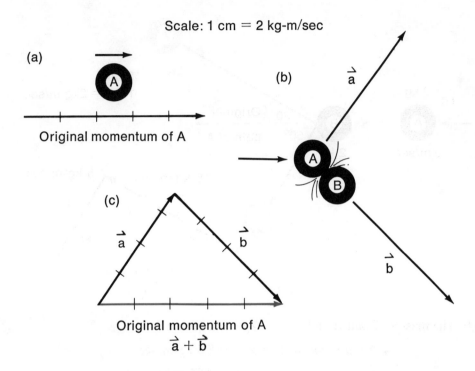

Figure 7-3.   The vector sum of the momenta is constant.

Sample Problem 4

Ball *A* of mass 2 kg moves at a speed of 5 m/sec. Ball *A* collides with a second stationary ball *B*, also of mass 2 kg. After the collision, ball *A* moves off in a direction 30° to the left of its original direction. Ball *B* moves off in a direction 60° to the right of ball *A*'s original direction. (a) Draw a vector diagram to determine the momentum of ball *A* and ball *B* after the collision. (b) What is the speed of each ball after the collision?

Solution:

(a) The vector sum of ball *A*'s momentum and ball *B*'s momentum after the collision must equal the momentum of balls *A* and *B* before the collision. Since ball *B* was at rest prior to the collision, this must be just the momentum possessed by ball *A* prior to the collision. The momentum of ball *A* (10 kg-m/sec) is represented by a vector which is resolved into two components **a** and **b** along the directions taken by balls *A* and *B* after the collision. This is done in Figure 7-4. Direct measurement to scale yields the magnitudes of the momenta:

$$a = 8.5 \text{ kg-m/sec}$$
$$b = 5.0 \text{ kg-m/sec}$$

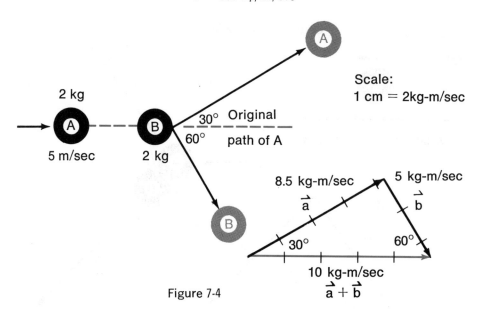

Figure 7-4

(b) The masses of ball A and B are 2 kg each. Hence:

$$a = mv = 2 \text{ kg} \times v = 8.5 \text{ kg-m/sec}$$
$$v = 4.25 \text{ m/sec}$$
$$b = mv = 2 \text{ kg} \times v = 5.0 \text{ kg-m/sec}$$
$$v = 2.5 \text{ m/sec}$$

Problems

21. Ball A of mass 5 kg moves at a speed of 4 cm/sec. It collides with a second stationary ball B, also of mass 5 kg. After the collision, ball A moves off in the direction 45° to the left of its original direction. Ball B moves off in the direction 45° to the right of ball A's original direction.
(a) Draw a vector diagram to determine the momentum of ball A and ball B after the collision. (b) What is the speed of each ball after the collision?

22. Body A of mass 6 kg moves at a speed of 3 m/sec. It collides with a second body B, also of mass 6 kg. After the collision, body A moves off in the direction 50° to the left of its original direction. Body B moves off in the direction 40° to the right of body A's original direction. (a) Draw a vector diagram to determine the momentum of body A and body B. (b) What is the speed of each body after the collision?

From PSSC PHYSICS, D. C. Heath & Company, Lexington, 1965

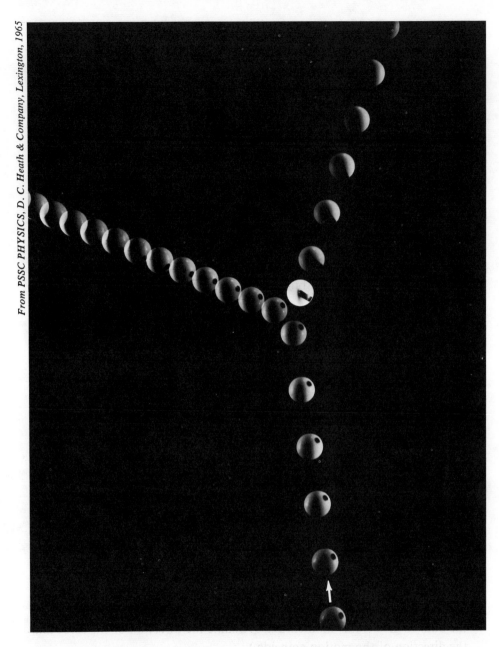

Figure 7-5.   This photograph accompanies Problem 23.

23. A billiard ball of mass 0.5 kg moves at a speed of 10 m/sec. It collides with a second stationary billiard ball, also of mass 0.5 kg. After the collision, the first ball moves off in a direction 60° to the left of its original direction. The second ball moves off in a direction 30° to the right of the first ball's original direction. (a) Draw a vector diagram to determine the momentum of each billiard ball. (b) What is the speed of each ball after the collision?

QUESTIONS

1. Define momentum.
2. Define impulse.
3. Your hand applies a force to a body for 6 sec. How long does the body apply a force to your hand?
4. State Newton's third law of motion.
5. Write an equation that expresses the momentum of any two particles before and after they collide.
6. Explain why an internal force cannot change the total momentum of any system.
7. Billiard ball A travels across a pool table and collides with a stationary billiard ball B. The mass of ball B is equal to the mass of ball A. After the collision, ball A is at rest. What must be true of ball B?
8. Would it be possible for a bullet to have the same momentum as a 10-ton truck? Explain.

PROBLEMS

1. A force of 50 nt is applied to a hockey puck for 2 sec. Calculate the magnitude of this impulse.
2. Assume the puck in Problem 1 has a mass of 0.5 kg and is at rest before the impulse acts upon it. With what speed does it move across the ice after the 2-sec period?
3. A 3200-lb automobile leaves a parking lot. Thirty seconds later it is moving along a highway at 60 mi/hr. (a) What is the automobile's change in momentum? (b) What average force does the motor produce to bring about this change in momentum?
4. A force of 8.0 nt acts on a 2.0-kg mass for 5 sec. (a) What is the change in momentum of the mass? (b) What is the change in the speed of the mass?
5. The mass of an auto is 1600 kg. The auto's velocity is 20 m/sec in a straight line. (a) What is its momentum? (b) How long must a force of 800 nt act on the auto to give it this momentum? (Assume the direction of the force and the direction of the motion coincide.)
6. Two plastic balls are moving in the same direction. One ball of mass 100 g moves with a speed of 20 cm/sec. It collides head on with a second plastic ball of mass 40 g moving with a speed of 10 cm/sec. After the collision, the 100-g mass has a velocity of 15 cm/sec in its original direction. What is the velocity (speed and direction) of the 40-g ball after the collision?
7. A bullet of mass 30 g is fired from a gun of mass 4 kg at a speed of 800 m/sec. What is the speed of recoil of the gun?

Motion in Two Dimensions

Motion in two dimensions refers to motion other than straight-line motion of a body. The pole-vaulter pictured above is increasing his distance above the ground. In what other direction is his body moving at the same time?

8:1 Projectile Motion

Previous chapters considered only straight line motion. What happens when motion does not occur in a straight line? Consider free fall under gravity when there is horizontal motion simultaneously. This is called the motion of a *projectile*. It includes all cases of bodies thrown or otherwise projected into the air. The path of the body is called its *trajectory*.

To begin the study of projectile behavior, consider the case of a projectile fired horizontally from a height. The vertical behavior and the horizontal behavior of such a projectile are independent of one another. In Figure 8-1, two golf balls are released simultaneously. Flash photography reveals the paths followed by the balls. One ball is projected horizontally while the other

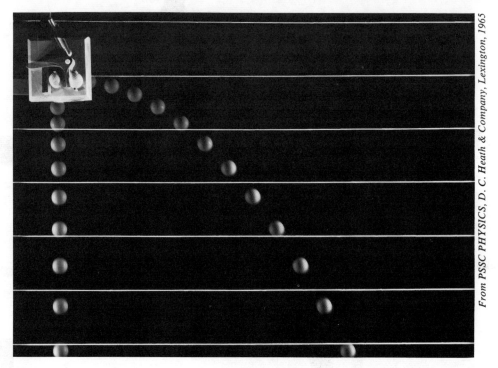

From PSSC PHYSICS, D. C. Heath & Company, Lexington, 1965

Figure 8-1.   A flash photograph of two golf balls released simultaneously. Both balls were allowed to fall freely, but one was projected horizontally with an initial velocity of 2.00 m/sec. The light flashes were 1/30 sec apart.

is dropped. Notice that even though the projected ball moves to the right, its vertical position is, at all times, the same as the position of the dropped ball. Vertically the projected ball behaves as if it had no horizontal velocity and is simply falling. Also notice that horizontally the projected ball moves to the right by the same amount during each time interval between flashes. The fact that the ball is falling does not change the rate at which it moves to the right. Both the horizontal and vertical velocities of the ball act as if the other velocity did not exist.

To determine the horizontal distance a projectile travels while it is falling, the horizontal velocity and the time of fall must be known. The horizontal distance then will be the horizontal velocity times the time of fall.

Sample Problem 1

A boy throws a stone horizontally at a speed of 15 m/sec. He is standing at the top of a cliff 44 m high. (a) How long does it take the stone to reach the bottom of the cliff? (b) How far from the base of the cliff does the stone strike the ground?

Solution:

(a) Find the time it takes for an object starting from rest to fall 44 m.

$$s = \frac{gt^2}{2}$$

$$t = \sqrt{\frac{2s}{g}}$$

$$t = \sqrt{\frac{2 \times 44 \text{ m}}{9.8 \text{ m/sec}^2}}$$

$$t = \sqrt{9 \text{ sec}^2}$$

$$t = 3 \text{ sec}$$

(b) The stone travels horizontally at 15 m/sec all the time it is falling.

$$s = vt$$

$$s = 15 \text{ m/sec} \times 3 \text{ sec}$$

$$s = 45 \text{ m}$$

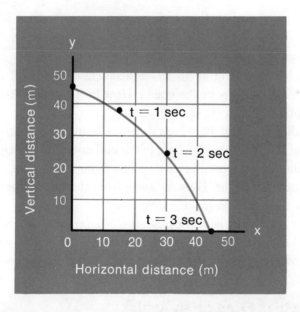

Figure 8-2. The path of the projectile for Sample Problem 1.

Problems

1. A steel projectile is shot horizontally from the top of a 49-m high tower at 20 m/sec. How far away from the base of the tower does it hit the ground?

2. A boy throws a stone horizontally at a speed of 30 ft/sec. He is standing at the top of a cliff 256 ft high. (a) How long does it take the stone to reach the bottom of the cliff? (b) How far from the base of the cliff does the stone strike the ground?

3. Sky jumpers fall from an airplane flying horizontally at 30 m/sec at a height of 1960 m. What horizontal distance do the ment ravel before striking the ground? (Neglect air resistance and effect of the parachute.)

Official U.S. Navy Photo

Figure 8-3. Sky divers forming a ''star'' two miles above the ground.

4. An automobile traveling at 38 ft/sec accidentally rolls off the edge of a cliff. The cliff is 64 ft above the ocean. How far from the base of the cliff is the automobile when it strikes the water?

5. A boy standing on a cliff 49 m high throws a stone with a horizontal velocity of 15 m/sec. How far from the base of the cliff does the stone hit the ground?

6. A bombardier drops a bomb from a plane flying at a height of 6400 ft. The plane's speed is 90 mi/hr. How far away from the target does the bombardier release the bomb to make a direct hit?

7. An arrow is fired directly at the bull's-eye of a target 60 m away. The arrow has a speed of 89 m/sec. The range is level and the arrow is 1 m above the ground. How far short of the target does it strike the ground?

8:2 Projectiles Fired at an Angle

The principle of independence of velocities still holds when a projectile is fired at an angle with the horizontal. The initial velocity of the projectile is resolved into two components. One component is directed vertically and the second component is directed horizontally. The component velocities then are treated separately.

Figure 8-4. The hunter sights the correct shooting angle so that the shot hits the bird.

Sample Problem 2

A shell is fired from a field gun with a speed of 128 ft/sec. The gun's barrel makes an angle of 30° with the horizontal. Calculate (a) the vertical velocity and the horizontal velocity of the shell. (b) the time the shell remains in the air. (c) the distance the shell travels horizontally.

Solution:

(a) Resolve $\vec{v}$ into its vertical and horizontal components either graphically or by calculation.

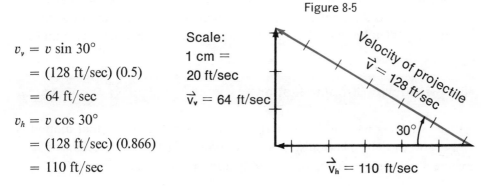

Figure 8-5

$$v_v = v \sin 30°$$
$$= (128 \text{ ft/sec}) (0.5)$$
$$= 64 \text{ ft/sec}$$
$$v_h = v \cos 30°$$
$$= (128 \text{ ft/sec}) (0.866)$$
$$= 110 \text{ ft/sec}$$

Scale:
1 cm =
20 ft/sec

$\vec{v_v} = 64$ ft/sec

Velocity of projectile
$\vec{v} = 128$ ft/sec

30°

$\vec{v_h} = 110$ ft/sec

(b) The initial vertical velocity of the shell is 64 ft/sec. It takes the acceleration of gravity 2 sec to bring the shell to a halt vertically and 2 sec more to return the shell to the earth. Total time in the air is 4 sec.

(c) While the shell is going up and down, the horizontal velocity of 110 ft/sec is constant. Since the shell spends 4 sec in the air, the horizontal distance it travels is,

$$s = vt$$
$$= (110 \text{ ft/sec}) (4 \text{ sec})$$
$$= 440 \text{ ft}$$

Problems

Assume no frictional effects.

8. A shell is fired from a field gun at such an angle that the vertical component of its velocity is 49 m/sec. The horizontal component of its velocity is 60 m/sec. (a) How long does the shell remain in the air? (b) What horizontal distance does the shell travel?

9. A shell is fired from a field gun with a speed of 128 ft/sec. The gun's barrel forms a 60° angle with the horizontal. Calculate (a) the vertical velocity and the horizontal velocity of the shell (b) the time the shell remains in the air (c) the horizontal distance the shell travels.

10. A projectile is fired at an angle of 53° with the horizontal. The speed of the projectile is 200 ft/sec. Calculate (a) the time the shell remains in the air. (b) the horizontal distance it travels.

11. A bullet has a muzzle velocity of 700 m/sec as it leaves the barrel of a rifle. The rifle is fired at an angle of 45° with the horizontal. Determine (a) the vertical and horizontal components of the bullet's velocity (b) the time the bullet spends in the air (c) the horizontal distance the bullet travels.

12. While standing on an open bed of a truck traveling 35 m/sec, an archer sees a duck flying directly overhead. He shoots an arrow at the duck and misses. The arrow leaves his bow with a vertical velocity of 98 m/sec. (a) How long does it remain in the air? (b) The truck maintains a constant speed of 35 m/sec and does not change its direction. Where does the arrow finally land? (c) What horizontal distance does the arrow travel while it is in the air?

8:3 Uniform Circular Motion

When studying motion of any sort it is well to bear in mind that motion is *always* governed by Newton's laws of motion. If a body is accelerated it is because a net force is acting on the body and that $F = ma$ *always*.

The Brush Beryllium Company

Figure 8-6. Each point along the rotating wheel of the gyroscope is accelerated toward the center of rotation. The centripetal acceleration is associated with the centripetal force acting toward the center.

In this section we will derive and use the equations that deal with the conditions for circular motion. The force needed to make an object go around in a circle will turn out to be $F = \dfrac{mv^2}{r}$ where m is the mass of the object, v is the speed with which to object goes around the circle and r is the radius of the circle. Although this equation looks different from $F = ma$ it actually is not. The acceleration of an object going about in a circle is found to be equal to $\dfrac{v^2}{r}$ and so $F = ma$ becomes $F = \dfrac{mv^2}{r}$. This is simply a more usable form of $F = ma$ where the acceleration is expressed in terms of the quantities that must be measured to calculate its value.

Circular motion results when a net force acting on a mass moving with a constant speed does not remain constant in direction but instead rotates in such a way as to keep itself always acting at right angles to the direction in which the mass is moving.

Figure 8-7 shows the path followed by a stone tied to the end of a string and being swung about in a circle. F_c is called the *centripetal* (center-seeking) force. This force is exerted on the stone through the string by the boy's hand. If the boy should release the string the force would at once disappear. The stone follows the first law of motion and travels off in a straight line at the point of release. This would be in a line tangent to the circle at the point of release.

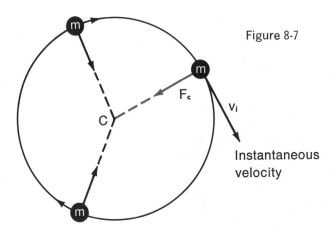

Figure 8-7

Instantaneous velocity

Note that in all positions in the diagram the centripetal force is perpendicular to the instantaneous velocity of the stone and so cannot change the magnitude of the instantaneous velocity. The force does change the direction of the velocity. Remembering that velocity is a vector quantity having both magnitude and direction it follows that a change in direction is a change in velocity: $\Delta \vec{v}$. A change in the velocity of the stone means that the stone is being accelerated. According to the second law of motion acceleration must always take place in the same direction as the applied force. *Since the force acting on the stone is always directed towards the center of the circular path the acceleration too is always directed towards the center of the circle. This acceleration is called the centripetal acceleration.*

By constructing a vector diagram we can analyze uniform circular motion and develop expressions for the magnitude of both the centripetal acceleration and the centripetal force. These expressions will hold for all circular motion. Whether we are concerned with the earth following its path about the sun, the stone tied to the end of a string and being swung about in a circle or a bit of rubber on the edge of the tire of an automobile is of no consequence. The equations hold.

In Figure 8-8 (a) , A and B are two successive positions of a mass moving with uniform circular motion in a circle of radius r. The vector $\vec{v}_1$ represents the initial velocity of the mass at A and the vector $\vec{v}_2$ represents the velocity of the mass at B. $\vec{v}_1$ and $\vec{v}_2$ are identical in magnitude.

In part (b) of Figure 8-8 the vectors $\vec{v}_1$ and $\vec{v}_2$ have been placed in a separate diagram. Notice that the two vectors are placed tail to tail in this diagram. We learned in Chapter 5 that placing two vectors head to tail gave us their vector sum. *By placing vectors tail to tail we get their vector difference.* This is the subtraction of vectors and in this case gives us the change in velocity or $\Delta \vec{v}$. By drawing in the vector $\Delta \vec{v}$ the vector $\vec{v}_2$ becomes the resultant of the addition of $\vec{v}_1$ and $\Delta \vec{v}$. Because $\vec{v}_1 + \Delta \vec{v} = \vec{v}_2$ it is apparent that $\Delta \vec{v} = \vec{v}_2 - \vec{v}_1$, Therefore $\Delta \vec{v}$ is the vector difference between $\vec{v}_1$ and $\vec{v}_2$.

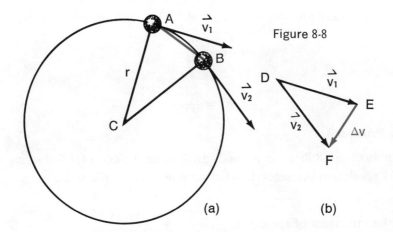

Figure 8-8

(a)   (b)

The triangles ABC and DEF are similar triangles because the corresponding sides of angle C are perpendicular to the corresponding sides of angle D. Therefore,

$$\frac{\Delta v}{v} = \frac{\text{chord } AB}{r}$$

The arc AB is the distance s the mass moves during the time interval Δt and may be expressed as $v\Delta t$. If we chose positions for A and B such that they are very close together the chord AB and the arc AB become the same length within a very small margin of error. Thus we may express the chord AB as $v\Delta t$.

$$\frac{\Delta v}{v} = \frac{v\Delta t}{r}$$

so,

$$\frac{at}{v} = \frac{v\Delta t}{r}$$

and,

$$a = \frac{v^2}{r}$$

This equation allows us to determine the magnitude of the centripetal acceleration of any body moving in a circle if the radius of the circle and the speed of the body along its path is known.

The time it takes for a body to traverse the circumference of its circular path once is called its period (T). Since the distance the body travels in a single revolution is the circumference of the circle $2\pi r$, its speed must be $2\pi r/T$. This expression for v can be substituted into the equation for centripetal acceleration to yield a form that is often useful.

$$a = \frac{v^2}{r}$$

$$a = \frac{(2\pi r/T)^2}{r}$$

$$a = \frac{4\pi^2 r}{T^2}$$

The magnitude of any force is equal to ma. The centripetal force must then be,

$$F_c = ma$$

$$F_c = \frac{mv^2}{r}$$

or,
$$F_c = \frac{m4\pi^2 r}{T^2}$$

Sample Problem 3

A boy twirls an 8-lb stone around his head on the end of a 5-ft string at the rate of 1 revolution per second. What tension exists in the string?

Solution:

First find the mass of the stone.

$$W = mg$$

$$m = \frac{W}{g}$$

$$m = \frac{8 \text{ lb}}{32 \text{ ft/sec}^2} = \frac{8 \text{ slug-ft/sec}^2}{32 \text{ ft/sec}^2} = 0.25 \text{ slug}$$

Then using the most convenient expression for F_c calculate its value.

$$F_c = \frac{m4\pi^2 r}{T^2}$$

$$= \frac{0.25 \text{ slug} \times 4 \times 9.9 \times 5 \text{ ft}}{(1 \text{ sec})^2}$$

$$= 49.5 \text{ slug-ft/sec}^2 = 49.5 \text{ lb}$$

Problems

13. An athlete twirls a 16-lb hammer about his head at a rate of 2 rev/sec. If his arms are 3 ft long compute the tension in them.
14. A 1-kg mass is attached to a string 1 m long and swings in a circle parallel with the horizontal at a rate of 4 rev/sec. (a) Compute the centripetal acceleration of the mass. (b) Calculate the centripetal force (the tension in the string).
15. What is the centripetal acceleration of an object moving along in a circular path of 20 m radius with a speed of 20 m/sec?
16. A 2-kg mass is attached to a string 1 m long and swings in a circle parallel with the horizontal. If the mass goes around its path once each 0.8 sec (a) what is its centripetal acceleration and (b) what tension is in the string?
17. A 600-kg racing car travels at a uniform speed about a circular race track of 50 m radius in 10 seconds. (a) What average force must the car's tires exert against the track to maintain its circular motion? (b) What is the acceleration of the car?

18. A child twirls his yo-yo top about his head rather than using it properly. The top has a mass of 0.2 kg and is attached to a string 0.8 m long. (a) If the top makes a complete revolution each second what tension must exist in the string? (b) If the child increases the speed of the top so that it makes two revolutions per second what tension must be in the string? (c) What is the ratio of the solution of (b) to (a) and why?

19. Using 32 ft/sec² as the acceleration of gravity and 4000 miles as the radius of the earth calculate the velocity at which any artificial satellite must be launched in order to achieve orbit (orbital velocity). (Change the 4000 miles to feet.)

20. The radius of the moon's orbital path about the earth is approximately 1.2×10^9 ft. The moon's period is 2.3×10^6 seconds or 27.3 days. Determine the centripetal acceleration of the moon.

8:4   Simple Harmonic Motion

Many motions such as the swinging of a pendulum or the vibrating of a guitar string are oscillatory. That is the bodies swing or vibrate back and forth in a regular way. Often this type of motion is related to circular motion in a very simple way which is why we will discuss this motion at this point.

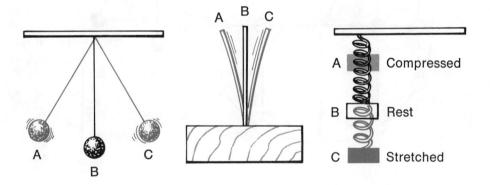

Figure 8-9.   Vibrating bodies undergo simple harmonic motion.

The frequency of a vibrating body is the number of times a body vibrates per unit of time. One vibration of a pendulum for example is from the highest point of its swing on one side of its rest position to the highest point of its swing on the other side and back again to its first position. If a pendulum does this five times in a second its frequency is 5 Hz. *The period of vibration is the time required for one vibration.* For the pendulum just described this would be $\frac{1}{5}$ second or 0.2 sec. The *amplitude of vibration is the distance from the vibrating body's rest position to the point of it's greatest displacement.*

Simple harmonic motion (SHM) is a special kind of vibrational motion characterized by the relationship between the acceleration of the body and the body's displacement (x) from its rest position. The acceleration of the body is always proportional to the displacement of the body. When the mass hanging from the spring in Figure 8-9 is pulled down the force tending to restore the mass to its rest position increases regularly with the distance the mass is pulled from its rest position. If the force increases regularly the acceleration it will give to the mass must do likewise because $F = ma$. Therefore the acceleration varies uniformly with the displacement or we may say it is proportional to the displacement. The body will undergo SHM. The acceleration of the mass is greatest at C, zero at B and in full magnitude again at A. Notice that at all times the acceleration is directed towards the rest position; this is another characteristic of SHM.

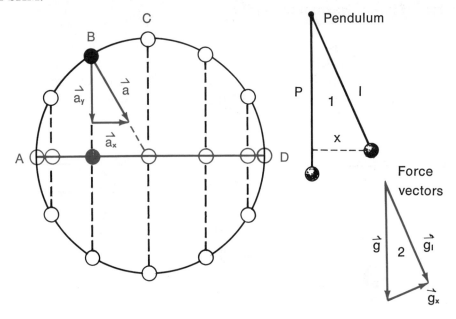

Figure 8-10

How SHM is related to circular motion is diagrammed in Figure 8-10. Here a body is shown going around a circle with uniform speed. At B the acceleration of the body is directed towards the center of the circle as it is at all times. However we can consider the acceleration to consist of the x and y components shown. The x component of the acceleration would be zero when the mass reaches point C and would be at its maximum value at points A and D. In between a_x fluctuates smoothly between zero and maximum. However a_x is always directed towards the center of the circle. Should a body be moving back and forth along the axis delineated by A and D in such a way as to always be perpendicularly beneath the mass going around the circle its acceleration would be the same as a_x and it would be undergoing SHM. *Simple harmonic motion is the projection of circular motion on one axis.*

It is apparent that the period of the body undergoing uniform circular motion and the body undergoing SHM would be the same. In the previous section we found that for uniform circular motion $a = \dfrac{4\pi^2 r}{T^2}$. The period of both circular motion and SHM must then be given by $T^2 = \dfrac{4\pi^2 r}{a}$.

To show the usefulness of the relationship between circular motion and SHM we will use the pendulum of Figure 8-10. For swings of short arc such a pendulum undergoes simple harmonic motion. In the diagram triangles 1 and 2 are similar (two corresponding sides parallel). Therefore the equation for the period of the pendulum can be derived in the following manner.

$$\frac{g_x}{x} = \frac{g}{l} \qquad\qquad\qquad T^2 = \frac{4\pi^2 x}{(g/l)x}$$

$$g_x = \frac{gx}{l} \qquad\qquad\qquad T^2 = \frac{4\pi^2 l}{g}$$

$$T^2 = \frac{4\pi^2 x}{a} \qquad\qquad\qquad T = 2\pi\sqrt{\frac{l}{g}}$$

Notice that the period of a pendulum does not depend upon the mass of the body nor on the amplitude of the swing but only upon its length (g being constant in any one location).

Sample Problem 4

Determine the period of a pendulum 6 ft in length.

Solution:

$$T = 2\pi\sqrt{\frac{l}{g}}$$

$$= 6.28\sqrt{\frac{6\text{ ft}}{32\text{ ft/sec}^2}}$$

$$= 6.28\,(0.43\text{ sec})$$

$$= 2.7\text{ sec}$$

Problems

21. Determine the period of a pendulum 1 foot long.

22. Determine the period of a pendulum 1 meter long.

23. What is the period of a pendulum 0.5 meter long?

24. The period of a pendulum is 1 second. Determine its length in feet.

25. The period of a pendulum is 2 seconds. If the pendulum is 3.25 ft in length determine the acceleration of gravity.

QUESTIONS

1. A hunter standing on a high platform aims the barrel of his rifle straight at a monkey who is hanging on a distant tree branch by one hand. The barrel of the rifle is parallel with the horizontal. Just as the hunter pulls the trigger of his rifle the monkey lets go of the branch and begins to fall. Will the bullet hit the monkey?

2. If an airplane is flying at a constant speed in a straight line parallel with the horizontal and the pilot drops a bomb where will the plane be relative to the bomb when it hits the target?

3. What relationship must exist between an applied force and a moving mass if uniform circular motion is to result?

4. What constitutes a complete vibration of a pendulum?

5. Distinguish between the frequency, the period, and the amplitude of a pendulum.

6. How is simple harmonic motion distinguished from other types of vibrational motion?

7.

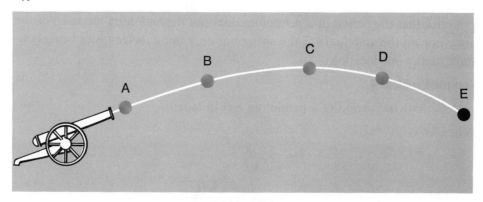

Figure 8-11

(a) At which point is the vertical velocity the greatest? (You may find two points)

(b) At which point is the horizontal velocity the greatest?

(c) Where is the vertical velocity least?

(d) Name the curve described by the ball.

1. A boy throws a stone horizontally at 25 ft/sec from atop a cliff 160 ft high. How far from the base of the cliff will the stone strike the ground?

2. A bridge is 176.4 m above a river. If a man throws a lead fishing weight from the bridge with a horizontal speed of 22 m/sec what horizontal distance will it travel before striking the water?

3. (a) If an object falls from rest from a height of 6400 ft how long will it remain in the air. (b) If the object had a horizontal velocity of 200 ft/sec when it began to fall what horizontal distance will it travel while falling?

4. A stone is thrown horizontally from the top of a cliff 122.5 m high. If the stone lands 40 m from the base of the cliff (a) how long did it take for the stone to fall to the base and (b) with what horizontal velocity was the stone thrown?

5. Divers at Acapulco dive from a cliff that is 200 ft high. If the rocks below the cliff extend outwards for 75 ft what is the minimum horizontal velocity a diver must have to clear them?

6. A projectile is fired at an angle of 37° with the horizontal. If the initial velocity of the projectile is 1000 ft/sec what horizontal distance will it travel?

7. A bullet is fired from a gun held at an angle of 45° with the horizontal. If the muzzle velocity of the gun is 1370 ft/sec how far will the bullet travel horizontally before striking the ground?

8. A projectile is fired at an angle of 30° with the horizontal and with a velocity of 256 ft/sec. (a) Determine the vertical and horizontal velocities of the projectile. (b) Make a table showing the magnitude of the vertical and horizontal velocities at the end of each second for an eight second period. (c) Plot a graph of the vertical velocity vs time using the data in your table. Describe the curve obtained. (d) Plot a graph of the horizontal velocity vs time. Describe the curve obtained.

9. An athlete twirls a 16 lb hammer tied to the end of a 4 ft rope about his head at the rate of 1 rev/sec. (a) What is the centripetal acceleration given to the hammer by the tension in the rope? (b) What is the tension in the rope?

10. A 0.5 kg mass is attached to a string 0.8 m long and swings in a circle parallel with the horizontal. If the mass is completing 4 revolutions per second what tension exists in the string?

11. What would be the period of a pendulum that is 9.8 meters long?

12. What would be the period of a pendulum that is 32 ft long?

13. Determine the period of a pendulum that is 4.9 m long.

14. How long must a pendulum be to have a period of 1.5 seconds. Determine your answer in meters.

9 Law of Gravitation

Gravity was originally thought to be a force which pulls everything to the earth. Limited everyday experience led to this conclusion. Newton reasoned that the reverse might also be true and he turned to the heavens for proof of his theory. From experience you know that the parachute pictured above will fall to the ground because of earth's gravitational pull. Does the parachute exert an attraction on the earth? If so, why is this attraction not apparent?

9:1 Kepler's Laws of Planetary Motion

The astronomical observations and calculations of Tycho Brahe and Johannes Kepler provided the basis for Newton's theory of universal gravitation. Born in Denmark in 1546, Tycho Brahe was an avid observer of heavenly bodies. He spent almost all his life tracing the orbits of the planets and the paths of stars. Near the end of his life, Brahe hired a young assistant named Johannes Kepler. Kepler lacked his employer's patience for long hours of observation, but he was an excellent mathematician. Kepler used the vast amount of data accumulated by Brahe to formulate three laws of planetary motion.

1. The paths of the planets are ellipses.

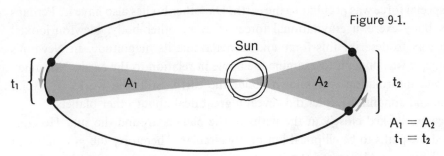

Figure 9-1.

$A_1 = A_2$
$t_1 = t_2$

2. An imaginary line from a planet to the sun sweeps out equal areas each second whether the planet is close to or far away from the sun.
3. If the radius of any planet's orbit about the sun is cubed and then divided by the planet's period (time for it to travel about the sun once) squared, the same number or constant (k) is always obtained. This is expressed mathematically as,

$$\frac{r^3}{T^2} = k$$

9:2   Universal Gravitation

Until Newton's time, gravitational force was considered a special surface characteristic of the earth. But Newton suspected that the earth was not unique among all the other heavenly bodies. Because of his understanding of the laws of motion, he believed that the behavior of all material bodies is governed by the same universal laws.

Figure 9-2. The gravitational force which shapes the Andromeda galaxy enables you to walk upright on the surface of earth.

Lick Observatory

Legend has it that while observing an apple fall from a tree, Newton recognized that the apple fell because an unbalanced force acted upon it. (Newton's second law of motion). This unbalanced force was gravity. Newton questioned whether this special force was peculiar to the earth. Did other bodies also have it? Perhaps every body exerts a gravitational force on every other body. Newton looked for a way to describe this force and to determine its magnitude. In Newton's lifetime, it was difficult to examine the apple in relation to the earth. Not much accurate information was known about the earth. Still, the works of Tycho Brahe and Johannes Kepler did reveal a great deal about other planets.

Newton looked closely at the paths of the planets around the sun. He concluded the paths to be elliptical but nearly circular. Therefore, the gravitational force between a planet and the sun supplies the centripetal force and conforms to the equation,

$$F_c = \frac{m4\pi^2 r}{T^2}$$

Kepler showed that for any planet $\frac{r^3}{T^2} = k$. Newton rewrote this equation as $T^2 = \frac{r^3}{k}$ and substituted it into the expression for F_c.

$$F_c = \frac{m4\pi^2 r}{T^2}$$

$$= \frac{m4\pi^2 r}{r^3/k}$$

$$= \frac{m4\pi^2 k}{r^2}$$

In this expression the $4\pi^2 k$ is considered a single factor because each factor's value does not change. The $4\pi^2 k$ is called K. Thus,

$$F_c = \frac{mk}{r^2}$$

This result told Newton that the centripetal force and therefore the gravitational force acting on a planet varies directly as the mass of the planet and inversely as the square of the distance between the planet and the sun. The force varies as the product of the masses of the two bodies. He assumed that gravity is a universal property of all matter and acts the same way between any two masses as it does between a planet and the sun. From these assumptions, Newton wrote his law of universal gravitation:

Every body in the universe attracts every other body
in the universe with a force that varies directly as
the product of their masses and inversely as the square
of the distance between the two masses.

Mathematically, this is written,

$$F = G\frac{m_1 m_2}{r^2}$$

In the equation, m_1 and m_2 are the masses of any two bodies in the universe; r is the distance between them and G is a universal constant that depends upon the units being used. For all problems dealing with universal gravitation, the value of G is either 6.67×10^{-11} m^3/kg-sec^2 or 3.41×10^{-8} ft^3/slug-sec^2 depending upon the units used in the problem.

Sample Problem 1

Two large locomotives of mass 3.0×10^5 kg each are located on adjacent tracks. Their centers are 9 m apart. What gravitational force exists between them?

Solution:

$$F = G\frac{m_1 m_2}{r^2}$$

$$= 6.67 \times 10^{-11} \text{ m}^3/\text{kg-sec}^2 \frac{(3.0 \times 10^5 \text{kg})(3.0 \times 10^5 \text{kg})}{(9 \text{ m})^2}$$

$$= 6.67 \times 10^{-11} \text{ m}^3/\text{kg-sec}^2 \frac{(9 \times 10^{10} \text{ kg}^2)}{81 \text{ m}^2}$$

$$= 0.074 \text{ nt}$$

Problems

1. Two bodies are 2 m apart. One body has a mass of 80 kg. The second body has a mass of 60 kg. What is the gravitational force between them?
2. (a) What is the gravitational force between two 1600-lb automobiles that are 10 ft apart? (b) What is the gravitational force between them when they are 100 ft apart?
3. Two ships are docked next to each other with their centers of gravity 40 ft apart. One ship weighs 16 000 tons. The other ship weighs 32 000 tons. What gravitational force exists between them?
4. Two space capsules weigh 3200 lb each when on earth. The two capsules are put into orbit side by side, 100 ft apart. (a) What gravitational force exists between them? (b) What is the initial acceleration given to each capsule by this force?
5. The mass of the moon is about 7.3×10^{22} kg. The mass of earth is 6.0×10^{24} kg. If the centers of the two are 3.9×10^8 meters apart, what is the gravitational force between earth and moon?
6. Use Newton's second law of motion to determine the acceleration given to the moon by the force calculated in Problem 5.

7. The mass of an electron is 9×10^{-31} kg. The mass of a proton is 1.7×10^{-27} kg. They are about 1.0×10^{-10} m apart in a hydrogen atom. What force of gravitation exists between the proton and the electron of a hydrogen atom?

9:3   Newton's Test of the Inverse Square Law

Newton lacked the necessary equipment to make a direct test of his law of universal gravitation, however, he compiled enough information about the moon to determine how earth's gravitational field varies with distance. He determined that earth's gravitational field varies inversely as the square of the distance from earth as his theory indicated it should.

Newton started with the acceleration of gravity as 32 ft/sec² on earth. If the force acting on the moon becomes weaker as the square of its distance from the earth and gravity supplies the force, then the acceleration of gravity given to the moon must become weaker in the same way. The moon is 60 earth radii from the earth. Newton reasoned if the inverse square law applies to the earth's gravitational field, the acceleration given to the moon by the earth should be $\frac{1}{(60)^2}$ or $\frac{1}{3600}$ of the acceleration found on the surface of the earth. This is,

$$32 \text{ ft/sec}^2 \times \frac{1}{3600} = 0.009 \text{ ft/sec}^2$$

Newton also knew the distance to the moon and its period. With this knowledge, he calculated the centripetal acceleration needed to keep the moon in its orbit.

$$a = \frac{v^2}{r} = \frac{4\pi^2 r}{T^2}$$
$$= \frac{4(3.14)^2(1.2 \times 10^9 \text{ ft})}{(2.3 \times 10^6 \text{ sec})^2}$$
$$= 0.009 \text{ ft/sec}^2$$

The calculation was in complete agreement indicating that earth's gravitational force does follow the inverse square law and gravity does keep the moon in its orbit. This was important evidence that the law of universal gravitation was correct.

9:4   The Cavendish Experiment

In 1798, the English scientist, Henry Cavendish, used another method to prove that Newton was correct. His method also proved that a small gravitational force exists between two small bodies. (Figure 9-3.) Cavendish attached two small lead balls to either end of a long rod. Carefully he suspended the rod at the end of a long wire. Then he placed two larger lead balls close to the small ones. The two large balls attracted the two small balls. This caused the

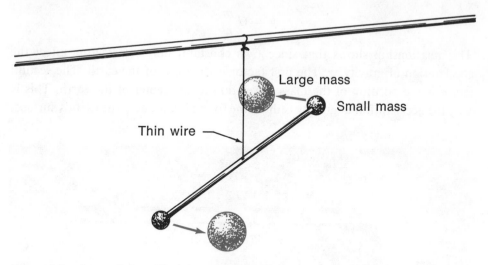

Figure 9-3.   Cavendish verified the existence of gravitational forces between masses by using apparatus similar to the type shown.

wire to twist. Cavendish measured the force required to twist the wire through given angles. From the amount of twisting, Cavendish determined the force between the lead balls. He knew the masses of the balls and the distance between their centers. Substituting these values into the law of gravitation, he solved for G. In the MKS system, the value of G is 6.67×10^{-11}m³/kg-sec².

9:5   The Law of Universal Gravitation and Weight

The force that draws any body toward the earth's surface is the gravitational attraction of the earth acting on that body. This force is called weight. It must conform to the law of universal gravitation. Therefore, the weight of any mass is:

$$W = G \frac{m_b m_e}{r^2}$$

In the equation, m_b is the mass of the body; and m_e is the mass of the earth. A spherical body behaves as though all its mass is concentrated at the center of the body. For this reason r is the radius of the earth. The weight of a body is the force that causes the mass to accelerate if it is allowed to fall Hence,

$$W = G \frac{m_b m_e}{r^2}$$

But W also equals mg

$$W = m_b g$$

$$m_b g = G \frac{m_b m_e}{r^2}$$

$$g = G \frac{m_e}{r^2}$$

This relationship shows that since G is constant, only two factors affect the acceleration of gravity, g. The first factor is the mass of the earth. The second factor is the position of the mass in relation to the center of the earth. This is why the acceleration of gravity is the same for all bodies near the earth's surface.

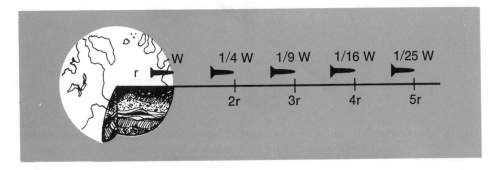

Figure 9-4. Variation of gravitational force with distance follows the inverse square law.

Figure 9-4 shows the variation in a rocket's weight as the distance between the rocket and the earth increases. The weight of the rocket varies inversely as the square of its distance from the earth's center.

9:6   Gravitational Fields

The force of gravitation is capable of action even though there is no direct connection between the two bodies involved. The sun and the earth are millions of miles apart. However the gravitational force of the sun keeps the earth in its orbital path. In an effort to describe and predict the behavior of forces acting at a distance the field concept has been developed. Essentially the field concept considers that the presence of a mass in space distorts the space around it setting up a gravitational *field* which is able to interact with any mass placed in the field.

A gravitational field is plotted by placing a small test mass in the field and observing its behavior. Figure 9-5 shows the pattern obtained if the earth's field is plotted. The force which acts on the test mass is of greater magnitude when it is closer to the earth. According to the inverse square law, this is to be expected.

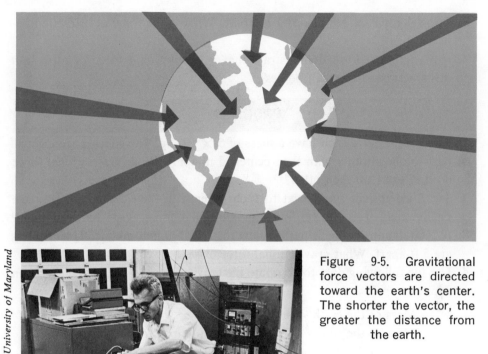

University of Maryland

Figure 9-5. Gravitational force vectors are directed toward the earth's center. The shorter the vector, the greater the distance from the earth.

Figure 9-6. Dr. Joseph Weber uses a massive aluminum cylinder equipped with numerous sensing devices to measure minute changes in the earth's gravitational field. He is looking for evidence that gravitation waves travel through space.

QUESTIONS

1. An imaginary line from a planet to the sun sweeps out equal areas in equal times. Does the planet move faster along its orbital path when it is close to the sun or when it is far away from the sun?

2. The radius of the earth is about 4000 miles. A 3600-lb spacecraft travels away from the earth. What would be the weight of the spacecraft at these distances from the earth's surface? (a) 4000 mi   (b) 8000 mi   (c) 12 000 mi (d) 16 000 mi   (e) 20 000 mi

3. Two 1-kg masses are placed 1 m apart. What is the force of attraction between them?
4. How did Cavendish demonstrate that a gravitational force of attraction exists between two small bodies?

PROBLEMS

1. Two lead spheres each have a mass of 5×10^5 kg. The spheres are located next to one another with their centers 5 m apart. What gravitational force do they exert on each other?
2. Two locomotives stand next to each other with their centers 10 ft apart. Each weighs 128 000 lb. What gravitational force exists between them?
3. A 1600-lb automobile is parked next to a 3200-lb automobile. Their centers are 5 ft apart. What gravitational force exists between them?
4. Use the following data to compute the gravitational force the sun exerts on Jupiter.

Mass of the earth $= 6 \times 10^{24}$ kg
Mass of the sun $= 3.3 \times 10^5$ times the mass of the earth
Mass of Jupiter $= 3 \times 10^2$ times the mass of the earth
Distance between Jupiter and the sun $= 7.8 \times 10^{11}$ m

Work and Power

10

"Work" in an everyday sense refers to any effort which is exerted or any task which is tiring. "Power" is used by the nonscientist to indicate strength. According to a physicist, is work done when the logs are merely suspended above the log pile? Is the weight of suspended logs a measure of the power of the machine?

10:1 Work

When a man lifts a crate, pushes a lawnmower, or shovels snow, we say he is doing work. All of these work examples share one thing in common — force is exerted through a distance. This is true of all work. In physics, work is done when a force acts on a body and moves it in the direction of the force.

To calculate the work done by a force, multiply the force by the distance the force moves the body in the direction of the force.

$$\text{Work} = \text{Force} \times \text{Distance}$$

$$W = Fs$$

Thus, if a man lifts a 10-lb box 3 ft, he performs 10 lb $\times$ 3 ft, or 30 ft-lb of work. In the English system, the unit of work is the foot-pound. In the MKS system, the unit of work is the newton-meter. A force of 6 nt acts through a distance of 5 m. The force does 30 nt-m of work. A newton-meter also is called a joule. Therefore, 30 nt-m of work is 30 joules of work or 30 j.

Sample Problem 1

A man applies a force of 60 nt for a distance of 20 m to push a desk across a floor. How much work is done by the man?

Solution:

$$W = Fs$$

$$W = (60 \text{ nt}) (20 \text{ m})$$

$$W = 1200 \text{ nt-m} = 1200 \text{ j}$$

Sample Problem 2

A worker pushes a crate 20 ft across a warehouse floor. He exerts a constant force of 50 lb on the crate. How much work does he do?

Solution:

$$W = Fs$$

$$W = (50 \text{ lb}) (20 \text{ ft})$$

$$W = 1000 \text{ ft-lb}$$

Problems

1. A force of 800 nt is required to push a car across a parking lot. Two students push a car 40 m. How much work is done in joules?
2. How much work is done to lift a 60-lb crate a vertical distance of 10 ft?
3. A worker lifts a crate from one floor to another in a warehouse. He exerts a force of 48 lb through a distance of 40 ft on the rope of a pulley system. How much work does he do?
4. A package weighs 35 nt. A delivery man carries the package from the ground floor to the fifth floor of an office building, a vertical distance of 15 m. (a) How much work does the delivery man do? (b) The man weighs 750 nt. How much total work does he do to move himself and the package from the ground floor to the fifth floor?

5. A man changing a tire exerts a force of 40 lb on the handle of a screw type bumper jack. The handle to which the steel shaft is attached has a radius of 1 ft. The man turns the handle through 30 rev. How much work does he perform to lift the automobile?

6. (a) What is the weight of a 49-kg crate? (b) What work is done to lift the crate a distance of 10 m?

7. A man carries cement blocks weighing 30 lb each up a ladder onto a scaffold 15 ft high. He carries them at the rate of 2/min. How much work does he do? (a) in 10 min (b) in 1 hr

8. A pile-driver hammer has a mass of 100 kg. The machine's engine lifts it to a height of 5 m every 10 sec. (a) How much does the hammer weigh? (b) How much work must the machine do to lift the hammer? (c) How much work does the machine do in 1 min?

9. A boy has a mass of 50 kg. He runs up a flight of stairs that takes him a vertical distance of 6 m. How much work does he do?

10:2   Work and the Direction of the Force

When work is calculated, the force to use is the component of the force which acts in the direction of the motion. In Figure 10-l, a 50-lb force is applied

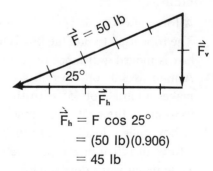

Scale: 1 cm = 10 lb

$\vec{F} = 50$ lb

$\vec{F}_v$

25°

$\vec{F}_h$

$\vec{F}_h = F \cos 25°$
$= (50 \text{ lb})(0.906)$
$= 45 \text{ lb}$

Figure 10-1

(*F*) to push a lawnmower. However, the force that moves the mower forward is the horizontal component of this force (F_h). Find the value of F_h by multiplying the force *F* by the cosine of the angle between *F* and the horizontal.

$$\cos \theta = \frac{\text{adjacent side}}{\text{hypotenuse}}$$

$$\cos \theta = \frac{F_h}{F}$$
$$F_h = F \cos \theta$$
$$W = F_h s$$
$$W = F \cos \theta \, s$$

Suppose a man lifts a 100-lb crate 3 ft from the floor. He performs 300 ft-lb of work. But, if he carries the same crate 20 ft down a corridor, he performs no work. Why? The force required to hold the crate does not act in the same direction as the motion of the crate. Nor does the force have a component in that direction.

Sample Problem 3

A boatman pulls his boat along a dock. He holds the rope at 60° with the horizontal and pulls on it with a force of 100 lb. (a) What horizontal force acts on the boat? (b) How much work does the man perform if he pulls the boat 30 ft?

Solution:

(a) $F_h = F \cos \theta$ (b) $W = F_h s$

      $F_h = (100 \text{ lb}) (0.5)$ $W = (50 \text{ lb}) (30 \text{ ft})$

      $F_h = 50 \text{ lb}$ $W = 1500 \text{ ft-lb}$

Problems

10. A force of 600 nt is applied to a metal box to pull it across a wooden floor. The rope used to pull the box is held at an angle of 46° with the floor. The box is moved a distance of 15 m. How much work in joules is done?
11. A man uses a rope to pull a one-ton boat 50 ft along a wharf. The rope makes an angle of 45° with the horizontal. The man exerts a force of 100 lb to move the boat. How much work does he do?
12. A boy pulls a loaded sled weighing 800 nt a distance of 200 m. He exerts a force of 120 nt on a rope which makes an angle of 60° with the horizontal. How much work does he do?
13. A cable attached to a small tractor pulls a barge through a canal lock. The tension in the cable is 500 lb. It makes an angle of 30° with the direction in which the barge is moving. (a) What force moves the barge along the lock? (b) If the lock is 200 ft long, how much work is done to get the barge through the lock?
14. Friction requires a force of 400 nt to drag a wooden crate across a wooden floor. The rope tied to the crate is held at an angle of 56° with the horizontal. (a) How much tension is needed in the rope to move the crate? (b) What work is done if the crate is dragged 25 m?

10:3   Power

Power is the rate at which work is done. Power is an important concept because it furnishes the means to evaluate workers and machines. Two machines may be similar, but if one machine accomplishes more work per second or per minute, it is more powerful than the other machine.

$$\text{Power} = \frac{\text{Work}}{\text{Time}}$$

In the MKS system of measurement, power is measured in watts. *A watt is one joule per second.* A machine that works at a rate of one joule per second has a power of one watt. Since a joule is a newton-meter, a watt is a newton-meter per second. A watt is a relatively small quantity of power. Therefore, power often is measured in kilowatts. A kilowatt is 1000 watts.

In the English system of measurement, power is measured in foot-pounds per second, foot-pounds per minute, or in horsepower. One horsepower (hp) is 550 ft-lb per second or 33 000 foot-pounds per minute. The term horsepower first was used by James Watt who timed a working horse. One horsepower was the average rate at which a horse could work. To determine the power of a machine in horsepower, first find the number of foot-pounds of work the machine is doing each second. Then divide this figure by the number of foot-pounds of work a horse can do per second, or 550 ft-lb/sec.

Sample Problem 4

A machine exerts a force of 40 nt through a distance of 100 m in 5 sec. (a) How much work does the machine do in this time? (b) What is the power of the machine in watts? (c) What is the power of the machine in kilowatts?

Solution:

(a) $W = Fs$

         $W = (40 \text{ nt}) (100 \text{ m})$

         $W = 4000 \text{ j}$

(b) $P = \dfrac{W}{t}$

         $P = \dfrac{4000 \text{ j}}{5 \text{ sec}}$

         $P = 800 \text{ watts}$

(c) $\dfrac{800 \text{ watts}}{1000 \text{ watts/kilowatt}} = 0.80 \text{ kw}$

Sample Problem 5

An electric motor lifts an elevator weighing 1100 lb to the sixth floor of a building in 1 min. The floors of the building are 10 ft apart. (a) At what rate does the motor work? (b) What is the motor's horsepower?

Solution:

(a)
$$P = \frac{W}{t}$$

$$P = \frac{Fs}{t}$$

$$P = \frac{(1100 \text{ lb})(60 \text{ ft})}{60 \text{ sec}}$$

$$P = 1100 \text{ ft-lb/sec}$$

(b)
$$hp = \frac{\text{Work per sec}}{\text{Work a horse can do per sec}}$$

$$hp = \frac{1100 \text{ ft-lb/sec}}{550 \text{ ft-lb/sec}}$$

$$= 2 \text{ hp}$$

Problems

15. A box that weighs 1000 nt is lifted a distance of 20 m straight up by a rope and pulley system. The work is done in 10 sec. (a) What amount of power is used in watts? (b) What amount of power is used in kilowatts?

16. A steam engine lifts the 225-lb hammer of a pile driver 30 ft into the air in 5 sec. (a) How much work is done on the hammer? (b) What is the power of the engine? (c) What is the horsepower of the engine?

17. A hiker carries a 20-kg knapsack up a trail. After 30 minutes, he is 300 m higher than his starting point. (a) What is the weight of the knapsack? (b) How much work in joules is done on the knapsack? (c) If the hiker weighs 600 nt, how much total work in joules is done? (d) What is the hiker's average power in watts during the 30 min? (e) What is his average power in kilowatts?

18. An electric motor lifts a 4000-lb elevator 55 ft in 40 sec. (a) How much work is done? (b) What is the power of the motor? (c) What is the horsepower of the motor? (d) If one horsepower equals 746 watts, what is the power of the motor in kilowatts?

19. It takes a winch 8 sec to lift a 5500-lb truck from a dock onto the deck of a ship. The vertical distance is 50 ft. Calculate the horsepower of the winch.

20. A motor operates an endless conveyor belt. The motor produces a force of 500 nt on the belt and moves it at the rate of 6.5 m/sec. What is the power of the motor in kilowatts?

QUESTIONS

1. Define work.

2. What is a joule?

3. What is a watt?

4. Define horsepower.

5. Explain why no work is done by the vertical force in Figure 10-1 on page 115.

6. What is power? What is the MKS unit of power? What is the English unit of power?

PROBLEMS

1. A force of 60 nt is needed to push a crate weighing 300 nt across a waxed floor. How much work is required to push the crate 15 m?

2. The third floor of a house is 22 ft above street level. How much work is required to move a 100-lb refrigerator from street level to the third floor?

3. A 50-kg mass is raised by a machine to a height of 20 m. Calculate the work done (a) in newton-meters (b) in joules.

4. Workers use a force of 1760 nt to push a piano weighing 8800 nt up a 20-m ramp. (a) How much work is done? (b) The piano is being moved from street level to the second floor of a building. The second floor is 4 m above street level. If the workers decide to lift the piano straight up by using ropes, how much work would they do?

5. A man applies a force of 150 nt to push a wheelbarrow with a constant speed. The man pushes the wheelbarrow 60 m in 20 sec. (a) How much work does he do? (b) what is his power in watts?

6. How much work does a 400-watt motor do in 5 min?

7. Calculate the horsepower of a gasoline engine that accomplishes 2.2×10^4 ft-lb of work in 10 sec.

8. Calculate the wattage of a motor that accomplishes 11 250 joules of work in 25 sec.

9. A loaded elevator weighs 1100 lb. An electric motor hoists the elevator 30 ft in 15 sec. (a) How much work is done? (b) What is the power in ft-lb/sec? (c) What is the horsepower of the motor?

10. A pump raises 30 liters of water per min from a depth of 100 m. What is the wattage expended? (A liter of water has a mass of 1 kg).

11. A horizontal force of 800 nt is required to drag a crate across a horizontal floor. A worker drags the crate by means of a rope held at an angle of 60°. (a) What force does he apply to the rope? (b) How much work does he perform in dragging the crate 22 m? (c) If the worker completes the job in 8 sec, what is his power in watts?

11 Energy and its Conservation

Energy, defined as the capacity to do work, exists in many forms. What forms of energy can you find in the accompanying photograph? Can you find any examples of energy transformations? What can you say about the total energy and matter in this situation?

11:1 Energy

Energy exists in many different forms. The forms are interchangeable. Some forms of energy are electricity, light, heat, sound, and nuclear. The chapter titles of this book reflect the different types of energy studied in physics.

Four rules concern energy:

1. Energy is the capacity to do work.
   (a) Like work, energy is a scalar quantity.
   (b) Energy has the same units as work.

2. Energy is converted readily from one form to another.
3. Work is the means by which energy changes form.
4. Regardless of its form, energy always is potential or kinetic. Potential energy is stored energy or energy of position. Kinetic energy is the energy a body possesses by virtue of its motion.

11:2   Potential Energy

Potential energy is the energy a body possesses because of its position or state. Suppose a 10-lb stone is lying on the ground. It is hard to think of it as having potential energy. However, lift this same stone to the top of a 20-ft wall and it has potential energy. Should the stone fall from the wall, it can do work. It can drive a stake into the ground, that is, exert a force through a distance. As long as the stone stays on the top of the wall, it remains a source of stored or potential energy. In the same manner, a drawn bow or a stretched spring has potential energy. It is a little more difficult to visualize the potential energy in a lump of coal or a drop of oil. Until fuels of this sort react chemically, their potential energy is locked in their internal molecular structure.

11:3   Base Levels

The potential energy a body has due to its position above the surface of the earth is called its gravitational potential energy. The potential energy a body releases to do work is equal to its change in potential energy as it falls from a higher to a lower level. This energy change is measured with reference to some base position or level (not necessarily the surface of the earth). Suppose a man on the third floor of a building drops a weight onto a nail. The potential energy of the weight when it is raised is measured with respect to the nail, not to the surface of the earth. A base level is only an arbitrary point and depends upon each situation.

11:4   Energy Units

Since energy is the capacity to do work, it is measured in the same units as work (joules or foot-pounds). Under ideal conditions, energy and work are completely interchangeable. For example, to lift a 20-nt stone to the top of a 10-m wall, requires 200 joules of work. If the same stone falls back to earth, once again it should be able to provide 200 joules of work. *The increase in the potential energy of any system is equal to the amount of work it requires to place the system in its final position.*

$$\text{Change in Potential Energy} = \text{Force} \times \text{Distance}$$
$$\Delta PE = Fs$$

If the potential energy of a mass is increased by raising it, the force required is the weight of the mass.

$$\Delta PE = Wh$$
$$\Delta PE = mgh$$

Sample Problem 1

A 5-kg mass is lifted to a height of 5 m. What is its increase in potential energy?

Solution:

$$\Delta PE = Fs$$
$$= mgh$$
$$= 5 \text{ kg} \times 9.8 \text{ m/sec}^2 \times 5 \text{ m}$$
$$= 245 \text{ nt-m}$$
$$= 245 \text{ j}$$

Sample Problem 2

The distance between each floor of a hotel is 10 ft. A 1000-lb elevator is raised from the ground floor to the fourth floor. By how much is the potential energy of the elevator increased?

Solution:

$$\Delta PE = Fs = Wh$$
$$= (1000 \text{ lb}) (40 \text{ ft})$$
$$= 40\,000 \text{ ft-lb}$$

Problems

1. The 200-kg hammer of a pile driver is lifted 10 m. Calculate the potential energy of the system when the hammer is at this height.
2. A 60-lb shell is shot from a cannon to a height of 400 ft. (a) What is the potential energy of the earth-shell system when the shell is at this height? (b) What is the change in potential energy of the system when the shell falls to a height of 200 ft?
3. A 150-lb man climbs 15 ft up a ladder. (a) What work does he do? (b) What is the increase in the potential energy of the earth-man system when he is at this height?
4. Calculate the potential energy of a 10-kg mass when it is raised to a height of 20 m above the ground.

5. A plumber using a 16-lb hammer works in a building which has 9 ft between each floor. (a) What is the potential energy of the hammer with respect to the ground floor when it is on the fifth floor? (b) How much energy is added to the system if the hammer is carried from the fifth to the eighth floor?

11:5   Kinetic Energy

A body has a mass m and rests on a frictionless surface. A constant force F acts on the body through a distance s. This force causes the body to be accelerated in accordance with Newton's second law of motion.

$$F = ma$$

The work done by the force, F, on the body is Fs. Multiply both sides of the equation by s. The Fs on the left side of the equation represents the work done on the mass.

$$Fs = mas$$

The speed of a body starting from rest is

$$v^2 = 2as$$

therefore,

$$as = \frac{v^2}{2}$$

Substitute this expression into $Fs = mas$ to get

$$Fs = \frac{mv^2}{2}$$

This expression relates the work done on a mass to the resulting speed of the mass. It also gives the work that a mass of speed v is able to do while being

Figure 11-1. The kinetic energy of a mass equals the work done upon the mass to give it that kinetic energy. Therefore the speed of a body is dependent upon the amount of work done on it.

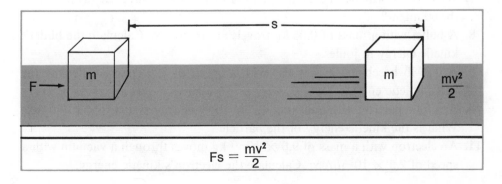

brought to rest. The quantity $\frac{mv^2}{2}$ is defined as the kinetic energy, *KE*, of the body.

$$KE = \frac{1}{2} mv^2$$

Sample Problem 3

An 8-kg mass moves at 30 m/sec. What is its kinetic energy?

Solution:

$$KE = \frac{1}{2} mv^2$$

$$= \frac{(8 \text{ kg})(30 \text{ m/sec})^2}{2}$$

$$= 3600 \text{ j}$$

Sample Problem 4

An 8-lb stone moves at 30 ft/sec. What is its kinetic energy?

Solution:

$$KE = \frac{1}{2} mv^2 = \frac{1}{2} \frac{W}{g} v^2$$

$$= \frac{\left(\frac{8 \text{ lb}}{32 \text{ ft/sec}^2}\right)(30 \text{ ft/sec})^2}{2}$$

$$= 112.5 \text{ ft-lb}$$

Problems

6. (a) A 10-kg mass moves with a speed of 20 m/sec. Determine its kinetic energy. (b) A 10-kg mass moves with a speed of 10 m/sec. Determine its kinetic energy. (c) What is the ratio of the solution of part (a) to the solution of part (b) Why?

7. What is the kinetic energy of a 3200-lb car which moves at (a) 30 mi/hr (b) 60 mi/hr?

8. A bullet with a mass of 0.06 kg travels at 700 m/sec. Calculate the bullet's kinetic energy in joules.

9. A 0.64-lb baseball leaves a bat with a speed of 120 ft/sec. Calculate the ball's kinetic energy.

10. An alpha particle with a mass of 4.7×10^{-27} kg travels at 1.6×10^7 m/sec. What is the kinetic energy of the particle?

11. An electron with a mass of 9.0×10^{-31} kg moves through a vacuum with a speed of 2.5×10^8 m/sec. Calculate the electron's kinetic energy.

12. (a) What potential energy does a 5-kg mass have when it is 10 m from the earth's surface? (b) What potential energy does the mass have if it falls to 5 m above the earth's surface? (c) How much potential energy does the mass lose if it falls 5 m? (d) What speed does the mass have after it falls the 5 m? (Assume that it starts from rest.) (e) What kinetic energy does the mass have after it falls 5 m?

11:6   The Conservation of Energy

The law of conservation of energy states that when energy is changed from one form to another it is always conserved. This law that energy exchanges always occur in equal amounts is one of the scientist's most useful tools.

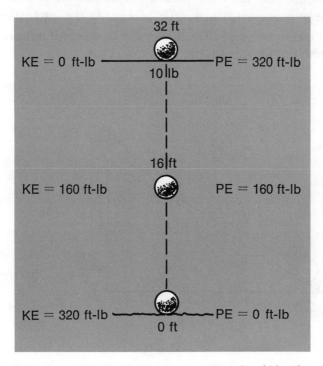

Figure 11-2. Loss of potential energy equals gain of kinetic energy.

As an example of the law of conservation of energy, consider what happens to a 10-lb body located 32 ft above the surface of the earth when it is allowed to fall freely. At the end of one second it will have fallen 16 ft and so will be located just 16 ft above the surface of the earth. Before the body was allowed to fall it must have had a potential energy of Fs or 10 lb × 32 ft which is 320 ft-lb. But at the end of one second it has fallen to a height of 16 ft and so can have only 10 lb × 16 ft or 160 ft-lb of PE. The 160 ft-lb difference in energy must have been converted to kinetic energy. Now at the end of one second of free fall the 10-lb weight must have a speed of 32 ft/sec. Its kinetic energy is then,

$$KE = \frac{mv^2}{2}$$

$$= \left(\frac{W}{g}\right) \frac{v^2}{2}$$

$$= \frac{10 \text{ lb } (32 \text{ ft/sec})^2}{(32 \text{ ft/sec}^2)2}$$

$$= 160 \text{ ft-lb}$$

The loss of potential energy by the body is equal to the gain in kinetic energy by the body. This transition of potential energy to kinetic energy occurs as the body falls. By the time the body reaches the earth's surface, all its previous potential energy is converted to kinetic energy. At the instant the body hits the earth, its kinetic energy is 320 ft-lb. This kinetic energy is transformed to heat energy as a result of the impact.

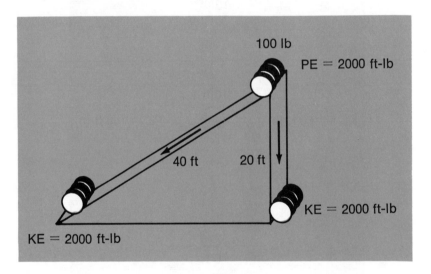

Figure 11-3

The path an object follows as it is raised to a certain height does not affect the potential energy of the object at the height. A 100-lb barrel 20 ft above the ground has 2000 ft-lb of potential energy whether it is raised straight up to that height or is pushed up a long incline to that height. The reverse also is true. The barrel's kinetic energy, neglecting friction, is 2000 ft-lb when it reached ground level. It makes no difference if the barrel falls straight down or rolls down the incline.

Sample Problem 5

An object with a mass of 15 kg falls 8 m. (a) What is the kinetic energy of the object just as it reaches earth? (b) What is the speed of the mass just as it reaches earth?

Solution:

(a) The kinetic energy of the object as it reaches the earth is equal to the potential energy the object possessed before it fell.

$$KE = PE$$

$$PE = mgh$$

$$= 15 \text{ kg} \times 9.8 \text{ m/sec}^2 \times 8 \text{ m}$$

$$= 1176 \text{ j}$$

(b) Since the $KE = 1176$ j

$$KE = \frac{mv^2}{2}$$

$$1176 \text{ j} = \frac{mv^2}{2}$$

$$v^2 = \frac{2 \times 1176 \text{ j}}{m}$$

$$v = \sqrt{\frac{2 \times 1176 \text{ j}}{15 \text{ kg}}}$$

$$v = \sqrt{\frac{157 \text{ m}^2}{\text{sec}^2}}$$

$$v = 12.5 \text{ m/sec}$$

Problems

13. A 15-kg mass moves with a speed of 12.5 m/sec. Calculate its kinetic energy.
14. An 8-kg mass drops 12 m. What is the kinetic energy of the mass just before it strikes the ground?
15. A 16-lb stone falls 40 ft. Find the stone's kinetic energy just before it strikes the ground.
16. An 8-lb block drops 64 ft. (a) Find the potential energy of the block at its highest point. (b) What is the kinetic energy of the block just as it strikes the ground? (c) What speed does the block have as it strikes the ground?
17. A man throws a 16-lb hammer straight up. To perform the throw, he does 320 ft-lb of work. How high does the hammer rise?
18. A 10-kg mass is shot straight up in the air. The mass has a kinetic energy of 1960 j just as it starts to rise. How high does it rise before it stops?

19. A 5-kg mass receives 600 j of energy. What speed is given to the mass? Assume the mass starts from rest on a horizontal, frictionless surface.
20. A 10-kg mass slides 16 m down a 30° incline. (a) Calculate the speed acquired (neglect friction). (b) What is the kinetic energy of the mass?
21. A 64-lb box slides 20 ft down a smooth incline that makes an angle of 37° with the horizontal. (a) Calculate the speed acquired (neglect friction). (b) What is the kinetic energy of the box?
22. A 5-kg mass is projected straight up with a speed of 15 m/sec. (a) What is the kinetic energy of the mass at the outset? (b) To what height does the mass rise?

11:7 Conservation of Energy in General

Energy is always conserved when it changes form. A given amount of potential energy produces an equal amount of kinetic energy. One liter of water at the top of a dam has a given quantity of potential energy. As the water falls, its potential energy is converted to kinetic energy. If this falling water is made to turn an electric generator, the generator generates a certain amount of electricity. This quantity of electricity generates just so much heat. If friction were absent, this quantity of electricity also could pump just one liter of water back up to the top of the dam. Energy never disappears. It just moves from place to place.

A law concerning the conservation of matter parallels the law of conservation of energy. This law states that matter neither can be created nor destroyed. Suppose fire destroys a piece of paper. After the fire is out, if all the original molecules of the paper from the gases and ash formed during the burning could be reassembled, there would be just as many molecules after the fire as before the fire. According to this law, matter can change form, but is never destroyed.

Until recently, the laws of conservation of energy and conservation of matter were thought to be completely true. However, discoveries in nuclear energy now show that matter can be converted into energy. The amount of energy obtained from a certain amount of mass is:

$$E = mc^2$$

E represents the energy released, m is the quantity of mass converted into energy, and c^2 the speed of light squared. This equation was derived by Dr. Albert Einstein. It has been verified by many experiments. Because mass and energy are equivalent, the law of conservation of energy and the law of conservation of matter are now combined into one law: *The sum total of matter plus energy in the universe is a constant.*

11:8 Elastic Collisions

An elastic collision is a collision in which the total kinetic energy of the bodies involved is the same after the collision takes place as it was before the collision occurred. Strictly speaking, all collisions between objects larger than molecules are inelastic. That is, kinetic energy decreases so the velocity of the objects involved in the collision decreases as well. The loss in energy is accounted for by an increase in the heat energy content of the bodies that collide; the generation of sound during the collision, or both. In any event, the energy is not lost. It merely changes form.

The collision between some fairly large objects is so nearly elastic that they may be considered to be elastic. Within negligible error, the collision that takes place between two billiard balls or two glass marbles moving across a smooth surface is nearly elastic.

Frederic Lewis

Figure 11-4. A golf ball collides with a hard surface. How can you tell if the collision is nearly elastic?

Although kinetic energy decreases during an inelastic collision, there is no change in momentum. For all collisions, the law of conservation of momentum holds. To illustrate, suppose a 1-kg ball of putty moves across a frictionless surface at 20 m/sec. This ball of putty collides head on with another stationary ball of putty also with a mass of 1 kg. The two balls stick together and move off as one mass. According to the law of conservation of momentum, the total momentum of the two balls stuck together is no more than the momentum possessed by the original ball of putty. That is,

$$mv = (1 \text{ kg}) (20 \text{ m/sec}) = 20 \text{ kg-m/sec}$$

In order for the momentum to be conserved, the two balls stuck together must have the same 20 kg-m/sec of momentum. This means that they move with a velocity of 10 m/sec in the direction of the moving ball of putty.

$$mv = (2 \text{ kg}) (10 \text{ m/sec}) = 20 \text{ kg-m/sec}$$

If the velocity had been different, the law of conservation of momentum would have been violated. However, the kinetic energy of the balls of putty before and after the collision is not the same.

Original KE

$$\frac{1}{2} mv^2 = \frac{1 \text{ kg} (20 \text{ m/sec})^2}{2}$$
$$= 200 \text{ j}$$

Final KE

$$\frac{1}{2} mv^2 = \frac{2 \text{ kg} (10 \text{ m/sec})^2}{2}$$
$$= 100 \text{ j}$$

While momentum is conserved, half the kinetic energy is converted to some other form of energy (such as heat). The collision is highly inelastic.

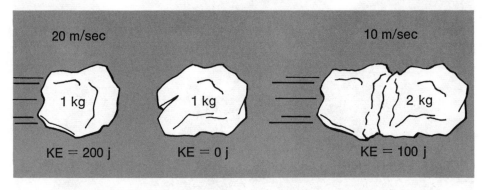

Figure 11-5.   Kinetic energy is not conserved in an inelastic collision.

The behavior of bodies involved in a highly elastic collision often can be predicted. This is done by considering the laws of conservation of energy and conservation of momentum together. For example, suppose a billiard ball of mass m moves with a speed v. This ball collides head on with a second, stationary billiard ball of equal mass. After the collision, if the two balls roll off together at just half the speed of the original billiard ball, the law of conservation of momentum is satisfied. This is the same as it was for the balls of putty discussed earlier. However, as was shown also for the balls of putty, the kinetic energy of the billiard balls together would constitute only half the kinetic energy of the first billiard ball before the collision took place. This collision could hardly be called elastic. What actually happens in a collision of this type is that the first ball comes to a complete halt. The second ball of equal mass moves off at exactly the speed of the first ball before the collision took place. Thus momentum and kinetic energy are strictly conserved.

Figure 11-6. (a) The golfer uses clubs of different materials to produce varying degrees of elastic collisions between the ball and club. (b) Direction and speed of the tennis ball are determined by control of the collision between racket and ball.

Problems

23. Two bowling balls each with a mass of 10 kg, roll together along a smooth ramp at 10 m/sec. They collide with a row of 10-kg bowling balls at rest.

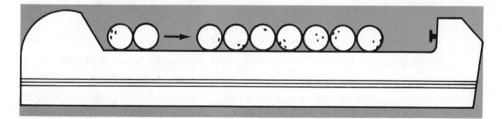

Figure 11-7

Collisions between bowling balls are highly elastic. (a) After the collision, can one bowling ball leave the opposite end of the row with a speed of 20 m/sec and satisfy the law of conservation of momentum? (b) If one bowling ball did leave the opposite end of the row at 20 m/sec, what kinetic energy would it possess? What was the total kinetic energy of the two original balls before the collision? Would energy be conserved under these circumstances? (c) Two bowling balls leave the opposite end of the row at 10 m/sec. Is the law of conservation of momentum obeyed? (d) Two bowling balls leave the opposite end of the row at 10 m/sec. Is the law of conservation of energy observed?

24. Use the same procedure as in Problem 23 to determine what happens if a single bowling ball with a mass of 10 kg moving at 10 m/sec and collides with a row of stationary bowling balls. That is, will one bowling ball moving at 10 m/sec move away from the opposite end of the row? Or, will two balls moving at 5 m/sec each move away from the opposite end of the row?

25. A railroad car with a mass of 5×10^5 kg collides with a second stationary railroad car of equal mass. After the collision, the two cars lock together and move off at 4 m/sec. (a) Before the collision, the first railroad car moved at 8 m/sec. What was its momentum? (b) What is the momentum of the two cars after the collision? (c) Calculate the kinetic energies of the two cars before and after the collision. (d) Account for the loss of kinetic energy.

QUESTIONS

1. What type of energy does a wound-up watch spring possess? What form of energy does a running watch use? When the watch runs down, what has become of the energy?

2. Describe the energy conversions a bullet undergoes from the time it is fired from a rifle to the time it enters a tree 500 m away.

3. Describe the types of energy the earth-sun system possesses.

4. The earth is approximately 4×10^6 miles closer to the sun in winter than it is in summer. The earth moves along its orbit faster in winter than it does in summer. Explain these two statements in terms of the earth's potential and kinetic energy.

5. A rubber ball is dropped from a height of 8 ft and, after striking the floor, bounces to a height of 5 ft. (a) If the ball had bounced to a height of 8 ft how would you describe the collision between the ball and the floor? (b) If the ball had not bounced at all how would you describe the collision between the ball and the floor? (c) What happened to the energy lost by the ball during the collision?

6. A film was produced that centered around the discovery of a mythical substance called "flubber." This substance could bounce higher than the height from which it was dropped. Explain why "flubber" is not likely to exist.

7. If "flubber" did exist, what changes would have to take place in the condition of the surface from which "flubber" bounced?

PROBLEMS

1. (a) How much work is required to hoist a 98-nt sack of grain to a storage room 50 m above the ground floor of a grain elevator? (b) What is the potential energy of the sack of grain at this height? (c) The rope tied to the sack of grain breaks just as the sack reaches the storage room. What kinetic energy does the sack have just before it strikes the ground floor?

2. A 3200-lb automobile travels at a speed of 30 mi/hr. What is its kinetic energy?

3. An automobile has a mass of 1500 kg. What is its kinetic energy if it has a speed of 108 km/hr? (Convert km/hr to m/sec.)

4. An archer puts an 4-oz (0.25 lb) arrow to his bowstring. He exerts an average force of 50 lb and draws the string back 2 ft. (a) Assuming no frictional losses, with what speed does the arrow leave the bow? (b) If the arrow is shot straight up, how high does it rise?

5. A 3200-lb automobile starts from rest and accelerates to 60 mi/hr in 20 sec. The average force needed to overcome friction during this period is 100 lb. (a) What distance does the auto travel during this period of acceleration? (b) What force does the engine produce upon the automobile during this time? (c) How much work does the engine do to overcome the friction? (d) How much work does the engine do to accelerate the auto? (e) Assume the engine works to capacity. What is its horsepower?

6. A man applies an average force of 82 lb in a direction straight up to a stone that weighs 8 lb. To what height does the stone rise if the man applies this force through a distance of 4 ft?

7. (a) A 20-kg mass is on the edge of a 100-m high cliff. What potential energy does it possess? (b) The mass falls from the cliff. What is its kinetic energy just as it strikes the ground? (c) What speed does it have as it strikes the ground?

8. A steel ball has a mass of 4 kg and rolls along a smooth, level surface at 60 m/sec. (a) Calculate its kinetic energy. (b) Originally, the steel ball was at rest on the surface. A force acted on it through a distance of 20 m to give it the speed of 60 m/sec. What was the magnitude of the force?

9. Calculate the amount of energy that is released if an entire kilogram of mass is destroyed completely. (The speed of light is 3.0×10^8 m/sec.)

10. A submarine's engines consume energy at the rate of 3000 j/sec. How long can a kilogram of mass propel the sub before it will stop? (Assume that one year is equivalent to 3.0×10^7 sec.)

11. Calculate the amount of matter that is destroyed to produce 30.0 j of energy.

12. A steel ball with a mass of 5 kg rolls along a frictionless, level surface at 40 m/sec. (a) Calculate its kinetic energy. (b) A chute changes the direction

of the ball. Now its direction is vertically perpendicular to the level (horizontal) surface. How high does it rise?

13. As shown, a bowling ball rolls down an incline. The surfaces involved are

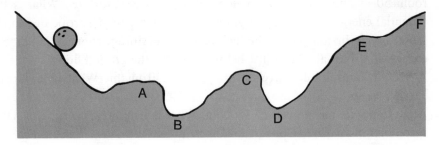

Figure 11-8

completely frictionless. (a) To what point does the ball rise on the opposite incline? (b) At what point in the diagram is the speed maximum? (c) At what point is the speed zero?

14. A railroad car with a mass of 100 slugs rolls along a level track at a speed of 20 ft/sec. It collides with a stationary car of equal mass. (a) The two cars lock together and then move off. What is their new velocity? (b) How much kinetic energy do the cars lose during the collision?

Measurement of Heat

Heat energy when transferred from one body to another, results in a temperature change or a change in state. The amount of heat transferred can be measured in terms of the physical effects which result, namely changes in state, volume, pressure, length, and electric resistance. Equal amounts of two substances at the same temperature may differ greatly in thermal energy. How do large bodies of water temper the climate of adjacent land areas?

12:1   What is Heat?

Before the nineteenth century, heat was thought to be an invisible fluid called "caloric." One body was thought to be warmer than another because it contained more caloric than the other. This theory explained why a cool body brought close to a warm body soon became warm itself. Caloric could supposedly flow from the warm body into the cool body.

By the middle of the nineteenth century, the caloric theory of heat was abandoned in favor of the kinetic theory of heat. The kinetic theory states that all matter is made up of molecules which are constantly in motion. Today the accepted theory is the kinetic theory. In the kinetic theory, heat is associated with internal energy. Internal energy is the total kinetic and potential energy associated with the motions and relative positions of the molecules of an object. Internal energy is separate and distinct from any kinetic or potential energy of the object as a whole. *Heat is the measure of the internal energy transferred from bodies of higher internal energy to bodies of lower internal energy.* Heat can be made to do work. Work can be made to generate heat.

12:2   Temperature and Heat Are Not the Same

Temperature and heat are two different quantities. *The temperature of a substance is a measure of the average kinetic energy of the molecules of the substance.* One substance is hotter than another because its molecules possess more kinetic energy than those of the other substance. However, the heat a body can supply depends upon more than just the kinetic energies of the molecules that make up that body. Molecules have potential energy as well as kinetic energy. Potential energy is a result of mutual attractions of the molecules in a substance. Thermal energy is the sum of the kinetic and potential energy of the molecules in a substance. Temperature only indicates the average kinetic energy of the molecules. It does not limit the heat a body can supply. Thus, a glass of water and a swimming pool of water might have exactly the same temperature. However, the water in the swimming pool is able to supply more heat because it contains more water.

12:3   Thermometry

In scientific work, temperature is measured with a mercury thermometer. A column of mercury is sealed in a glass tube and an appropriate scale is placed on the tube. Increases or decreases in temperature cause the column of mercury to expand or contract. Mercury expands at a greater rate per degree temperature change than does glass. Therefore, the level of the mercury in the tube varies with the temperature.

Mercury and alcohol thermometers are common. However, the use of them is limited to a short range of temperatures. Mercury is limited by its freezing point ($-39°$ C) and its boiling point ($357°$ C). For low temperatures, either hydrogen or helium gas are suitable. For high temperatures, devices that measure a property other than expansion usually are used. The temperature of incandes-

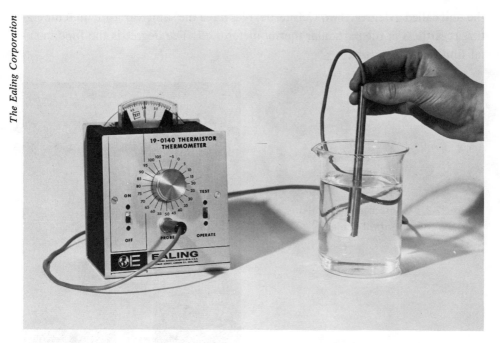

Figure 12-1.   Electrical resistance changes with temperature. This thermistor thermometer indicates temperature with great accuracy by using this principle.

cent substances can be estimated by an analysis of the color of light the substance emits. Another means to determine high temperatures utilizes the knowledge that the electrical conductivity of wire depends upon the temperature of the wire. Platinum wire often is used to measure temperature because of its precise variation in conductivity with temperature.

12:4   Temperature Scales

The Celsius scale was established by selecting two fixed temperatures. These were the freezing and boiling points of water. At fixed atmospheric pressure, these points are reproduced easily. On the Celsius scale, the freezing point of water is 0°. The boiling point of water is 100°. Therefore, there are 100 degrees between these two points. For this reason the Celsius scale often is called the "centigrade scale." The Celsius scale is thought of as the metric temperature scale.

The English system uses the Fahrenheit scale. On the Fahrenheit scale, the freezing point of water is 32°. The boiling point of water is 212°. Therefore, there are 180° between these two points.

On a thermometer, the actual size of a degree depends upon the thermometer itself. The linear distance between two marks on a scale has nothing to do with the unit called a degree. Two Celsius degrees have the same variation in temperature regardless of the particular thermometer used. The degree is the fundamental unit of temperature.

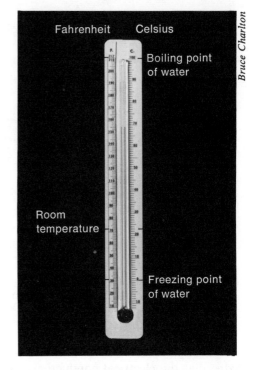

Figure 12-2.   Comparison of Celsius and Fahrenheit scales.

12:5   The Absolute or Kelvin Scale

Temperatures do not appear to have an upper limit. The interior temperature of the sun ranges above 1.5×10^7 degrees Celsius. Other stars may have even higher temperatures. However, temperatures do appear to have a lower limit. The random motion of molecules is thought to approach zero at $-273°$ C. At this temperature, the average kinetic energy of the molecules of a material is zero. So temperature, as defined, must be zero as well. This does not mean that the molecules do not retain any energy. The molecules would have rotational motion as well as other forms of internal energy not related to temperature.

Lord Kelvin, an eminent 19th century physicist, devised a scale known as the Kelvin temperature scale. This scale extends the Celsius scale to absolute zero and places zero degrees at that point. The Kelvin scale is the same as the Celsius scale except zero is at $-273°$ C. Any temperature on the Celsius scale is converted to the Kelvin scale by adding 273°.

$$°K = °C + 273°$$

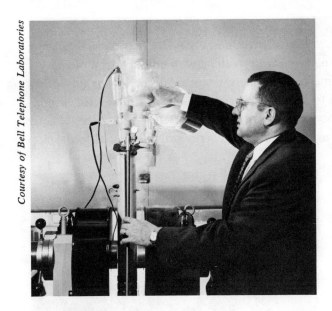

Courtesy of Bell Telephone Laboratories

Figure 12-3. A metallurgist pours liquid nitrogen into the apparatus to cool it to −200°C (73°K). At this temperature the tin alloy in the tube becomes superconducting (has almost no electrical resistance).

Sample Problem 1

Convert 20° C to degrees Kelvin.

Solution:

$$°K = °C + 273°$$
$$= 20° + 273°$$
$$= 293° K$$

Sample Problem 2

Convert 50° K to degrees Celsius.

Solution:
$$°K = °C + 273°$$
$$50° = °C + 273°$$
$$°C = −223°$$

Problems

1. Convert 40° C to degrees Kelvin.
2. Convert 40° K to degrees Celsius.
3. Convert 273° C to degrees Kelvin.
4. Convert 273° K to degrees Celsius.
5. Convert 200° K to degrees Celsius.
6. Convert these Kelvin temperatures to Celsius temperatures.
   (a) 100°   (b) 22°   (c) 373°   (d) 323°   (e) 400°
7. Convert these Celsius temperatures to Kelvin temperatures.
   (a) 100°   (b) −100°   (c) 300°   (d) 20°   (e) −23°

12:6   The First Law of Thermodynamics

The first law of thermodynamics reasserts the law of conservation of energy. This law states that when mechanical energy, electrical energy, or any other kind of energy is converted to heat, all energy is conserved. The heat, if converted to mechanical, electrical, or any other form of energy, develops exactly the same amount of energy as the amount of energy originally used to develop the heat.

Figure 12-4. Heat is converted directly to electricity in this thermocouple. More than 2 amperes of current are produced when the flame heats the junction of two dissimilar thermoelectric materials.

Westinghouse Photo

12:7   The Second Law of Thermodynamics

The quantity of heat a body supplies is not necessarily indicated by its temperature. Temperature serves chiefly to describe which way heat flows when two bodies of different temperatures are brought together. For example, a hot iron bar is placed in cold water. The heat travels from the metal bar into the water. The iron bar is "hot" because its molecules have a higher average kinetic energy than do those of the water. Collisions between the water molecules and the more energetic iron molecules impart energy to the water molecules. The energy spreads out into the entire system. However, the reverse process never occurs. The hot iron bar does not become hotter while the water becomes colder. This is known as the second law of thermodynamics. Heat flows from hot to cold. This law prohibits the transfer of energy from areas of low concentration to areas of high concentration.

The second law of thermodynamics sometimes is stated in terms of entropy. Entropy is the "unavailability" of energy. Dissipated energy cannot be retrieved without additional energy input. The entropy of the universe always is increasing.

12:8 Heat Units

The metric system measures heat in calories (cal) or kilocalories (kcal). *A calorie is the amount of heat needed to raise the temperature of one gram of water one Celsius degree.* Since the calorie is a relatively small unit of heat, the kilocalorie often is used. It is one thousand calories, the amount of heat needed to raise the temperature of one kilogram of water one Celsius degree. The increasing use of the joule to measure heat will be discussed in the next chapter.

The English system measures heat in the British Thermal Unit or the Btu. This unit is similar to the calorie. *A Btu is the amount of heat needed to raise the temperature of the mass of one pound of water one Fahrenheit degree.*

12:9 Specific Heat

The specific heat of a substance is the amount of heat needed to raise the temperature of a unit mass of that substance through one degree. In the metric system, specific heat is expressed in calories per gram-Celsius degree or in kilocalories per kilogram-Celsius degree. For example, it requires 0.2 calories of heat to raise the temperature of one gram of aluminum through one Celsius degree. The specific heat of aluminum is 0.2 cal/g-C°. The specific heat of aluminum also could be expressed as 0.2 kcal/kg-C°. In the English system, specific heat is expressed as Btu per pound-Fahrenheit degree. Numerically, specific heat is the same in either the English or metric systems. So the specific heat of aluminum is 0.2 Btu/lb-F°.

Table 12-1

Material	Specific Heat (cal/g-C° or Btu/lb-F°)	Material	Specific Heat (cal/g-C° or Btu/lb-F°)
Alcohol	0.58	Ice	0.50
Aluminum	0.20	Iron	0.11
Brass	0.09	Lead	0.03
Carbon	0.17	Silver	0.056
Copper	0.093	Steam	0.5
Glass	0.20	Water	1.0
Gold	0.030	Zinc	0.09

Most materials require less than one calorie to raise the temperature of one gram through one Celsius degree. Therefore, most specific heats are less than the specific heat of water. Copper requires only about 0.09 calories per gram for a temperature increase of one Celsius degree. One calorie of heat raises the temperature of one gram of copper by more than eleven Celsius degrees. Table 12-1 gives the specific heats of some common materials.

When the specific heat of a material is known, the amount of heat lost or gained by any given mass of that material as it undergoes a temperature change is readily calculated. One gram of water heated through a temperature increase of 1 C° indicates the heat absorbed by the water is 1 cal. Ten grams of water heated through 1 C° indicates the heat absorbed is 10 cal. Ten grams of water heated through 5 C° indicates the heat absorbed is 50 cal. Thus mass, change in temperature, and specific heat determine the quantity of heat gained or lost by a mass as it changes temperature. As an equation,

$$\Delta H = ms\Delta t$$

In the equation, ΔH is the heat gained or lost, m is the mass involved, s is the specific heat of the mass, and Δt is the change in temperature.

Sample Problem 3

A 400-g block of iron is heated from 20° C to 50° C. How much heat is absorbed by the iron?

Solution:

$$\Delta H = ms\Delta t$$

$$\Delta H = \left(400 \text{ g}\right)\left(0.11 \frac{\text{cal}}{\text{g-C}°}\right)\left(30 \text{ C}°\right)$$

$$\Delta H = 1320 \text{ cal}$$

Sample Problem 4

A 30-lb aluminum ladder is taken from a heated garage (70° F) into the outside air (42° F). Later on, the ladder's temperature is the same as the outside air. How much heat is liberated by the ladder?

Solution:

$$\Delta H = ms\Delta t$$

$$\Delta H = \left(30 \text{ lb}\right)\left(0.2 \frac{\text{Btu}}{\text{lb-F}°}\right)\left(-28 \text{ F}°\right)$$

$$\Delta H = -168 \text{ Btu}$$

Problems

8. Calculate the heat absorbed by 250 g of water when it is heated from 10° C to 85° C.

9. Calculate the heat absorbed by 60 g of copper when it is heated from 20° C to 80° C.

10. A 38-lb block of lead is heated from −26° F to 180° F. How much heat does it absorb during the heating?

11. A 5-kg gold ingot is cooled from 120° C to −20° C. How much heat is removed from the ingot?

12. A 400-g glass coffee cup at room temperature (20° C) is plunged into hot dishwater (80° C). Later, the temperature of the cup reaches that of the dishwater. How much heat does the cup absorb?

13. A woman transfers 5 lb of ice cubes from the freezing compartment of a refrigerator into a home freezer. The refrigerator's freezing compartment is kept at 25° F. The home freezer is kept at 0° F. How much heat does the freezer's cooling system remove from the ice cubes?

14. A 500-lb cast-iron auto engine contains 30 lb of water as a coolant. The engine's temperature is 95° F when it is shut off one evening. The air temperature is 50° F. How much heat does the engine and the water in it give up in cooling?

15. Steam enters one end of a turbine at 450° C. It leaves the other end at 175° C. How much heat does each kilogram of steam give up to the turbine as it passes through?

12:10 Conservation in Heat Transfer

One hundred grams of water at 10° C are mixed with 100 g of hot water at 90° C. The container in which they are mixed is insulated to prevent heat loss. The hot water gives up heat to the cold water. Assuming very little loss to the surroundings, the temperature of the mixture when measured with a thermometer is 50° C. The temperature of the cold water increases by 40 Celsius degrees while the temperature of the hot water decreases by 40 Celsius degrees.

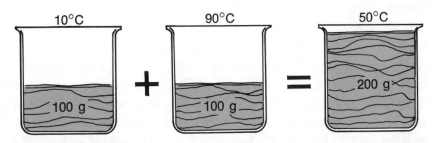

Figure 12-5. Heat lost by the hot water equals the heat gained by the cold water.

To heat 100 g of water by one Celsius degree requires 100 calories. To heat 100 g of water by 40 Celsius degrees requires 40 × 100 calories or 4000 calories. The cold water gains 4000 calories of heat. Similarly, the 100 g of hot water is cooled through 40 Celsius degrees. As a result, the hot water gives up 40×100 cal or 4000 calories of heat. The heat gained by the cold water is equal to the heat lost by the hot water. This is according to the first law of thermodynamics.

To solve problems of heat transfer, assume that the heat lost by one substance is equal to the heat gained by the second substance. Heat lost or gained by a substance is equal to $ms\Delta t$. This is expressed:

$$\text{Heat Lost} = \text{Heat Gained}$$

$$ms\Delta t = ms\Delta t$$

Sample Problem 5

A 500-g block of iron at 100° C is placed in 500 g of water at 20° C. What is the final temperature of the iron and water mixture? (The specific heat of iron is 0.11 cal/g-C°.)

Solution:

The temperature of the iron decreases. Its temperature change (Δt) is 100° C $- t_2$ where t_2 represents the final temperature of the mixture. The temperature of the water increases. Its temperature change is $t_2 - 20$° C. Hence,

$$\text{Heat lost by iron} = \text{Heat gained by water}$$

$$ms\Delta t = ms\Delta t$$

$$(500 \text{ g})(0.11 \text{ cal/g-C°})(100 \text{ C°} - t_2) = (500 \text{ g})(1 \text{ cal/g-C°})(t_2 - 20° \text{ C})$$

$$55(100 - t_2) = (500)(t_2 - 20° \text{ C})$$

$$5500 - 55\, t_2 = 500\, t_2 - 10\,000$$

$$15\,500 = 555\, t_2$$

$$t_2 = 28° \text{ C}$$

Problems

16. 200 g of water at 80° C are mixed with 200 g of water at 10° C. Assume no heat loss to surroundings. What is the final temperature of the mixture?
17. 600 g of water at 90° C are mixed with 400 g of water at 22° C. Assume no heat loss to surroundings. What is the final temperature of the mixture?
18. 400 g of alcohol at 16° C are mixed with 400 g of water at 85° C. Assume no heat loss to surroundings. What is the final temperature of the mixture?
19. A 100-g mass of brass at 90° C is placed in a glass beaker containing 200 g of water at 20° C. Assume no heat loss to the glass or surroundings. What is the final temperature of the mixture?
20. A 100-g mass of aluminum at 100° C is placed in 100 g of water at 10° C. The final temperature of the mixture is 25° C. What is the specific heat of the aluminum?

21. A 20-lb piece of zinc at 160° F is placed in a container of water. The water weighs 40 lb and has a temperature of 50° F before the zinc is added. What is the final temperature of the water and zinc?

12:11   Latent Heat and Change of State

The particle nature of matter implies that some force holds the particles together. Otherwise an object would have no shape. The forces holding molecules together are called cohesive forces. They help to explain how a substance can absorb heat without reflecting the heat gain as an increase in temperature. For example, the specific heat of ice is 0.5 cal/g-C°. If a gram of ice at −10° C has 5 cal of heat added to it, the temperature of the ice becomes 0°C, or the melting point of ice. Once the gram of ice is warmed to this temperature, it continues to absorb heat. Yet it shows no increase in temperature. The ice at 0° C absorbs 80 calories of heat to become water at 0° C. The 80 calories causes the ice to change state, but they do not change its temperature. The 80 calories needed to change the state is called the latent heat of fusion of ice.

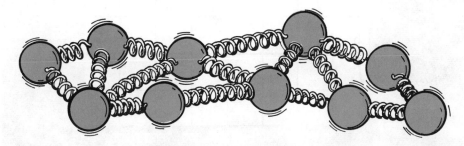

Figure 12-6.   Molecules of a solid behave as if they were held together by springs.

As the ice melts, the heat it absorbs must be stored in some form other than the kinetic energies of its molecules. If the kinetic energies of the molecules are increased, the temperature of the ice is increased. But this does not happen. The absorbed energy is used to do work on the ice molecules and to help separate them. Since molecules attract one another, work is required to force them apart. As the molecules are forced apart, their potential energies are increased. The potential energy of each molecule increases in relation to all the molecules about it. Whereas its kinetic energy content remains more or less constant.

As the space between each molecule of the ice increases, the cohesive forces decrease. This allows each individual molecule more freedom of movement. Eventually the intermolecular forces are reduced to the point where the molecules can slide over one another and the mass undergoes a change in state and becomes liquid.

Once the gram of ice has absorbed 80 calories of heat and has changed to water, the water continues to absorb heat if it is available. The temperature of the water increases one Celsius degree for each calorie of heat it absorbs. As heat is added, the temperature continues to rise until the water acquires a temperature of 100° C. This is called the boiling point of water. After the boiling point is reached, any heat absorbed is used to change the water from liquid state to

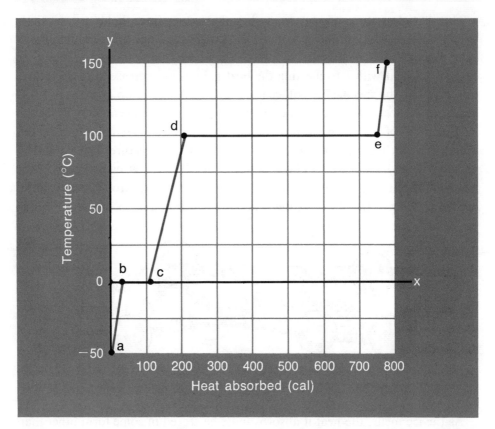

Figure 12-7.   Graph of the heat absorbed by 1.0 g of ice as its temperature is raised from −50°C to 150°C. Notice that the slope of the graph is steeper from *a* to *b* and from *e* to *f* than it is from *c* to *d*. This is because the specific heats of ice and steam are less than the specific heat of water. What do the horizontal portions of the graph indicate? Can you read the heat of vaporization and heat of fusion from the graph?

gas state. To completely change the entire gram of water at 100° C to steam at 100° C requires 540 cal of heat. This amount of heat is known as the latent heat of vaporization of steam.

The latent heat of vaporization of steam is considerably higher than the latent heat of fusion of ice. The result of this large energy input is that the gas molecules are more free of intermolecular attraction than are liquid molecules.

Sample Problem 6

Heat is applied to 100 g of ice at 0° C until the ice melts and the temperature of the resulting water rises to 20° C. How much heat is absorbed?

Solution:

First, calculate the heat the ice absorbs to cause a change of state from solid ice to liquid water. Each gram requires 80 calories to bring about the change,

$$100 \text{ g} \times 80 \frac{\text{cal}}{\text{g}} = 8000 \text{ cal}$$

Next, calculate the heat the water absorbs to change its temperature from 0° C to 20° C.

$$\Delta H = ms\Delta t$$

$$\Delta H = \left(100 \text{ g}\right)\left(1 \frac{\text{cal}}{\text{g-C}°}\right)\left(20 \text{ C}°\right)$$

$$\Delta H = 2000 \text{ cal}$$

Total: 8000 cal + 2000 cal = 10 000 cal

Sample Problem 7

100 g of water at 80° C is heated until it becomes steam at 130° C. How much heat is absorbed?

Solution:

First, calculate the heat the water absorbs to increase its temperature to 100°C.

$$\Delta H = ms\Delta t$$

$$\Delta H = \left(100 \text{ g}\right)\left(1 \frac{\text{cal}}{\text{g-C}°}\right)\left(20 \text{ C}°\right)$$

$$\Delta H = 2000 \text{ cal}$$

Next, determine the heat the water absorbs at 100° C to become steam at 100° C. Each gram requires 540 cal to bring about the change,

$$100 \text{ g} \times 540 \frac{\text{cal}}{\text{g}} = 54\ 000 \text{ cal}$$

Finally, calculate the heat the steam absorbs to increase its temperature from 100° C to 130° C. The specific heat of steam is 0.5 cal/g-C°.

$$\Delta H = ms\Delta t$$

$$\Delta H = \left(100 \text{ g}\right)\left(0.5 \frac{\text{cal}}{\text{g-C}°}\right)\left(30 \text{ C}°\right)$$

$$\Delta H = 1500 \text{ cal}$$

Total: 2000 cal + 54 000 cal + 1500 cal = 57 500 cal

Problems

22. How much heat is needed to change 50 g of ice at 0° C to water at 0° C?

23. How much heat is needed to change 50 g of water at 100° C to steam at 100° C?

24. How much heat is absorbed by 100 g of ice at −20° C to become water at 0°? The specific heat of ice is 0.5 cal/g-C°.

25. 200 g of water at 60° C is heated to steam at 140° C. How much heat is applied?

26. How much heat is needed to change 300 g of ice at −30° C to steam at 130° C?

27. How much heat is removed from 60 g of steam at 100° C to change it to 60 g of water at 20° C?

28. The specific heat of mercury is 0.033 cal/g-C°. Its latent heat of vaporization is 71 cal/g. How much heat is needed to completely vaporize a kilogram of mercury at 10° C? The boiling point of mercury is 358° C.

29. Years ago a home icebox required a cake of ice with a mass of about 20 kg. The temperature of the ice was 0° C when delivered. As it melted, how much heat in calories did this size ice cake absorb?

QUESTIONS

1. How is heat described in terms of the kinetic theory?

2. Distinguish between heat and temperature.

3. Why are the readings of thermometers of different diameters the same under identical conditions?

4. Describe the Celsius temperature scale.

5. How is the Kelvin temperature scale different from the Celsius temperature scale?

6. A wheel is stopped by a friction brake. The brake gets hot, and the internal energy of the brake increases. The kinetic energy of the wheel decreases by the same amount as the increase in internal energy of the brake. The first law of thermodynamics would be satisfied if the hot brake were to cool and give back its internal energy to the wheel, causing it to resume rotation. This does not happen. Why?

7. Ten grams of aluminum and ten grams of lead are heated to the same temperature. The pieces of metal are placed on a block of ice. Which metal will melt the most ice?

PROBLEMS

1. Convert these Celsius temperatures to Kelvin temperatures. (a) 50° (b) 150° (c) −200° (d) 300°

2. Convert these Kelvin temperatures to Celsius temperatures. (a) 50° (b) 150° (c) 273° (d) 300°

3. How much heat in Btu is needed to raise the temperature of 50 lb of water from 40° F to 180° F?

4. How much heat in calories must be added to 50 g of aluminum at 20° C to raise its temperature to 120° C?

5. Suppose the same amount of heat needed to raise the temperature of 50 g of water through 100 C° is applied to 50 g of zinc. What is the temperature change of the zinc?

6. A copper wire has a mass of 165 g. An electric current runs through the wire for a short time and changes its temperature from 20° C to 38° C. What minimum quantity of heat is generated by the electric current?

7. A pound of water has a mass of 454 g. A Fahrenheit degree is $\frac{5}{9}$ of a Celsius degree. (a) How many calories are equivalent to a Btu? (b) How many kilocalories?

8. 500 g of water at 90° C are mixed with 500 g of water at 30° C. Assume no heat loss to surroundings. What is the final temperature of the mixture?

9. 200 g of brass at 300° C are placed in a calorimeter cup which contains 260 g of water at 20° C. Disregard the absorption of heat by the cup and calculate the final temperature of the mixture. The specific heat of brass is 0.09 cal/g-C°.

10. 100 g of tungsten at 100° C are placed in 200 g of water at 20° C. The mixture reaches equilibrium at 21.6° C. Calculate the specific heat of tungsten.

11. How much heat is added to 10 g of ice at −20° C to convert it to steam at 120° C?

12. 40 g of chloroform condensed from a vapor at 61.6° C to a liquid at 61.6° C. It liberated 2360 calories of heat. What is the latent heat of vaporization of chloroform?

13. 50 g of ice at 0° C are placed in a glass beaker containing 400 g of water at 50° C. All the ice melts. What is the final temperature of the mixture? Disregard heat loss to the glass. Remember also that when ice melts it becomes water.

13

Heat as Energy

Heat is considered a form of energy because it produces measurable amounts of work. Heat energy can also be converted to other forms of energy such as light, electrical and mechanical energy. Metallurgical processes require huge amounts of heat energy. What are some suitable sources of this heat energy? How might the heat source affect the geographical location of the foundry?

13:1 The Mechanical Equivalent of Heat

Heat is conserved as it moves from one body to another. Since heat is a form of energy, the heat supplied by a body also is conserved when it is changed into another form of energy. Recall that energy is the capacity to do work. So much heat produces so much work, and so much work produces so much heat.

Early experiments to relate work and heat in a quantitative way were performed by Count Rumford*. At the time of the experiments, Count Rumford was Minister of War of Bavaria. Rumford did not go along with the caloric theory of heat. His work did much to discredit it. While supervising the boring of cannons at the arsenal in Munich, Rumford noticed that friction caused the drills to become extremely hot. To overcome the heat, he ordered the cannons to be submerged in tubs of water. Horses were being used to turn the boring shafts. Rumford kept a record of the time the horses worked and the temperature increase of the water in the tubs. He found that while the horses worked, the water temperature increased steadily. Although the experiment was not precise, it did establish a relationship between heat and work. The Count's writings summed up the experiments this way. If the heat added to the water originated anywhere, it was the result of the work done by the horses rather than the transfer of some mysterious fluid.

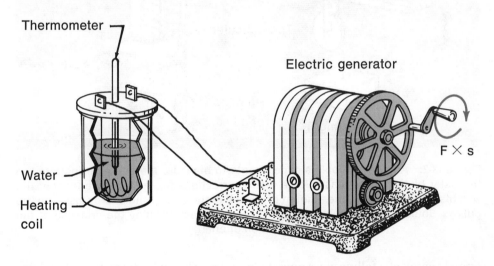

Figure 13-1.   One of Joule's early experiments to investigate the relationship between the forms of energy. How many energy transformations do you observe in the figure?

In 1830, James Prescott Joule began a brilliant series of precise experiments in England. His aim was to establish the equivalence of the various forms of energy. In an early experiment, Joule carefully measured the work (Fs) required to drive an electric generator. Then he measured the heat produced by the electric current put out by the generator. His findings were consistent. For every 4.2 newton-meters or joules of work put into turning the generator, one

---

*Count Rumford was born Benjamin Thompson in 1755 in Woburn, Mass., the son of a poor farmer. Almost entirely self-educated, he became a superb scientist, a count of the Holy Roman Empire (the name by which he came to be known), Minister of War of Bavaria, and an English Knight.

calorie of heat was produced. This 4.2 joules of work needed to develop a calorie of heat is called the mechanical equivalent of heat.

$$1 \text{ calorie} = 4.2 \text{ joules}$$

In the English system, the mechanical equivalent of heat is

$$1 \text{ Btu} = 778 \text{ ft-lb}$$

Joule performed many experiments to measure the mechanical equivalent of heat. Figure 13-2 diagrams one of his best-known. In this experiment, the po-

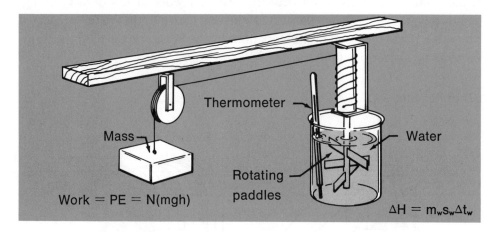

Figure 13-2.   Another of Joule's experiments to measure the energy transferred to the water by the falling mass. Joule made corrections for the kinetic energy of the weights hitting the floor, the amount of stretch of the string, and energy losses in the pulleys. Joule's experiments were instrumental in establishing the principle of the conservation of energy.

tential energy of a falling mass operates a pulley. The pulley turns a set of paddles submerged in a water-filled calorimeter. When the falling mass has the proper weight, the force it applies to the pulley turns the pulley smoothly and steadily. The potential energy of the mass is converted to work to turn the paddles and is not used to accelerate the mass. From the experiments, Joule assumed that the work done by the paddles on the water was equal to the loss of potential energy (*mgh*) of the mass as it fell. The work done on the water by the paddles was converted to heat. As a result, the temperature of the water rose steadily. To gain a large difference in the water temperature, Joule repeated the process several times. Hence, he found the total work done on the water was equal to N (*mgh*) where N is the number of times the mass is allowed to fall.

To determine the heat produced, Joule measured the change in water temperature with a thermometer. He knew the mass in grams and the specific heat of the water. Therefore, the heat energy added to the water was $m_w s_w \Delta t_w$. He divided the total work done by the heat generated and allowed adjustments for experimental error. Again, Joule found that for every 4.2 joules of work done, a calorie of heat is generated.

Joule established a definite relationship between heat and other forms of energy. Then it became possible to predict the quantity of heat that is generated when other forms of energy are converted to heat.

Sample Problem 1

A man does 630 j of work to lift a cement block from the ground to a platform. The block falls off the platform. How much heat is generated when it strikes the ground?

Solution:

Assume that all the potential energy of the block is converted to kinetic energy as the block falls. Then assume that all the kinetic energy is changed to heat energy when the block strikes the ground. Then, the heat energy produced must be equal to the original potential energy of the block. This, in turn, is equal to 630 j, or the work done on the block. Since 1 calorie requires 4.2 j of work, the number of calories of heat developed by 630 j is:

$$H = \frac{630 \text{ j}}{4.2 \text{ j/cal}}$$

$$H = 150 \text{ cal}$$

Sample Problem 2

A 1600-lb car traveling at 20 ft/sec is braked to a halt. How much heat is generated by the car's brakes?

Solution:

The car's braking system uses friction to convert the kinetic energy of the car to heat. This brings the car to a halt. First calculate the kinetic energy of the car. The mass of the car is 50 slugs.

$$KE = \frac{1}{2} mv^2$$

$$KE = \frac{50 \text{ slugs } (20 \text{ ft/sec})^2}{2}$$

$$KE = 10\ 000 \text{ ft-lb}$$

Since 778 ft-lb generates 1 Btu of heat, 10 000 ft-lb generates

$$H = \frac{10\ 000 \text{ ft-lb}}{778 \text{ ft-lb/Btu}}$$

$$H = 13 \text{ Btu}$$

Problems

1. A 10-kg mass weighing 98 nt falls 20 m. How much heat is generated when the mass strikes the ground?

2. The 500-lb hammer of a pile driver falls 7.78 ft onto a piling. How much heat is generated in Btu?

3. How much heat does 1 j produce?

4. An iron object weighing 196 nt falls 10 m. The object absorbs all the heat generated when the mass strikes the earth. What is the temperature increase of the object? (The specific heat of iron is 0.11 cal/g-C°.)

5. A mass weighing 30 nt falls 1.5 m. It falls 10 times. All the work done by the falling mass converts to heat. What temperature change does it bring about in 150 g of water?

6. How much heat could two of Count Rumford's horses generate in one hour? (A horsepower is 550 ft-lb/sec.)

7. An electric generator connected to a 500 watt heater operates at 100% efficiency. (a) How many calories of heat does it produce each minute?
(b) How much work is done each minute by the energy source turning the generator?
(c) If the generator is turned by water falling over a dam 5 m high, what is the minimum amount of water that must pass through the electric generator each minute? (One liter of water weighs 9.8 nt.)

8. A 0.020-kg bullet traveling at 700 m/sec becomes embedded in a tree. How many calories of heat are generated by the kinetic energy of the bullet?

13:2 The Joule as a Universal Unit of Energy

In mid 19th century, the physicist Hermann von Helmholtz used mathematics to demonstrate that all forms of energy — light, heat, electric, and mechanical — are equivalent. (Add nuclear energy to this list today.) This was the first clear statement of the law of conservation of energy. To a large extent, it could be called the culmination of Joule's work.

Because all forms of energy are equivalent, it is to everyone's advantage to use the same unit of measurement for all forms of energy. This basic unit is the joule. Scientists use the joule exclusively to measure electric energy, light energy, mechanical energy, and nuclear energy. For practical reasons, engineers still use foot-pounds.

When a scientist sees that the temperature of a gram of water increases a Celsius degree, he does not say that a calorie of heat is added to the water. Instead, he says that 4.2 joules of energy are added to the gram of water. Conversely, if a kilogram of water decreases 5 Celsius degrees, the scientist calculates that 4.2 j/g-C° × 1000 g × 5 C° or 21 000 j of energy are liberated by the water. Eventually the term calorie may be dropped altogether.

PROBLEMS

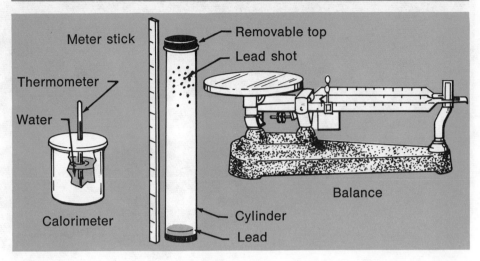

Figure 13-3

1. Figure 13-3 shows the laboratory apparatus commonly used to determine the mechanical equivalent of heat. Look at the apparatus carefully and explain how it is used.

2. A 20-kg mass falls 30 m. How much heat is generated when the mass strikes the ground? (A 20-kg mass weighs 196 nt.)

3. A 3200-lb automobile traveling at 30 mi/hr is brought to a halt by its brakes. How much heat in Btu is developed in the brakes? Assume all heat is absorbed by the braking system.

4. When the first transcontinental railroad was completed, a ceremony was held to drive the "final" spike. The spike was made of gold ($s = 0.03$ cal/g-C°) and had a mass of 200 g. What was the spike's change in temperature if it was driven by a hammer with a mass of 5.0 kg traveling at 10 m/sec? (It took 6 blows to drive the spike.) Assume the heat is absorbed equally by the hammer and the spike.

5. How much heat is liberated by a 150-watt soldering iron in 30 sec?

6. Niagara Falls is approximately 160 ft high. Calculate the difference in temperature between the water at the top of the falls and the water at the bottom of the falls.

7. A 50-kg boy coasts down a hill on a sled that has a mass of 10 kg. The hill is 80 m long and rises 2 m for every 10 m of its length. The speed of the boy and sled at the bottom of the hill is 15 m/sec. (a) How much heat was generated by the friction between the sled runners and the snow as the boy coasted down the hill? (b) The steel runners have a specific heat of 0.11 cal/g-C°. Assume that half the heat goes into the runners. What is the increase in temperature of the runners if they represent 2 kg of the sled's mass?

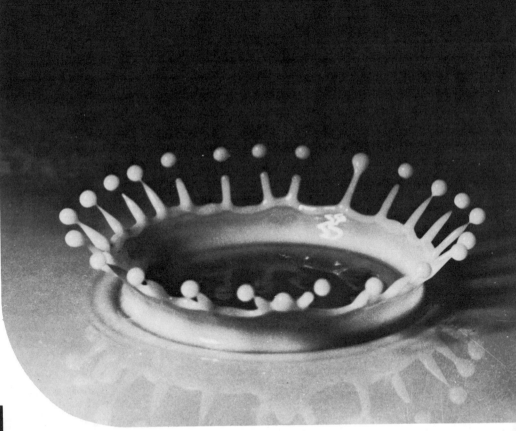

Kinetic Theory and the Structure of Matter

The kinetic theory helps to explain the nature of the three common physical states of matter, solids, liquids and gases. How can you explain the fact that water exists in all three states? In the accompanying photograph of the splash from a milk drop, note the liquid shapes which resulted. Using the kinetic theory, how can you explain their formation?

14:1 Assumptions of the Kinetic Theory

The kinetic theory of matter forms the basis of our understanding of heat. The three basic assumptions in the kinetic theory are:

1. All matter is made up of extremely small particles.
2. These particles are in constant motion.
3. A mutual force of attraction acts between particles of the same kind. These forces are called cohesive or van der Waals forces. Cohesive forces are greatest in solids, strong in liquids, and weak in gases.

There is much evidence to support these assumptions. The assumption that matter consists of particles is supported by the evaporation of water. Water left in a dish for a few days gradually disappears. If water were a continuous material, there could be no reasonable explanation for this evaporation.

The motion of molecules can be detected by a method first employed by the biologist Robert Brown in 1827. Brown suspended small grains of pollen in a drop of water and observed them under a microscope. He found that the grains moved in an erratic zigzag pattern. The result of Brown's experiment can be explained in this way. Many water molecules constantly struck each pollen grain. Occasionally one side of a grain was struck by more molecules than was the opposite side. As a result, the grain moved a short distance in the direction of the

Figure 14-1. A model of Brownian motion. The time intervals between successive positions of the particle are the same.

net force. Further evidence to substantiate the motion of molecules is the detection of odors. The smell of a drop of perfume in a room moves to all parts of the room in a short time. Therefore, the perfume consists of particles which move very fast.

Acceptance of the first two assumptions of the kinetic theory requires the acceptance of the third assumption. If all matter is made of particles, some force must hold the particles together. Otherwise, no object would have a shape. All materials would just drift apart. This does not happen so scientists know these forces do exist.

14:2   Thermal Expansion of Matter

Most materials expand when heated and contract when cooled. To understand why this is so consider what happens when a given particle in a substance is passed by a second particle. According to the third assumption of the kinetic theory, a force of attraction acts between the two particles. Assume that the force depends upon the distance between the two particles. If the first particle passes the second particle at high speed, the force of attraction between the two particles has less time to draw the particles together. Therefore, when the temperature of the material is high and the particles move fast, the force of attraction between the particles is less effective. The material expands. Conversely, when the temperature of the material is low and the particles move slowly, the force of attraction between the particles is more effective. The material contracts.

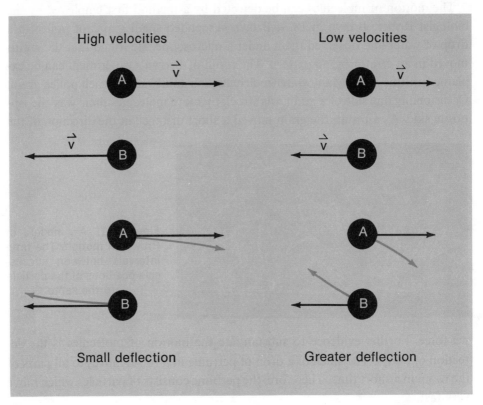

Figure 14-2.   As molecule A passes molecule B, the attractive force between them is less effective if their relative velocities are high.

14:3   Temperature and the Kinetic Theory

Temperature relates to the kinetic energies of the particles of matter. All the particles of a uniform material are similar. Their kinetic energies $\left(\frac{1}{2}mv^2\right)$ increase if they move faster. However, the particles move at random. Some particles move very fast while others move very slowly. *Temperature is the average kinetic energy of all the particles.*

The thermometer in Figure 14-3 is placed in a substance. The particles of the substance collide with the glass particles. If the substance is hot, its high-energy particles increase the motion of the glass particles. This is done by means of momentum exchange. If the substance is cold, the faster moving glass particles lose energy to the substance. The glass loses heat. The mercury molecules in the glass tube interact with the glass particles in the same way. If the speeds of the mercury molecules increase, the mercury expands. If the speeds of the mercury molecules decrease, the mercury contracts. Mercury expands and contracts at a greater rate per degree temperature change than does glass. For this reason, the level of mercury rises or falls in a glass thermometer.

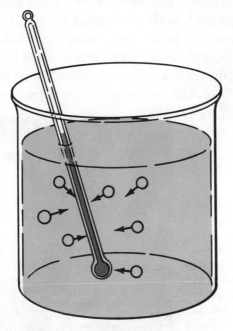

Figure 14-3. Mercury expands and contracts at a greater rate per degree than does glass.

14:4   Surface Tension

The third assumption of the kinetic theory explains "skin effect," also known as surface tension. Many materials (mostly liquids), display surface tension. In Figure 14-4, molecule A is located below the surface of a liquid. It is surrounded

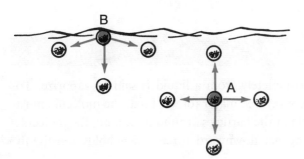

Figure 14-4. The net downward force on Molecule B draws the surface molecules together.

by molecules on all sides. The molecules exert an equal attraction on *A* more or less in all directions. Molecule *B* is near the surface of the liquid. It is not subjected to an upward force because no liquid molecules are above it. This results in a net downward force. The downward force draws the first several layers of the liquid molecules closer together. The top layers then have a higher density than the liquid below. As a result, the top layers act as a "skin." This phenomenon is referred to as surface tension. Water bugs can stand on the surface of quiet water pools because of surface tension. The surface tension of water also supports objects such as razor blades or small needles. Otherwise, according to the laws of flotation, such objects would sink in water. Surface tension accounts for the tendency of an unconfined liquid to form drops. Notice that a small drop of water forms a sphere when placed on a smooth surface.

Figure 14-5. Raindrops on leaves of grass. Notice how the large drops are more flattened and the small drops are nearly spherical. Some of the drops cling to the nearly vertical surfaces —can you explain this in terms of molecular force?

USDA Photo

However, the weight of the water droplet usually causes it to flatten out. Compared to water, liquid mercury has a much stronger cohesive force between its molecules. Thus, small amounts of mercury form spherical drops when placed on a smooth surface.

14:5   Vaporization

A molecule which escapes completely from a liquid is said to vaporize. To make the escape, it must overcome three major forces. First, the molecule must overcome the force of attraction of the particles around it. Second, the molecule must break through the strong net downward force which holds the tightly

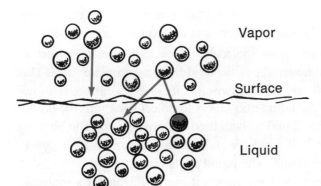

Vapor

Surface

Figure 14-6. The vapor above a liquid slows the rate of evaporation.

Liquid

packed surface layers. And third, the molecule must overcome the atmospheric pressure just above the surface. To overcome these forces, a molecule needs high energy. Only those molecules which have a high speed and therefore a high kinetic energy, manage to escape the liquid. Therefore, because it is the high energy molecules that vaporize, or escape from a liquid, the average kinetic energy of the entire liquid decreases. The decrease in the average kinetic energy of the molecules of vaporizing liquid results in a decrease in the temperature of the liquid. This is known as the cooling effect of evaporation.

Figure 14-7. The vaporization curve for water showing how boiling point varies with pressure.

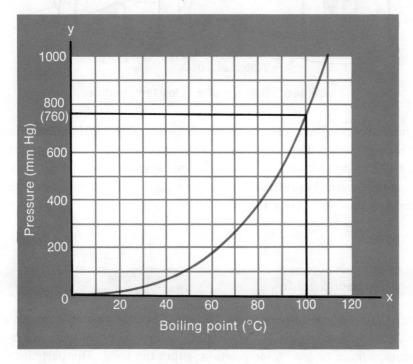

A molecule which escapes from a liquid expends much of its kinetic energy. The net downward force of the surface layers and the atmospheric pressure are enough to slow down the vaporizing molecule. These molecules have lost so much speed that they tend to hover above the liquid and accumulate there. This accumulated vapor above a liquid slows down the rate of evaporation. It allows some molecules to return to the liquid and others to reflect back into the liquid. Often a person blows on a hot liquid to help it cool more rapidly. The blowing causes the removal of vaporized particles and accordingly more high energy particles are able to leave the liquid. The liquid cools faster.

An increase in pressure above a liquid makes it more difficult for a molecule to escape from a liquid. Increased pressure means the molecules need an even higher speed for vaporization to take place. Under increased pressure, the temperature of a liquid increases noticeably before boiling takes place. Boiling is very rapid evaporation. When a liquid boils, fast moving molecules form vapor pockets. Then the pockets of vapor leave the liquid as a whole.

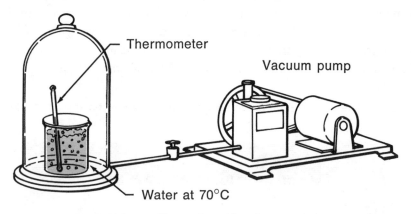

Figure 14-8.   Boiling water at low temperatures.

At normal atmospheric pressure, water boils at 100° C. If the pressure above water is decreased, boiling occurs at lower temperatures. To demonstrate this (Figure 14-8), place a small container of warm water inside a bell-jar. Evacuate the air from the jar. As pressure lowers, the water boils vigorously even though its temperature is well below 100° C.

14:6   The Solid State

When liquids freeze the particles of the liquids lose their ability to move about freely. As the molecules slow down the cohesive forces between them causes them to assume a more or less stable position within the solid. The particles of the solid do not stop moving completely but rather occupy a set position and vibrate about that position. The position of each particle is influenced by the cohesive forces around it. Molecules of the same material have similar cohesive attractions for one another. Therefore, the molecules of a solid often have a uniform arrangement in relation to one another. Crystals form in this way and result in such interesting structures as snowflakes and diamonds.

NOAA

Optovac, Inc.

Optovac, Inc.

Figure 14-9. Ice crystals (top) have an open lattice structure. Fluorite (bottom left) forms an octahedron, and potassium chloride (bottom right) forms a cube.

As liquids freeze and the particles occupy their positions within the crystalline lattice, the cohesive forces are stronger. The particles usually are closer together than they were in the liquid state. Water is an important exception to this rule. Water particles in a crystalline structure require more space than they did as a liquid. This causes water to expand as it freezes. It is fortunate that water does this. If water were to contract as it froze, ice would have a higher density than water and would sink. Lakes and rivers would freeze from the bottom up. In summer, the water above the ice would act as an insulator. Many lakes and rivers never would thaw completely. The impact on land masses in the higher latitudes would be tremendous.

Increased surface pressure on a liquid forces the particles closer together. Then the cohesive forces become stronger. This means that for most liquids, the particles assume a solid state more readily. In general the freezing point of a liquid increases as the pressure on the liquid increases. Again, water is the exception. Because water expands as it freezes, an increase in pressure prevents this expansion. The freezing point of water lowers under increased pressure. Skaters use this knowledge effectively. Increased pressure from the skate blades melts the ice under the blades. Thus the water which forms acts as a lubricant to make skating easier and faster.

QUESTIONS

1. List the three basic assumptions of the kinetic theory.
2. Most materials expand when heated and contract when cooled. Why?
3. Liquids display surface tension. Account for it.
4. Why does a swimmer feel cold on a breezy day even though the air is warm?
5. Denver, Colorado has the highest altitude of any city in the United States. Why do most Denver housewives use pressure cookers?
6. A drop of water, a drop of mercury, and a drop of ether are placed on a smooth, flat surface. The water and the mercury take a definite shape. The ether spreads out over the surface. What does this tell you about the cohesive forces between ether molecules? Does this explain why ether vaporizes so rapidly?
7. Use the answer to Question 6 to explain why ether has a very low freezing point.
8. Explain why hot water evaporates more rapidly than cold water.

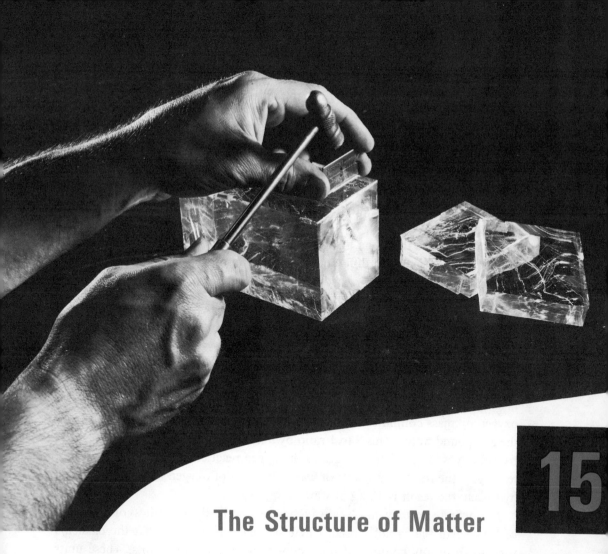

The Structure of Matter

Matter was thought by the early Greeks to consist of four fundamental substances, fire, earth, air, and water. According to modern theory all substances are composed of tiny stable particles called atoms and molecules. What determines the chemical and physical properties of these elements and compounds? Why does the crystal pictured above cleave geometrically rather than shatter when struck in the manner illustrated?

15:1   Elements and Compounds

The assumptions of the kinetic theory help us to understand heat. Each time a theory explains the behavior of matter, the theory becomes more credibile. Consider the idea that matter is composed of particles. This theory provides a logical explanation for many observable phenomena. The more the theory that matter is composed of particles provides a logical explanation for observable phenomena the stronger becomes our belief that matter is indeed composed of particles.

However, the kinetic theory is not the only evidence that points toward the particle nature of matter. Between 1790 and 1820 several important investigations in chemistry also indicated the particulate nature of matter.

During the eighteenth century, Lavoisier and others revealed that all matter exists as either elementary substances called elements, or combinations of two or more elements called compounds. In every case, however, when a compound is reduced to its component parts, the parts or elements cannot be further reduced chemically.

There are more than one hundred known elements, some of which are synthetic. The thousands of different substances found on earth are either these elements in their pure form or compounds of these elements.

15:2   The Law of Definite Proportions

In the study of the chemical combination of elements, scientists noticed that *whenever two or more elements combine chemically they do so in definite proportions by mass*. This is the law of definite proportions. For example, 8 parts of oxygen by mass combine chemically with 1 part of hydrogen by mass to form the compound water. This 8 to 1 ratio by mass of oxygen to hydrogen is always true of any water sample. If 8 grams of oxygen react chemically with 1 gram of hydrogen, the result is 9 grams of water. If 16 kg of oxygen react with 2 kg of hydrogen, the result is 18 kg of water.

This definite ratio by mass is always adhered to rigidly, regardless of how large or how small the samples used. Chemists began to suspect that the elements used to form any compound must consist of tiny discrete units. These units combine with each other in some definite way, such as particle for particle, or particle for two particles.

15:3   The Law of Combining Volumes of Gases

In 1808 the chemist Joseph Gay-Lussac (1778-1850) was experimenting with gases. He brought hydrogen gas and oxygen gas together and allowed them to combine chemically. Results showed twice as much hydrogen gas by volume as oxygen gas by volume entered into the compound. Two liters of hydrogen required exactly one liter of oxygen to be completely used up in the manufacture of the gas steam. Furthermore, he found that the resulting gas occupied a volume of exactly two liters.

This was only the beginning of Gay-Lussac's work with gases. He found that one unit volume of nitrogen combined chemically with exactly one unit volume of oxygen. This formed two unit volumes of nitrogen(II) oxide gas. Similarly,

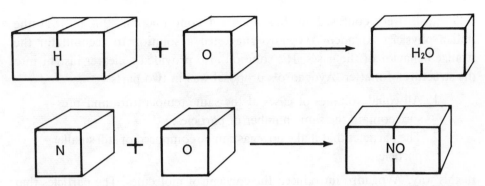

Figure 15-1. A model of the law of combining volumes of gases. At a given temperature and pressure gases combine in simple proportions by volume and the volume of any gaseous product bears a whole-number ratio to that of any gaseous reactant.

three unit volumes of hydrogen required exactly one unit volume of nitrogen to form two unit volumes of ammonia gas. Gay-Lussac allowed volumes of gases at the same temperature and pressure to react chemically. Every time he found that *the volumes of the gases involved in a chemical reaction are related by simple whole numbers.* This is the law of combining volumes of gases.

The explanation for why volumes of gases combine in the ratio of simple whole numbers is that equal volumes of gases kept at the same pressure and temperature contain equal numbers of particles. The acceptance of this idea explains why equal volumes of nitrogen and oxygen combine completely to form nitrogen(II) oxide. Assuming that each volume of gas contains the same number of particles, the particles simply combine in a one to one ratio.

A major objection to this solution soon came up. Nitrogen is a gas, oxygen is a gas, and nitrogen(II) oxide is a gas. Assume each particle of nitrogen combines with each particle of oxygen. The total number of nitrogen(II) oxide particles should be the same as the number of particles in either the original volume of oxygen or the original volume of nitrogen. Now assume that all

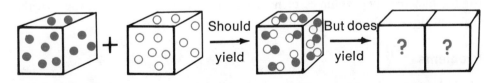

Figure 15-2

volumes of gases with the same number of particles have the same volume. Then one volume of oxygen gas, combined particle for particle with one volume of nitrogen gas, should yield one volume of nitrogen(II) oxide gas. However, this does not happen. Instead two volumes of nitrogen(II) oxide gas are formed.

Scientists were confused by this apparent contradiction. But in 1811 the Italian physicist Amadeo Avogadro suggested a solution to account for the strange behavior of the gases. His solution also provided a clearer insight into the structure of matter. Avogadro's proposal was in two parts:

1. All equal volumes of gases at the same temperature and pressure contain the same number of particles.
2. The particles that make up a gas can be composed of still smaller particles.

In this way, Avogadro introduced the concept of molecules. The particles that combine chemically (molecules) are made up of even smaller sub-particles called atoms. This proposal accounted for the manner in which gases combine. If nitrogen molecules have two atoms each and oxygen molecules have two atoms each, then one volume of nitrogen plus one volume of oxygen gives two volumes of nitrogen(II) oxide. Figure 15-3 illustrates how this proposal accounts

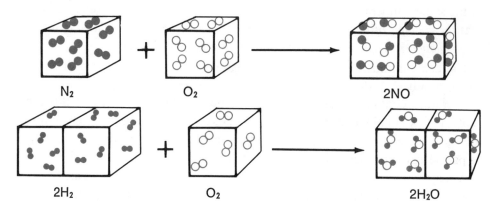

Figure 15-3. A model of Avogadro's proposal that equal volumes of gases contain equal numbers of particles.

for the fact that two volumes of hydrogen plus one volume of oxygen yields two, not three, volumes of steam.

Problems

1. Two atoms of nitrogen combine chemically with one atom of oxygen to form the compound nitrogen(I) oxide (N_2O). Both the nitrogen and oxygen are diatomic (the molecule of each contains two atoms). (a) A liter of nitrogen and a liter of oxygen are at the same temperature and pressure. What volume of oxygen combines chemically with what volume of nitrogen to form N_2O? (b) How many liters of N_2O are formed from 12 liters of nitrogen and 8 liters of oxygen?

2. Nitrogen and hydrogen molecules are diatomic. How many liters of nitrogen and how many liters of hydrogen are formed by the decomposition of 8 liters of ammonia gas (NH_3)? (NH_3 means that an ammonia gas molecule contains one atom of nitrogen and three atoms of hydrogen.)

3. How many volumes of hydrogen and how many volumes of oxygen are formed by the decomposition of 10 volumes of steam? Assume all volumes are under equal pressure and temperature.

15:4　Atomic Mass Units

The knowledge that equal volumes of gases at the same temperature and pressure contain an equal number of molecules made it possible to determine the relative masses of the particles themselves. Equal volumes of hydrogen gas and oxygen gas kept at the same temperature and pressure were weighed. Results showed that the oxygen gas had a mass of about sixteen times as much as the hydrogen gas. The volume of hydrogen gas contained the same number of molecules as did the volume of oxygen gas. This meant that each oxygen molecule must have a mass of sixteen times as much as a hydrogen molecule. Each molecule of oxygen contains two atoms and each molecule of hydrogen contains two atoms. Therefore, an oxygen atom must have sixteen times as much mass as a hydrogen atom.

Because the oxygen atom was assigned an atomic mass of sixteen units, *the relative masses of the other elements result in nearly whole numbers. These relative mass units are called atomic mass units (a.m.u.)* Today an isotope of carbon has replaced oxygen as the standard. It is known as carbon 12. Using carbon 12 as a standard, the relative masses of the atoms of each element are very nearly whole numbers. Thus, the mass of a hydrogen atom in a.m.u. is very nearly 1. The mass of a neon atom is nearly 20 a.m.u. The mass of a lead atom is 207 a.m.u.

The mass of a molecule is equal to the sum of the masses of the atoms it contains. For example, an oxygen molecule contains two atoms of oxygen. Each atom of oxygen has a mass of 16 atomic mass units. Therefore, the mass of the oxygen molecule is 32 atomic mass units. To find the mass of a molecule in a.m.u. add the masses of the atoms it contains.

Problem

4. What is the mass of each molecule in atomic mass units? (a) F_2　(b) N_2　(c) CO　(d) CO_2　(e) H_2　(f) NH_3　(g) NO　(h) N_2O
   (Fluorine atoms have a mass of 19 a.m.u. and nitrogen atoms have a mass of 14 a.m.u.)

15:5   Avogadro's Number and the Mole

A mole of any substance is that quantity, the mass of which in grams, is numerically equal to the mass of one of its particles in atomic mass units (a.m.u.). The oxygen molecule contains two oxygen atoms of 16 atomic mass units each. Hence the mass of the oxygen molecule is 32 a.m.u. and a mole of oxygen is 32 grams of oxygen. Hydrogen gas molecules are diatomic also and since the mass of a hydrogen atom is 1 a.m.u. the mass of the hydrogen molecule is 2 a.m.u. and 2 grams of hydrogen gas is a mole of hydrogen.

The relative masses of the elements were first determined by weighing equal volumes of gases kept at the same temperature and pressure. It was found for example that oxygen molecules weigh sixteen times as much as do hydrogen molecules. Now a mole of oxygen is 32 grams of oxygen and a mole of hydrogen is 2 grams of hydrogen. A mole of oxygen therefore has sixteen times the mass of a mole of hydrogen and a mole of oxygen and a mole of hydrogen, must occupy the same volume. By similar reasoning *a mole of any gas must occupy the same volume as does a mole of any other gas. This volume is 22.4 liters when the gas is at normal atmospheric pressure and 0°C.*

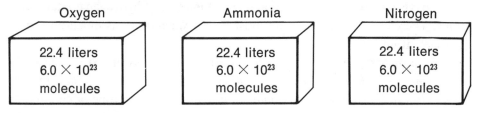

Figure 15-4. Avogadro's principle was used to calculate the number of particles in one mole of gas. One mole of any gas at standard temperature and pressure occupies 22.4 liters and contains 6.0×10^{23} particles.

By Avogadro's principle a mole of any gas, or of any material for that matter (solid, liquid, or gas), must always contain the same number of molecules. This number is known as *Avogadro's number and is 6.0×10^{23} molecules.* This is the number of hydrogen molecules contained in 2 grams of hydrogen. A number this huge is beyond comprehension. For instance this is more than twice the number of teaspoons of water in the Atlantic Ocean. It follows from this that the size of a molecule is much too small to be visualized.

The mass of a single molecule of a substance can be determined by dividing the mass of a mole of the substance by Avogadro's number.

Sample Problem 1

A mole of oxygen is 32 grams of oxygen. (a) What is the mass of a molecule of oxygen? (b) What is the mass of a single atom of oxygen?

Solution:

(a) $\dfrac{32 \text{ g/mole}}{6.0 \times 10^{23} \text{ molecules/mole}} = 5.3 \times 10^{-23} \text{ g/molecule}$

(b)   The oxygen molecule contains two atoms of oxygen.
The mass of a single oxygen atom is,

$$\frac{5.3 \times 10^{-23} \text{ g/molecule}}{2 \text{ atoms/molecule}} = 2.7 \times 10^{-23} \text{ g/atom}$$

Problems

5. A mole of hydrogen gas is 2 grams of hydrogen. A hydrogen molecule contains two atoms of hydrogen. (a) What is the mass of a hydrogen molecule? (b) What is the mass of a hydrogen atom?
6. Helium is monatomic. The mass of a mole of helium is 4 g. What is the mass of a helium atom?
7. The mass of a radon atom is 3.7×10^{-22} g. How many grams are in a mole of radon if radon is monatomic?

15:6   The Diameter of a Molecule

Molecule size is estimated in several ways. One method is to determine the diameter of a molecule of oleic acid. Oleic acid is not soluble in water. Therefore, a small amount of it on the surface of a pan of water spreads out to form a layer one molecule thick.

To determine the diameter of an oleic acid molecule, dissolve a very small amount of it in alcohol. For example, 5 cm³ of acid may be dissolved to form 1000 cm³ of a solution of oleic acid and alcohol. When one drop of this solution

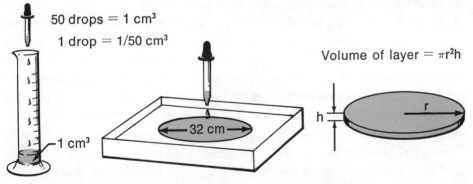

50 drops = 1 cm³
1 drop = 1/50 cm³

Volume of layer = $\pi r^2 h$

32 cm

1 cm³

h   r

Figure 15-5.   Measuring the diameter of a molecule.

is placed on the surface of water the alcohol dissolves in the water. Then the oleic acid spreads out to form a circular layer approximately 32 cm in diameter.

To determine the volume of a single drop of the solution, count the number of drops that occupy a volume of one cubic centimeter. This is done by adding solution drop by drop to a cylinder until there is 1 cm³ of solution. A typical measurement is 50 drops/cm³. The volume of the oleic acid in a single drop is:

$$V = \frac{5 \text{ cm}^3 \text{ acid}}{1000 \text{ cm}^3 \text{ sol'n}} \times \frac{1 \text{ cm}^3 \text{ sol'n}}{50 \text{ drops sol'n}} = \frac{5}{5 \times 10^4}$$

$$= 1 \times 10^{-4} \text{ cm}^3 \text{ acid/drop sol'n}$$

The circular layer of oleic acid forms a very shallow cylinder. The volume of the cylinder is $B \times h = \pi r^2 h$. Calculate the height of the cylinder.

$$V = \pi r^2 h$$

$$h = \frac{V}{\pi r^2}$$

$$= \frac{1 \times 10^{-4} \text{ cm}^3}{3 (16 \text{ cm})^2}$$

$$= \frac{1 \times 10^{-4} \text{ cm}^3}{770 \text{ cm}^2}$$

$$= 1.3 \times 10^{-7} \text{ cm}$$

Since the oleic acid forms a layer one molecule thick, the height of the cylinder is the diameter of a molecule of oleic acid. This calculation gives 10^{-7} cm as the order of magnitude of the diameter of an oleic acid molecule.

QUESTIONS

1. Distinguish between an element and a compound.
2. State the law of definite proportions. Give an example of the law.
3. State the law of combining volumes of gases.
4. Could Avogadro explain the formation of two volumes of nitric oxide from one volume of nitrogen and one volume of oxygen by assuming that the nitrogen molecule and the oxygen molecule contain four particles each?
5. Equal volumes of gases at the same temperature and pressure contain the same number of molecules. Explain how this knowledge made it possible to determine the relative weights of molecules of the elements.
6. Pure carbon is a solid except at extreme temperatures. How can the relative weight of carbon be determined by using equal volumes of gases?
7. Gas A and gas B are kept at the same volume, temperature, and pressure. Gas A weighs three times as much as gas B. (a) How do the number of molecules in each gas compare? (b) How does the mass of a molecule of gas A compare with the mass of a molecule of gas B?
8. How many molecules are in a mole of CO_2? In a mole of NH_3?

PROBLEMS

1. How many grams of these substances equal a mole? (Refer to Table C-1 in the Appendix.) (a) H_2SO_4 (b) HCl (c) SO_2 (d) SO_3

2. How many molecules are contained in 128 g of oxygen?

3. A carbon dioxide molecule consists of 1 atom of carbon of mass 12 a.m.u. and two atoms of oxygen of mass 16 a.m.u. each. (a) What is the mass of a mole of carbon dioxide? (b) How many molecules are contained in 33 g of carbon dioxide?

4. Neon is a noble gas. The mass of a neon atom is 20 a.m.u. What is the mass of a neon atom in grams?

5. A solution of oleic acid and alcohol contains 5 cm³ of oleic acid in 1000 cm³ of solution. A student places a single drop of this solution on the surface of a tray of water. The solution forms a circular expanse 20 cm in diameter. The student then determines that the volume of a single drop of the solution is $\frac{1}{50}$ cm³. What is the diameter of an oleic acid molecule if the acid forms a monolayer on water?

6. The sample calculation on page 172 in the text gives the diameter of an oleic acid molecule as 1.3×10^{-7} cm. Assume that each molecule of oleic acid is a cube having an edge equal to its thickness. Calculate the volume of a molecule of oleic acid.

7. The density of oleic acid is 0.9 g/cm³. Use the value determined for the volume of an oleic acid molecule in Problem 6 to calculate the mass of a single molecule of the acid.

8. A mole of oleic acid has a mass of 282 g. Use the value determined for the mass of a single molecule of the acid in Problem 7 to calculate the number of oleic acid molecules in a mole of oleic acid. The answer should be Avogadro's number, $N = 6.02 \times 10^{23}$ molecules.

9. The solution to Problem 8 should be of the right order of magnitude to agree with Avogadro's number. The oleic acid molecule is thought to be rodlike and not cubic in shape. It also stands with its long diameter perpendicular to a water surface. Explain why the solution to Problem 8 is not in complete agreement with Avogadro's number.

16 The Gas Laws

Gas volumes change predictably as the pressure and temperature of the gas are varied within certain limits. From the material you have already studied and knowing that both the temperature and pressure of the earth's atmosphere decrease with an increase in altitude, what do you predict will happen to the giant plastic helium-filled balloon pictured above as it soars high into the atmosphere?

16:1 Standard Pressure

Gas particles distribute themselves homogeneously throughout an enclosed volume. Therefore, the volume of a gas is the volume of the container that encloses it. Three quantities are necessary to describe the condition of a gas. These quantities are temperature, pressure, and volume.

Pressure is force per unit area. Pressure units are force units divided by area units, such as nt/m^2, lb/ft^2, and lb/in^2. Standard gas pressure is normal atmospheric pressure, 1.01×10^5 nt/m^2 or 14.7 lb/in^2. Another way to indicate pressure is in atmospheres (atm). Atmospheres are multiples of normal atmospheric pressure. Ten atmospheres (10 atm) indicates a pressure of 1.01×10^6 nt/m^2. One tenth of an atmosphere (0.1 atm) indicates a pressure of 1.01×10^4 nt/m^2.

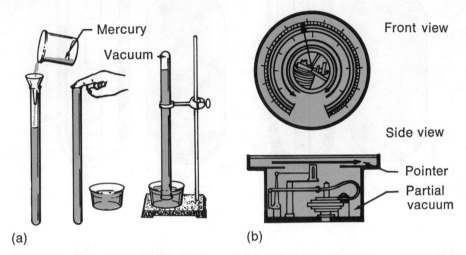

(a)   (b)

Figure 16-1. (a) The mercury barometer measures air pressure by using the height of a column of mercury supported by the atmosphere. (b) The aneroid barometer measures air pressure by means of changes in the size of an evacuated chamber.

There are many methods of measuring atmospheric pressure. The most popular method uses a column of mercury. Figure 16-1 (a) shows a tube 100 cm in length completely filled with mercury. When the tube is inverted and placed in a dish of mercury the mercury in the tube falls and leaves an empty space at the top of the tube. The pressure inside the empty space is nearly zero. The pressure on the mercury in the dish is atmospheric pressure. Normal atmospheric pressure supports a column of mercury 760 millimeters (76 cm) high. Pressure at the bottom of a column of mercury 760 mm high is 1.01×10^5 nt/m^2.

An increase in atmospheric pressure causes the pressure on the mercury in the dish to increase. The height of the mercury column in the tube must increase accordingly. Conversely, a decrease in atmospheric pressure causes the height of the mercury column in the tube to decrease. Therefore the level of mercury in the tube is a measure of atmospheric pressure.

A mercury barometer is large and awkward to handle. For this reason an aneroid barometer generally is used (Figure 16-1 b). An aneroid barometer consists of an evacuated flat can. The top of the can moves as air pressure fluctuates. A needle attached to the top of the can indicates these changes in air pressure. The scale of the barometer usually is calibrated in inches or milli-meters of mercury or both.

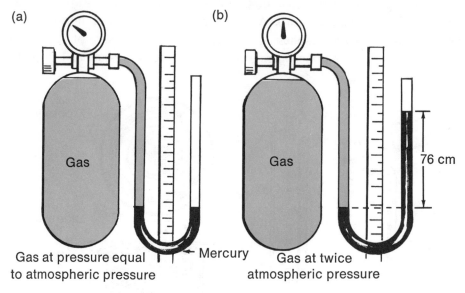

Figure 16-2.   Mercury U-tube pressure gauge.

Figure 16-2 illustrates a gauge often used in the laboratory. This gauge indicates the difference between atmospheric pressure and the pressure of a confined gas. The right arm of the U-tube is exposed to the pressure of the atmosphere. The left arm of the U-tube is exposed to the pressure of the confined gas. The level of the mercury in Figure 16-2 (a) is the same in each side of the tube. This indicates that the pressure of the gas and the pressure of the atmosphere are the same. The pressure may or may not be 1.01×10^5 nt/m² (14.7 lb/in.²). The result depends upon atmospheric conditions at the time the measurement is made.

The gas pressure in Figure 16-2 (b) supports a column of mercury 760 mm higher in the right arm than in the left arm. In addition to normal atmospheric pressure, the pressure of the gas is 760 mm of mercury. Therefore, the gas pressure is twice atmospheric pressure. This assumes normal conditions at the time the measurement is made. When the atmosphere supports a column of mercury 380 mm higher in the left tube than in the right tube, the pressure of the gas is half standard atmospheric pressure.

16:2   Boyle's Law

Figure 16-3 (a) shows a gas-filled cylinder. A kilogram mass is placed on the piston. This produces a force on the piston which in turn exerts pressure on the gas. Molecules of the gas collide with the underside of the piston. This produces pressure on the piston. Even a small sample of gas has a large number of molecules. This causes many collisions to take place between the gas molecules and the piston in any given instant. The large number of molecules in the cylinder also guarantees statistically that the number of collisions taking place at any given instant between the gas molecules and the surface of the piston is constant. Therefore, the pressure on the underside of the piston also is constant.

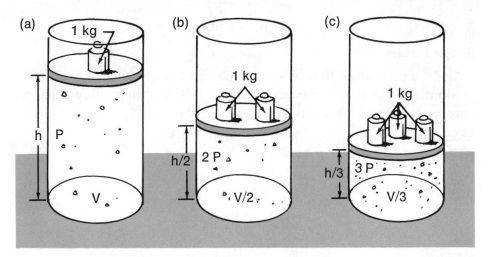

Figure 16-3.   The volume of a gas decreases as the pressure applied to it increases.

In Figure 16-3 (b) a second kilogram mass is placed on the piston. Now the piston produces twice the pressure on the gas as it did in Figure 16-3 (a). Molecular collisions account for the gas pressure on the walls of the container. This means twice as many collisions per second act must on the underside of the piston before equilibrium is regained. Twice as many collisions per second will occur if the piston sinks to just half its previous distance from the bottom of the cylinder. This is because the distance each molecule travels between collisions is reduced to one-half its former value when the piston is at this new position. With only half the distance to travel, the molecules strike the underside of the piston twice as often. This results in twice as much pressure on the piston.

Following this line of reasoning, three times the pressure on the top of the piston pushes the piston down to one-third its original height; four times the pressure pushes the piston down to one-fourth its original height. Since the cylinder is a regular shape, twice the pressure reduces the volume of the gas to one-half its original value; three times the pressure reduces the volume of the gas to one-third its original volume. Thus the kinetic theory predicts *Boyle's Law: the volume occupied by a gas varies inversely as the applied pressure. Therefore, the product of volume and pressure is a constant (PV = k).*

If P_1 = measured pressure, V_1 = measured volume, P_2 is standard pressure, and V_2 is standard volume, then:

$$V_1 = \frac{k}{P_1} \text{ and } V_2 = \frac{k}{P_2}$$

In the first equation $k = V_1P_1$. Since k is a constant, substitute $k = V_1P_1$ into the second equation:

$$V_2 = \frac{V_1P_1}{P_2}$$

or

$$V_2P_2 = V_1P_1$$

Sample Problem 1

Under a pressure of 10 lb/in.^{2} a confined gas has a volume of 2.6 ft^3. The pressure acting on the gas is increased to 50 lb/in^2. The temperature of the gas remains unchanged. What is the volume of the gas?

Solution:

$$P_1V_1 = P_2V_2$$
$$V_2 = \frac{P_1V_1}{P_2}$$
$$= \frac{10 \text{ lb/in.}^2 \times 2.6 \text{ ft}^3}{50 \text{ lb/in.}^2}$$
$$= 0.52 \text{ ft}^3$$

Sample Problem 2

A gas occupies a volume of 620.0 liters when under an external pressure of 760 mm of mercury. The pressure on the gas is increased to 1140 mm of Hg. What is the new volume of the gas?

Solution:

$$P_1V_1 = P_2V_2$$
$$V_2 = \frac{P_1V_1}{P_2}$$
$$= \frac{760 \text{ mm} \times 620.0 \text{ l}}{1140 \text{ mm}}$$
$$= 413 \text{ l}$$

Problems

1. Pressure acting on 60 m^3 of a gas is raised from 760 mm of Hg to 1520 mm of Hg. The temperature is kept constant. What new volume does the gas occupy?
2. Pressure acting on 8.0 ft^3 of a gas is 20 lb/in^2. The pressure is reduced steadily until the volume of the gas is 20 ft^3. What is the new pressure acting on the gas?

3. A gas occupies a volume of 20.0 liters under a pressure of 76 cm of Hg. The pressure is increased to 304 cm of Hg. What is the volume of the gas?

4. A volume of 50 m³ of neon gas is compressed until its volume becomes 12.5 m³. The original pressure acting on the gas was 2.0×10^5 nt/m². What is the pressure acting on it at its new volume?

5. An inflated balloon occupies a volume of 2 ft³. The balloon is tied with a string and weighted with a heavy stone. What is its volume when it reaches the bottom of a pond 68 ft deep? Note: One atmosphere of pressure supports a column of water 34 ft high. Assume the pressure acting on the balloon before it submerges is one atmosphere.

6. A helium-filled balloon occupies a volume of 16 ft³ at sea level. The balloon is released and rises to a point in the atmosphere where the pressure is 570 mm of Hg. What is its volume?

7. A helium-filled balloon occupies a volume of 2 ft³ at sea level. The balloon rises to a height in the atmosphere where its volume is 6 ft³. What is the pressure at this height? (a) in mm of Hg (b) in lb/in.²

8. A diver works at a depth of 170 ft in fresh water. A bubble of air with a volume of 2 in.³ escapes from his mouthpiece. What is the volume of the same bubble as it breaks the surface of the water?

16:3   Charles' Law

Boyle's Law assumes that gas temperatures remain constant. It neglects the effects of temperature variations on gas volume. Now it is time to consider the relationships that exist between the temperature and the volume of a gas and the temperature and the pressure of a gas.

Jacques Charles (1746–1823) discovered by experimentation that all gases expand equally if the temperature is increased equally while the pressure on the gas is kept constant. Charles kept a gas at 0° C under a pressure of 76 cm of Hg. He increased its temperature to 1° C and the gas expanded $\frac{1}{273}$ of its original volume. He increased the temperature of the gas to 2° C. Its volume increased $\frac{2}{273}$ of the first volume. At 273° C, the volume doubled. Charles obtained similar results when he reduced the temperature of the gas below 0° C. For each Celsius degree that the temperature was lowered below 0° C, the gas shrunk $\frac{1}{273}$ of its original volume. The discovery led to startling implications.

Theoretically, it meant that at −273° C a gas ceases to exist. However a substance does not remain a gas as its temperature is lowered. A point is reached where a phase change occurs and the gas becomes a liquid. Any further decrease in temperature of a liquid causes it to follow quite a different rate of contraction.

Figure 16-4 plots the volume of a gas against its temperature. The volume of the gas at 0° C is the basic volume. Today it is possible to measure most of the data needed to plot such a graph in the laboratory. However, in Charles' day,

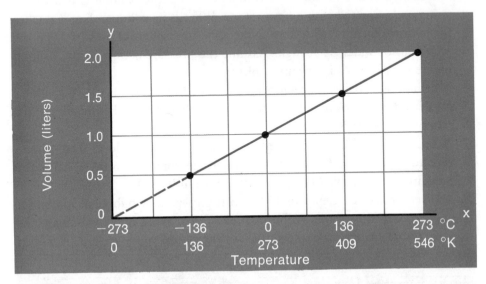

Figure 16-4.   A graph of the temperature of a gas versus its volume. The straight line indicates that the volume varies directly as the temperature. The constant of proportionality, taken from the slope of the graph, is $\frac{\Delta y}{\Delta x}$. What is the numerical value of the slope from this graph? The dotted line indicates extrapolation of the curve.

it was not possible to attain temperatures much below −20° C. Charles extended the line of the graph down to temperatures below −20° C to see what theoretical lower limits might be possible. To extend a graph beyond measureable points is called extrapolation. Although information implied by extrapolation is not based on precise data, it is far superior to no information at all.

Figure 16-5 indicates that the lowest possible volume of a gas occurs at −273° C. This leads to the conclusion that −273° C is the lowest possible temperature. Lord Kelvin chose this point as zero on what is called the Kelvin temperature scale. The temperature −273° C or 0° K is called absolute zero.

In his work with gases, Charles accomplished two things. He postulated the point of absolute zero and established a relationship between Kelvin temperature and the volume of a gas. *Charles' Law states that under constant pressure, the volume of a gas varies directly as its Kelvin temperature.*

$$\frac{V_1}{V_2} = \frac{T_1}{T_2}$$

Sample Problem 3

A volume of 22.0 m³ of nitrogen gas at 20° C is heated under constant pressure to 167° C. What is the new volume of the nitrogen gas?

Solution:

First change the temperatures to Kelvin temperatures.

$$T_1 = 20°C = 20° + 273° = 293° \text{ K}$$
$$T_2 = 167° \text{ C} = 167° + 273° = 440° \text{ K}$$
$$\frac{V_1}{V_2} = \frac{T_1}{T_2}$$
$$V_2 = \frac{V_1 T_2}{T_1}$$
$$= \frac{22.0 \text{ m}^3 \times 440° \text{ K}}{293° \text{ K}}$$
$$= 33.0 \text{ m}^3$$

Problems

9. A volume of 30.0 m³ of argon gas is kept under constant pressure. It is heated from 20° C to 293° C. What is the new volume of the gas?

10. Thirty liters of oxygen gas are kept under constant pressure. The gas is cooled from 20° C to −146.5° C. What is the new volume of the gas?

11. 0.02 m³ of a gas at 60° C is heated to double its volume. The gas is kept under constant pressure. To what temperature is it heated?

12. A volume of 4 m³ of a gas is kept under constant pressure. Its temperature is increased from 40° C to 140° C. What is the new volume of the gas?

16:4   The General Gas Law

By combining Boyle's and Charles' laws an equation can be derived which relates the pressure temperature, and volume of gases.

$$\frac{P_1 V_1}{T_1} = \frac{P_2 V_2}{T_2}$$

This is called the General Gas Law. It holds fairly well for all gases at moderate pressures. Under extreme pressures and low temperatures, the law is modified. The general gas law reduces to Boyle's Law if the temperature is constant. It reduces to Charles' Law if the pressure is kept constant.

Sample Problem 4

Twenty liters of gas are kept under a pressure of 760 mm of Hg and at a temperature of 273° K. The gas temperature is lowered to 91° K. The pressure upon it is increased to 1140 mm of Hg. What is the new volume of the gas?

Solution:

$$\frac{P_1V_1}{T_1} = \frac{P_2V_2}{T_2}$$

$$V_2 = \frac{P_1V_1T_2}{P_2T_1}$$

$$= \frac{760 \text{ mm} \times 20 \text{ l} \times 91° \text{ K}}{1140 \text{ mm} \times 273° \text{ K}}$$

$$= 4.4 \text{ liters}$$

Problems

13. Ten cubic feet of hydrogen gas are confined in a cylinder under a pressure of 1 atm at a temperature of 91° K. The volume is kept constant but the temperature is increased to 182° K. What pressure does the gas exert on the walls of the container?

14. 200 liters of gas at 0° C are kept under a pressure of 760 mm of Hg. The temperature of the gas is raised to 273° C. The pressure is increased to 1520 mm of Hg. What volume does the gas occupy?

15. 50 ft³ of gas are kept at a temperature of 200° K and under a pressure of 15 lb/in². The temperature of the gas is increased to 400° K. The pressure is decreased to 7.5 lb/in². What is the volume of the gas?

16. 100 ft³ of gas are kept under pressure of 1 atm and at a temperature of 27° C. The pressure on the gas is increased to 4 atm. The temperature is increased to 327° C. What is the new volume of the gas?

16:5   The Universal Gas Constant

A mole of any gas contains Avogadro's number of particles. Therefore, a mole of any gas contains the same number of particles as does a mole of any other gas. Under standard temperature and pressure, a mole of any gas also should occupy the same volume as a mole of any other gas. This is because equal numbers of particles of different gases occupy the same volume under these conditions. Careful measurements show that a mole of any gas at standard temperature and pressure occupies a volume of 0.0224 m³. This is 22.4 liters.

According to the general gas law, $P_1V_1/T_1 = P_2V_2/T_2$ which would also equal P_3V_3/T_3. Thus, the product of the pressure and the volume of any given quantity of a gas divided by its Kelvin temperature is a constant.

$$\frac{PV}{T} = k$$

For a mole of any gas, the constant k always must have the same value. This constant is called R. It is known as the universal gas constant.

$$\frac{PV}{T} = R \quad \text{or } PV = RT \quad \text{(for each mole)}$$

To determine the value of R, substitute 1.013×10^5 nt/m² for standard pressure, 273° K for standard temperature, and 0.0224 m³ for V. With these units, R equals 8.31 joules per mole-Kelvin degree. This known value is useful when making calculations dealing with gases.

Sample Problem 5

One mole of a gas has a pressure of 2.03×10^5 nt/m². Its temperature is 546° K. What volume does the gas occupy?

Solution:

$$PV = RT$$
$$V = \frac{RT}{P}$$
$$= \frac{8.31 \text{ j/mole-K}° (546° \text{ K})}{2.03 \times 10^5 \text{ nt/m}^2}$$
$$= \frac{8.31 \text{ nt-m/mole-K}° (546° \text{ K})}{2.03 \times 10^5 \text{ nt/m}^2}$$
$$= 2.24 \times 10^{-2} \text{ m}^3/\text{mole}$$

Problems

17. One mole of a gas has a pressure of 0.50×10^5 nt/m². Its temperature is 1000° K. Calculate the volume of the gas.
18. One mole of air at normal atmospheric pressure has a temperature of 293° K. What volume does the air occupy?
19. One mole of a gas occupies a volume of 0.04 m³. Its temperature is 40° C. What is the pressure of the gas?

QUESTIONS

1. A gas is compressed to 0.2 of its original volume. The gas is kept at a constant temperature during the compression. By what amount is the pressure on the gas increased?
2. Give the values for standard pressure in four different units.
3. State Boyle's Law.
4. State Charles' Law.
5. State the general gas law.
6. Use the general gas law to explain what happens if a gas is heated while its volume is kept constant.

7. The molecules of a gas produce a greater pressure on the walls of a container if the gas is heated. Explain why.

8. Charles' experiments with gases revealed the location of absolute zero. Describe how.

PROBLEMS

1. Convert to atmospheres: (a) 380 mm of mercury (b) 29.4 lb/in.^{2} (c) 5.05 $\times$ 10^5 nt/m^2

2. A bubble of air with a volume of 0.05 cm^3 escapes from a pressure hose at the bottom of a tank. The tank is filled with mercury to a height of 6.84 m. What is the volume of the air bubble as it reaches the surface of the mercury? Assume the pressure at the surface which acts on the bubble is 0.76 m of mercury. The pressure at the bottom of the tank is the pressure due to the mercury plus the pressure at the surface.

3. Pressure acting on 50 m^3 of a gas is reduced from 1000 mm of mercury to 250 mm of mercury. (a) What is the new volume of the gas? (b) The gas is kept at 0° C while the pressure is reduced. If the gas resumes its original volume, to what temperature in degrees Celsius is the gas cooled?

4. Pressure acting on a volume of 50 m^3 of air is 1.01 $\times$ 10^5 nt/m^2. The air is at a temperature of $-50°$ C. The pressure acting on the gas is increased to 2.02 $\times$ 10^5 nt/m^2, and the gas occupies a volume of 30 m^3. What is the temperature of the air at this new volume?

5. 2 m^3 of a gas at 30° C is heated until its volume is doubled. Assume constant pressure during the heating. To what temperature is the gas heated?

6. A cubic meter of gas at standard temperature and pressure is cooled to 91° K. The pressure is not changed. What volume does the gas occupy?

7. A cubic meter of gas at standard temperature and pressure is heated to 364° C. The pressure acting on the gas is kept constant. What volume does the gas occupy?

8. A volume of 10 ft^3 of carbon dioxide at 27° C is heated to 177° C. The pressure on the gas is kept constant. What new volume does the gas occupy?

9. A volume of 500 cm^3 of air at 0° C is under a pressure of 1.01 $\times$ 10^5 nt/m^2. The pressure acting on it is increased to 2.02 $\times$ 10^5 nt/m^2, and it is heated to 273° C. What volume does the gas occupy?

10. 10 m^3 of nitrogen at 40° K is under 4.00 $\times$ 10^5 nt/m^2 pressure. The pressure acting on the nitrogen is increased to 2.0 $\times$ 10^6 nt/m^2. Its volume remains constant. To what temperature does the nitrogen rise?

11. A balloon contains 200 m^3 of helium while on the surface of the earth. Atmospheric pressure is 75 cm of mercury. Temperature is 20° C. The balloon expands freely and rises to a height where the pressure is only 50 cm

of mercury, and the temperature is $-50°$ C. What is the new volume of the balloon?

12. One mole of gas has a pressure of 1.0×10^5 nt/m² and a temperature of $500°$ K. Calculate its volume.

13. One mole of gas occupies a volume of 2.6×10^{-4} m³. Its temperature is $80°$ C. What is its pressure?

Waves and the Transfer of Energy

Waves are already somewhat familiar to you from your own past experience. You have seen them at the beach or observed them traveling along a metal spring. There are other waves which you have probably not recognized as such, but all waves have one property in common. They all transfer energy. Can you see any evidence of energy transfer in the above photograph of a bug swimming in water?

17:1 Waves — A Means of Transferring Energy

Two methods are used to transfer energy between any two points. The first method involves the transfer of matter. The second method involves wave motion. To illustrate, two boys in a rowboat want to destroy an ant's nest on the waterline of a pond. They can throw stones to break up the nest or generate waves to wash away the nest. The boys could use other projectiles, such as bullets. Or, they could use other waves, such as highly concentrated sound waves. But to destroy the ant's nest, they are limited to the use of either projectiles or waves. There is no third way to transfer energy. Since physics is the study of energy transfer, wave motion is an important aspect of physics.

17:2   Different Kinds of Waves Follow the Same Rules

All types of waves come under the general rules of wave behavior. For example when a water wave is reflected from a barrier, the angle at which the wave is reflected is the same as the angle at which the wave approached the barrier. Sound waves, light waves, and all other waves are reflected from barriers in exactly the same way. Learning the rules of wave behavior for one type of wave develops an acquaintance with the rules for all waves.

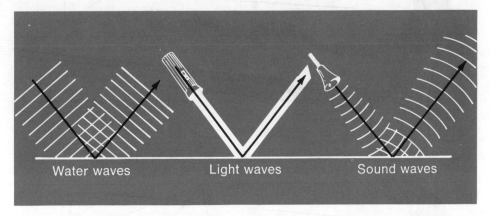

Figure 17-1.   Different kinds of waves follow the same rules. Water waves (a), light waves (b), and sound waves (c) all reflect from barriers according to the law of reflection — incidence angle equals reflection angle.

17:3   Mechanical Waves and Electromagnetic Waves

Mechanical waves are waves which require a material medium for energy transfer. Some examples of mechanical waves are water waves, waves that travel along a coiled rope or spring, and sound waves. Mechanical waves are easy to understand. Most of them can be observed and their behavior can be noted.

Electromagnetic waves constitute a large, important family of waves. Some examples of electromagnetic waves are light waves, radio waves, and X rays. These waves are more difficult to understand because they require no medium for energy transfer. Electromagnetic waves are both electric and magnetic in nature.

17:4   Transverse and Longitudinal Waves

The two general types of waves are transverse waves and longitudinal waves. A water wave is a transverse wave. A transverse wave, as Figure 17-2 (a) shows, can be generated along a rope. Figure 17-2 (b) shows a longitudinal wave. The most important longitudinal waves are sound waves.

Particles disturbed by a wave do not move along with the wave. Instead, they vibrate about a central position. As the wave moves along, whether it is transverse or longitudinal, the particles vibrate.

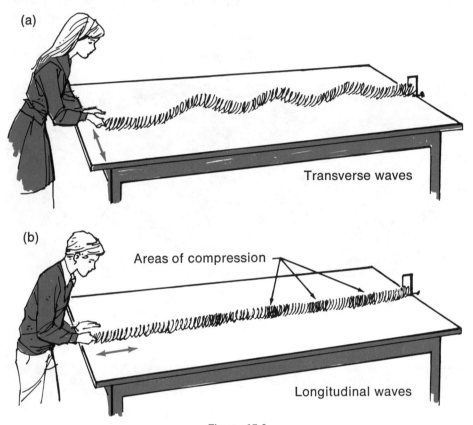

(a)

Transverse waves

(b)

Areas of compression

Longitudinal waves

Figure 17-2

Although both types of waves cause the particles of the medium to vibrate, the direction of the vibration differs in the two types of waves. A transverse wave causes the particles of the medium to vibrate in a direction perpendicular to the direction in which the wave is moving. A longitudinal wave causes the particles of the medium to vibrate in the same direction in which the wave is moving.

17:5 Pulses and Waves

A pulse is a single disturbance in a medium (Figure 17-3 a). When a single pulse is generated in a rope or coiled spring any point which is undisturbed before the pulse arrives will be undisturbed after the pulse passes.

(a)

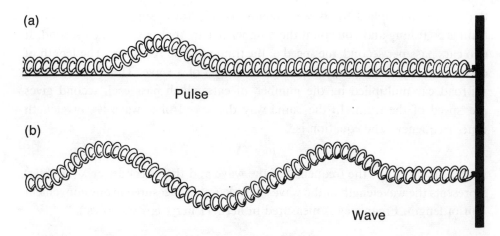

Pulse

(b)

Wave

Figure 17-3.   Waves end pulses in a long spiral spring. (a) You can find the speed of the pulse by dividing the distance covered by the elapsed time. (b) The speed of a wave depends upon the distance the wave travels per unit of time.

When a series of pulses are generated at regular intervals waves are formed as illustrated in Figure 17-3 (b). When a wave passes, any given point vibrates regularly in response to the passing of the wave.

17:6   Wavelength, Frequency and Velocity of a Wave

Consider the transverse wave in Figure 17-4. The wavelength (λ) of a wave is the linear distance between any two corresponding points on consecutive waves. Points C of the diagram are called crests. Points T of the diagram are called troughs. The wavelength of the wave is the distance from one C to the next C, or one T to the next T. Points A and A' are also one wavelength apart. However, points A and A'' are two wavelengths apart.

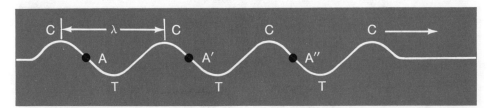

Figure 17-4.   Points C represent crests, points T represent troughs of the wave.

The frequency of a wave is the number of wavelengths that pass any given point per second. To determine the frequency of a wave, the number of wavelengths that pass each second is counted. If the wavelength is known or can be measured, the speed of the wave can be calculated. To do this, the frequency of the wave is multiplied by its wavelength. To illustrate, suppose each car of a train is 50 ft long and you count the number of cars that pass by each second. If two cars pass per second, the speed of the train must be 100 ft/sec. The length of each railroad car compares with the wavelength of a wave. The length of each railroad car multiplied by the number of cars which pass each second gives the speed of the train. In the same way the speed of a wave is wavelength times frequency. The equation is,

$$v = f\lambda$$

In the equation, f is the frequency of the wave and the Greek letter λ (lambda) represents the wavelength of the wave. Wavelength is measured in any convenient unit of length. Frequency is measured in hertz (1 hertz is 1 wave/sec).

Sample Problem 1

Transverse waves traveling along a rope have a frequency of 12 hertz (12 waves/sec). They are 2.4 ft long. What is the speed of the waves?

Solution:

$$v = f\lambda$$
$$= 12/\text{sec} \times 2.4 \text{ ft}$$
$$= 28.8 \text{ ft/sec}$$

17:7   Sound Waves

The frequency of a given wave is the same as the frequency of whatever generates the wave. Waves in a coiled spring often are generated by hand. In such a case, the frequency of the wave would be determined by the person generating the wave. Sound waves are generated by vibrating objects. Therefore, the frequency of a sound wave is the same as the frequency of the vibrating object.

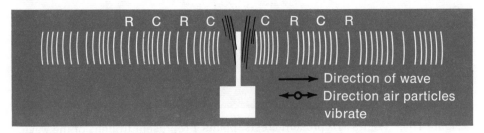

Figure 17-5.   Sound waves are generated by vibrating objects.

A vibrating object moves back and forth. As the object moves forward, it compresses the air on one side. When the object moves in the opposite direction, it rarifies rather than compresses the air. Then the process is repeated as the object swings to the other side of the rest or equilibrium position. (Figure 17-5). The areas of compression and rarefaction of the air correspond to the crests and troughs of a transverse wave. Sound waves, however, are longitudinal. Sound waves cause the particles of the medium to vibrate back and forth in the same direction as the movement of the wave.

The period of a wave is the time required for a full wave to pass a given point. The frequency of the wave determines the period of a wave. For example, if a wave has a frequency of 10 hertz. Then ten waves must pass a given point per second, the time for one wave to pass a given point is $\frac{1}{10}$ sec. The period of any wave is found in a similar manner. The period (T) of a wave is the reciprocal of its frequency.

$$T = \frac{1}{f}$$

Sample Problem 2

A sound wave has a frequency of 250 hertz. What is the period of the sound wave?

Solution:

$$T = \frac{1}{f}$$
$$= \frac{1}{250 \text{ hertz}}$$
$$= 0.004 \text{ sec}$$

Problems

1. Sound waves traveling through air have a frequency of 250 hertz. The sound waves are 4.4 ft in length. What is the speed of sound in air?
2. A radio wave has a frequency of 18 600 hertz. It is 10 miles long. What is the speed of the radio wave?
3. Water waves in a small tank are 6 cm long. They pass a given point at the rate of 4.8 waves per second. What is the speed of the water waves?
4. What is the period of the waves in Problem 3?
5. Microwaves are electromagnetic waves. They travel through space at the rate of 3.0×10^8 m/sec. A microwave has a wavelength of 0.20 m. (a) What is the frequency of the microwave? (b) What is the period of the microwave?
6. A sound pulse is directed toward a sheer stone cliff 2200 ft from the source. The reflected pulse is detected 4 sec after the pulse is generated. (a) What is the speed of sound in air? (b) The sound pulse has a frequency of 500 hertz. What is its wavelength? (c) What is the period of the sound pulse?

7. The speed of sound waves in air is 330 m/sec. A sound wave has a frequency of 500 hertz. (a) What is the wavelength of the wave as it travels through air? (b) What is the period of the sound wave?
8. An Angstrom unit is 10^{-10} m. A typical light wave has a wavelength of 5800 Å. (a) What is the length of the light wave in meters? (b) The speed of light is 3.0×10^8 m/sec. What is the frequency of the wave?

17:8   Energy and the Amplitude of a Wave

The energy content of a wave is characterized by the wave's amplitude. The amplitude of a wave is its maximum displacement from the rest or equilibrium position. Figure 17-6 shows two waves traveling along identical ropes. Each wave has the same frequency, velocity, and wavelength. However, the amplitudes are different. The source that generates wave A has the same frequency as the source that generates wave B. But the source that generates wave A puts more energy into the generation of the wave. This produces a wave of greater amplitude.

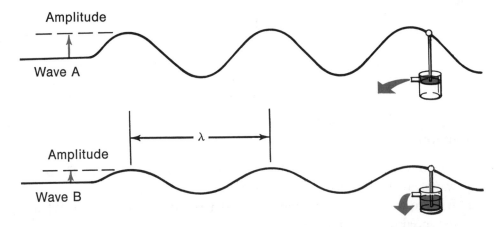

Figure 17-6.   The relationship of the amplitude of a wave to the work it can perform. The greater the work done to create the wave, the greater the amplitude of the wave. The greater the amplitude of the wave, the more work it can do. Waves transfer energy.

Since wave A has a greater amplitude than wave B, wave A transfers more energy. Wave A can do more work than wave B. Suppose that pumps are attached to each rope and the waves pump water. (Figure 17-6.) The pumps lift water through a distance and transform the wave energy into useful work. Ideally the waves disappear at the pumps and work is accomplished. Wave A is capable of performing more work per unit time than is wave B.

17:9 Wave Speed in a Medium

When waves travel in a medium, the speed at which mechanical waves are propagated depends upon the properties of the medium. Figure 17-7 represents

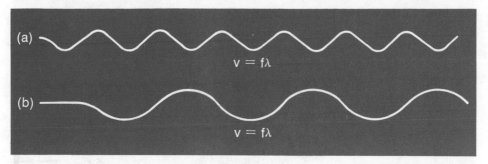

Figure 17-7. The speed of a wave is a function of the medium in which the wave travels. The product of frequency and wavelength gives the speed.

two waves generated at different times in the same medium. The wavelengths of the waves and the frequencies of the waves are entirely different. Their speeds are the same. Wave (*a*) has a high frequency and a short wavelength. Wave (*b*) has a low frequency and a long wavelength. In either case, the product of the frequency and the wavelength ($f\lambda$) result in the same speed (v_1). It makes no difference what frequency wave is generated in the medium. The only result is a change in wavelength that keeps the speed of the wave constant in the medium. The amplitude of the wave also has no effect on its speed. An increase in amplitude of a wave causes it to transfer more energy. But an increase in amplitude does not increase the speed of the wave. In general, the medium determines the speed of the waves that pass through it.

The speed of light in a vacuum is 3.0×10^8 m/sec. There is no way to change it. All light waves and other electromagnetic waves travel through space at this speed. Similarly all sound waves travel through air at approximately 330 m/sec (1100 ft/sec). What would be the consequences if this were not so? Consider an orchestra playing a musical work. If the sound waves from each instrument traveled different speeds, what would the music sound like?

17:10 Behavior of Waves at Boundaries

Transverse waves are easier to draw and to visualize than are longitudinal waves. Therefore, transverse waves will be used as examples to discuss wave behavior. However, the rules of wave behavior apply to both transverse and longitudinal waves.

Suppose a wave traveling in a medium reaches the boundary of a new medium. The wave is partially reflected and partially transmitted into the new medium. The portion of the wave that is reflected and the portion that is transmitted depend upon the difference between the two media. If the difference between the two media is slight, the amplitude of the reflected wave is small. This indicates that most of the energy is transmitted.

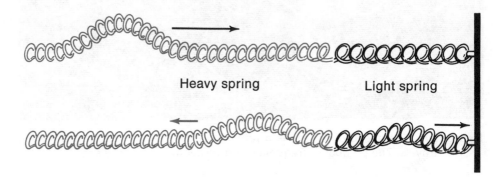

Figure 17-8.   A pulse reaching a boundary between two media is partially reflected and partially transmitted.

The result is different when a coiled spring is attached to a rigid object, such as the wall of a room. When the pulse reaches the spring-wall boundary, the pulse encounters a medium that is extremely different from the spring. The reflected pulse is practically identical in amplitude with the oncoming pulse. In theory, a small amount of the energy of the pulse does enter the wall. Figure 17-9 shows that the amplitude of the reflected pulse is almost equal to the ampli-

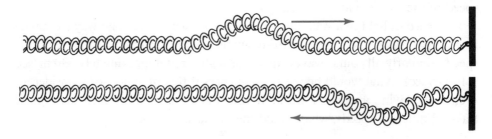

Figure 17-9.   The pulse that is reflected from the rigid wall returns inverted. Notice that the amplitude of the reflected pulse is nearly equal to the amplitude of the incident pulse.

tude of the oncoming pulse. But the pulse is inverted upon reflection from the rigid wall. When a wave is reflected at the boundary of a more rigid medium, it undergoes inversion.

In Figure 17-10 a pulse proceeds along a coiled spring that is supported by light threads. As in Figure 17-9, when the pulse reaches the end of the coiled spring, it passes into a different medium. In this case, the medium is air. This difference in the media causes a nearly total reflection in the pulse. In this case,

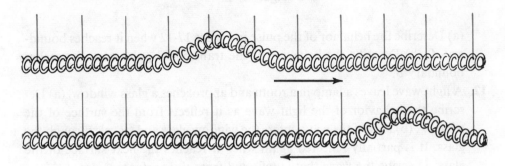

Figure 17-10. A pulse reflected from an open-ended boundary returns erect.

the pulse is reflected from the boundary of a medium less rigid than the one from which it came. The reflected pulse is erect. *When a wave is reflected from the boundary of a less rigid medium, its reflected wave is erect. In all cases there is a reflected wave at a boundary. The amount of reflected energy depends upon the difference in the properties of the two media. A pulse passing from a less rigid medium into a more rigid medium produces a reflected pulse that is inverted. A pulse entering a less rigid medium from a more rigid medium produces a reflected pulse that is erect.*

Problems

9. A long coiled spring passes along the floor of a room and out a door. A pulse is sent along the spring. After a while, an inverted pulse of almost the same amplitude returns along the spring. Is the spring attached to the wall in the next room or is it lying loose on the floor?

10.

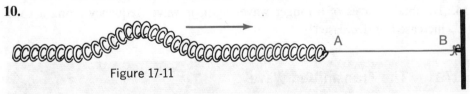

Figure 17-11

A pulse is sent along a coiled spring. (Figure 17-11.) The coiled spring is attached to a light thread which ends at a wall. (a) Describe the behavior of the pulse when it reaches *A*. (b) Is the reflected pulse from *A* erect or inverted? (c) Describe the behavior of the transmitted pulse when it reaches *B*. (d) Is the reflected pulse from *B* erect or inverted?

11.

Figure 17-12

(a) Describe the behavior of the pulse in Figure 17-12 when it reaches boundary *A*. (b) Describe the behavior of the transmitted pulse when it reaches boundary *B*.

12. A light wave leaves a lamp in a room and approaches a glass window. (a) Describe the behavior of the light wave as it reflects from the surface of the window. (b) Part of the wave enters the window glass and travels through the glass. It is partially reflected again when it reaches the next surface of the glass. Describe the wave that is reflected from this surface.

13.

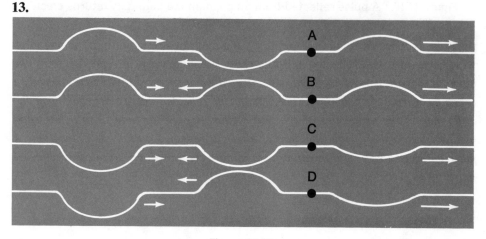

Figure 17-13

Figure 17-13 shows a pulse on the left. Its transmitted and reflected pulse is shown on the right. Describe the boundaries *A*, *B*, *C*, and *D*.

14. To obtain waves of a longer wavelength, is wave frequency along a rope increased or decreased?

17:11   The Transmitted Wave

The speed of a wave in a medium depends upon the medium in which the wave travels. When a wave reaches a boundary between two media, it passes into the new medium and has a different speed. The wave in the new medium is generated directly by the wave in the old medium. Therefore, the frequency of the wave in the new medium is exactly the same as the frequency of the wave in the old medium. Because the speed of the transmitted wave changes and the frequency remains the same, the wavelength must change. This is true because $v = f\lambda$. Figure 17-14 shows a wave passing into a new medium. Since the speed in the

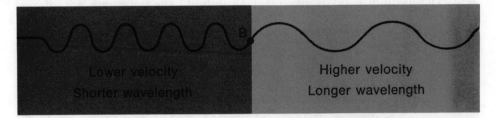

Figure 17-14.   The speed and wavelength are different in the new medium.

new medium is greater, a longer wavelength results. Conversely, if the wave in the diagram were to pass from the right hand medium to the left hand medium, it would have a slower speed in the new medium. Therefore, its wavelength would decrease.

17:12   Interference

Suppose two or more waves travel through the same medium at the same time. When the waves meet, they superimpose their amplitudes. This process is called interference. Waves interfere constructively or destructively. For simplicity, the interference of single pulses will be used to describe each type of interference.

Figure 17-15 shows the constructive interference of two pulses. When pulse a and pulse b meet, they combine momentarily. This forms an exceptionally strong pulse, $a + b$. The amplitude of $a + b$ is the algebraic sum of the amplitudes of the two pulses. Notice that once the two pulses pass through one another, they still are completely unaffected and retain their original form.

Figure 17-15

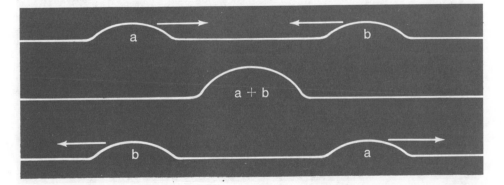

Figure 17-16 shows the destructive interference of two equal but opposite pulses, *a* and −*b*. Again note that the two pulses combine momentarily. They form a pulse equal to the algebraic sum of *a* and −*b*. In this case the sum is zero. The medium is undisturbed, for an instant. The pulses are not affected

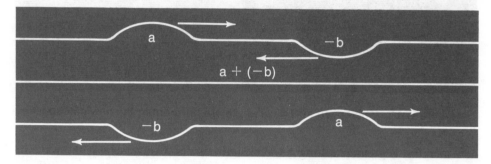

Figure 17-16.   Destructive interference of two pulses.

permanently by their momentary union. *An important characteristic of waves is their ability to pass through one another and not to change in any way.*

If the pulses that meet in a medium are unequal in amplitude when they meet, their combined amplitude is still the algebraic sum of the two. When the amplitudes are unequal in magnitude, the combined amplitude can not equal zero.

Figure 17-17

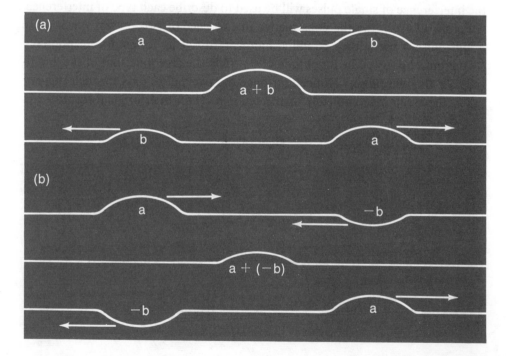

17:13 Nodes

Suppose two equal pulses are symmetrical but of opposite phase (180° difference). When they meet, there will be a point in the medium that is completely unaffected. This point is called a *node*. In Figure 17-18 a nodal point occurs.

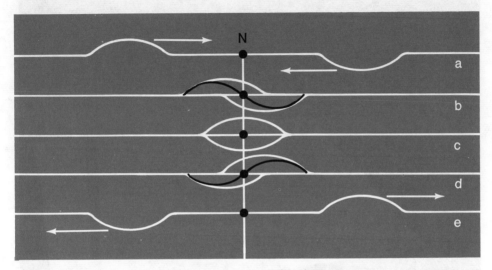

Figure 17-18. The nodal point is undisturbed during the meeting of two equal and opposite pulses or waves.

Notice parts *b*, *c*, and *d* of the diagram. The amplitude of the portion of the pulse above the nodal point is always the same as the amplitude of the portion of the pulse below the nodal point. Cancellation always takes place at the nodal point during the crossing of the two pulses.

When a wave train (series of identical waves) moving in one direction meets an identical wave train moving in the opposite direction, the same process occurs. But the process is on a more complex scale. Nodal points appear all along the path of the waves while between these points the waves interfere constructively and destructively. The two interfering waves appear to be vibrating in segments. The result is called a *standing wave*.

17:14 Ripple Tanks

A ripple tank is a shallow, rectangular tank with a glass bottom. When a ripple tank is filled with water to a depth of one or two centimeters, waves may be generated and their behavior studied. Often this is done by mounting a bright light above the tank and observing the shadows of the waves cast upon a screen below the tank.

Eduquip Inc.

Figure 17-19. The ripple tank is a useful device for demonstrating wave behavior. Several types of waves and pulses can be generated. This photograph shows two circular waves. The image of the waves is shown on the white paper below the tank.

To generate straight waves along the surface of the water, dip a ruler into the water at the end of the tank. This can be done automatically in most ripple tanks with a motorized wave generator. Use such a device to observe the characteristic wave behavior illustrated in the next few sections.

17:15   The Law of Reflection

Waves are reflected from a barrier at the same angle at which they approach the barrier. The angle of incidence is equal to the angle of reflection. This is called the law of reflection.

Figure 17-20 shows a pulse sent toward a barrier. Approach and reflection directions of the pulse are designated by lines drawn perpendicularly to the wave fronts. These imaginary lines are called rays. Frequently wave behavior is illustrated by ray diagrams. Ray diagrams show only the directions of the waves

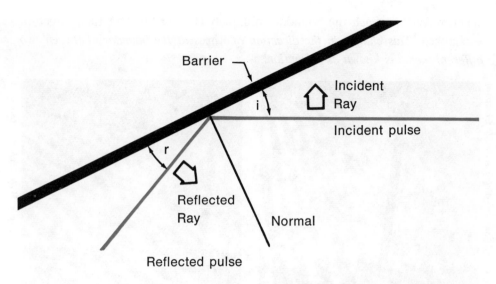

Figure 17-20.   The incident pulse approaches the barrier. The ray is the arrow which indicates the direction that the pulse moves. The ray is perpendicular to the front of the pulse. The angle between the incident pulse and the barrier (*i*) equals the angle between the reflected pulse and the barrier (*r*). The angle the incident *ray* would make with the normal equals the angle the reflected ray would make with the normal. The normal is a line perpendicular to the barrier at the point the pulse strikes it.

and not the waves themselves. Ray diagrams are particularly useful in the study of light, known as optics.

17:16   Refraction of Waves

The speed of a wave depends upon the medium in which it travels. Waves produced in different media have different speeds. As a wave travels from one medium into a new medium, the speed of the wave changes accordingly.

The behavior of waves as they move from one medium into another is observed in a ripple tank. The water above a glass plate placed in the tank is shallower than the water in the rest of the tank. It acts as a different medium.

The speed of waves in deep water is greater than the speed of waves in shallow water. To verify this, place the edge of the glass plate parallel to the advancing waves. Observe the decrease in the wavelength of the waves as they pass into the shallow water. Waves in the shallow water are generated by waves in the deep water. Therefore, their frequency and period are exactly the same as the frequency and period of the waves in the deep water. Because $v = f\lambda$ the decrease in the wavelength of the waves can only indicate a lower speed.

When waves approach the boundary between two media parallel with the boundary, they continue straight into the new medium. (Figure 17-21a.)

When waves approach the boundary obliquely (Figure 17-21b), their direction is changed. *This change in the direction of waves at the boundary between two different media is known as refraction.*

Figure 17-21. (a) Straight waves enter a different medium (shallow water) head-on. Notice the change in wavelength. (b) The straight waves enter the shallow water at an angle. Notice that the change in media causes the waves to bend at the boundaries of the barrier. This is refraction.

17:17   Diffraction of Waves

Diffraction is the bending of a wave around obstacles placed in its path. Diffraction may be observed in a ripple tank by placing a small barrier in the

Figure 17-22. Diffraction may be observed as water waves bend around a twig in a smoothly flowing stream.

path of straight waves. The waves bend around the edges of the obstacle. Eventually they form again some distance beyond. The undisturbed water behind the obstacle forms a shadow.

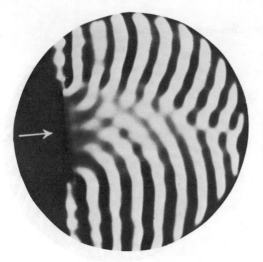

Figure 17-23. Straight waves hit the barrier from the direction of the arrow. Notice the bending of the straight wave beyond the barrier.

The Ealing Corporation

Create a diffraction pattern by placing three straight barriers as shown in Figure 17-24. Make the spaces between the barriers small in comparison to the wavelength of the approaching waves. The diffraction of the waves around the edges of the openings causes each opening to produce new circular waves. The two circular waves interfere with one another. Along the points marked by dashed lines, wave crest is superimposed on wave crest. At these points the

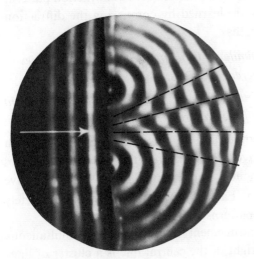

Figure 17-24. Waves diffract at two openings in the barrier. At each opening a set of circular waves is formed. The circular waves interfere constructively with each other forming lines marked by the dashed lines.

The Ealing Corporation

water is displaced doubly from its normal position. It forms points of severe agitation. These points of reinforcement all lie along the same line. They form a line of reinforcement. Between these lines of reinforcement are areas where each crest lies in a trough. Cancellation takes place and the water is relatively undisturbed. The undisturbed areas lie in definite paths or lines. They are called nodal lines.

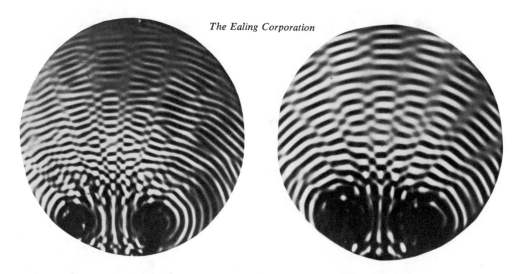

The Ealing Corporation

Figure 17-25. Changing the frequency of the wave changes the pattern produced by interference. The nodal lines are much closer together in (a) than in (b). The central line of wave maxima is present in both (a) and (b).

By varying the frequency of waves in the ripple tank, waves of different wavelengths are sent at the barriers. Each wavelength produces a diffraction pattern. Two facts about diffraction patterns are learned by comparing the diffraction patterns for several different wavelengths.

1. *Different wavelengths produce similar diffraction patterns, but the lines of reinforcement are in slightly different positions.*

2. *Regardless of the wavelength of the wave, the central line of reinforcement always falls in the exact center of the pattern.*

Different waves pass through one another and do not change each other. With this knowledge and the two facts above, a conclusion is reached. Several waves of different wavelengths can be sent at a barrier simultaneously. Each wave produces its own diffraction pattern. Each diffraction pattern is completely independent of the other diffraction patterns.

A very strong central line of reinforcement is the result of simultaneous diffraction patterns. To the left and right of the central line is a cluster of lines of reinforcement. There is one for each wavelength which falls upon the barrier. Ripple tanks do not lend themselves well to the generation of several wavelengths at once. The pattern that results is most difficult to analyze. A much clearer pattern is obtained by using light waves (Chapter 21).

17:18　The Doppler Effect

The Doppler effect is the change in frequency of waves received by an observer when the wave source and the observer are in relative motion. The source and the observer must move toward or away from each other. The Doppler effect applies to all kinds of waves. Figure 17-26 illustrates how the wavelength of the waves is shorter in front of the moving source and longer behind the moving source.

Vance A. Tucker

Figure 17-26.　A whirligig beetle swimming on the surface of the water provides an example of the Doppler effect. The wavelength of the waves ahead of the beetle (right) is noticibly shorter than the wavelength of the waves behind the beetle (left). The speed of the beetle can be determined by the difference in wavelength.

The Doppler effect also explains a phenomenon often observed by astronomers. Stars that are moving in a direction away from the earth tend to display light of longer wavelengths than they should. This is known as the "red-shift" because the longer wavelengths of light are red in color. The wavelengths observed coming from a star will show a shift towards the red but may not be necessarily red. The shift towards the longer wavelengths indicates that the stars are moving away from the earth and is evidence that the universe is expanding.

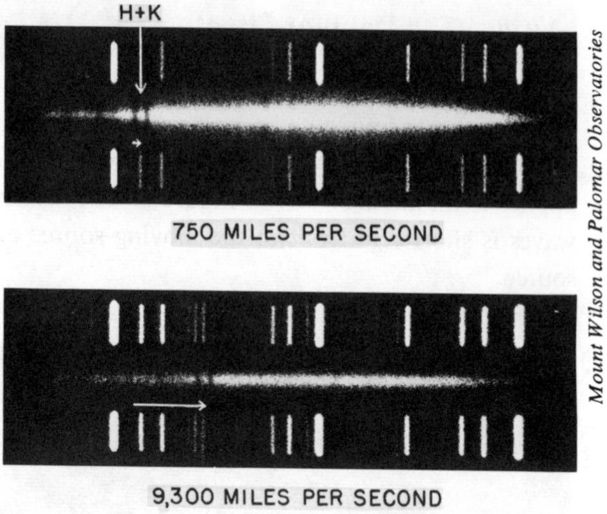

H+K

750 MILES PER SECOND

Figure 17-27. Astronomers use the Doppler shift of spectral lines to calculate the speed of a star. The arrows indicate the shift of the *H* and *K* lines of calcium. Notice how the lines are farther to the right in the lower photograph.

9,300 MILES PER SECOND

Mount Wilson and Palomar Observatories

QUESTIONS

1. How many general methods of energy transfer are there? Give two examples of each.
2. There are many kinds of waves. How is it possible to learn the rules of wave behavior for all kinds of waves without an extensive study of each kind of wave?
3. Distinguish between a mechanical wave and an electromagnetic wave.
4. How does a transverse wave differ from a longitudinal wave? Give an example of each.
5. If a pulse is sent along a rope, how does the rope behave at any given point once the pulse has passed?
6. A pulse differs from a wave. How?
7. Distinguish between the wavelength, frequency, and period of a wave.
8. Write an equation used to determine the velocity of a wave.
9. What does the amplitude of a wave represent?
10. An instructor sends waves along a coiled spring of fixed length. Can he change the speed of the waves in the spring? How can he change the frequency of a wave in the spring?
11. The top of a drum vibrates at a frequency that cannot be changed without altering the drum itself. Therefore, all sound waves coming from the drum must have the same frequency. If the drum is hit harder, what is different about the sound waves?
12. Reflection takes place when a wave reaches the boundary of a new medium. What determines the amount of reflection?

13. A pulse reaches the boundary of a medium more rigid than the one from which it came. Is the reflected pulse erect or inverted?

14. A pulse reaches the boundary of a medium less rigid than the one from which it came. Is the reflected pulse erect or inverted?

15. A light wave is reflected from the surface of a pond. Is the reflected wave erect or inverted?

16. When a wave passes into a new medium, what remains the same? What changes?

For Questions 17-21, sketch the result of wave a and wave b (a) when they meet (b) when they pass one another.

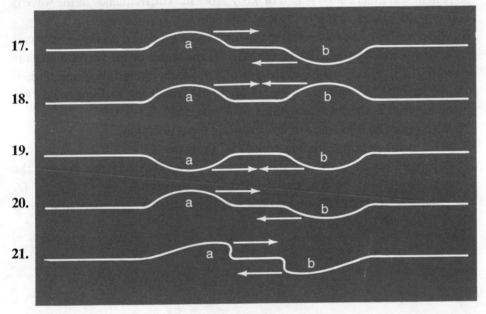

17.

18.

19.

20.

21.

Figure 17-28

22. In Questions 17-21: (a) In which diagrams do the pulses produce constructive interference when they meet? (b) In which diagrams do the waves produce destructive interference when they meet?

23. In Questions 17-21, in which diagrams are nodes formed as the pulses pass through one another?

24. List three different means of changing the direction of a wave.

25. State the law of reflection.

26. What is diffraction?

27. List two important facts about the diffraction patterns produced by waves of different wavelengths as they pass through the same pair of openings.

28. How do the waves in front of a moving source differ from the waves behind a moving source?

PROBLEMS

1. What is the wavelength of a sound wave that has a frequency of 50 hertz?
2. An ocean wave has a wavelength of 30 ft. A wave passes by every 2 sec. What is the speed of the wave?
3. A sonar signal (sound wave) of frequency 1000 hertz has a wavelength of 5 ft in water. (a) What is the speed of sound in water? (b) What is the period of the sound wave in water? (c) What is the period of the sound wave in air?
4. A sound wave in a steel rail has a frequency of 500 hertz and a wavelength of 33 ft. What is the speed of sound in steel?
5. A light wave has a wavelength of 4.0×10^{-7} m. The frequency of the wave is 7.5×10^{14} hertz. What is the speed of light?
6. Waves of frequency 2 hertz are generated along a coiled spring. The waves have a wavelength of 0.45 m. (a) What is the speed of the waves along the spring? (b) What is the wavelength of the waves along the spring if their frequency is increased to 6 hertz? (c) If the frequency is decreased to 0.5 hertz, what is their wavelength?
7. Determine the frequency of a microwave 6 cm in length.
8. What is the period of the microwave in Problem 7?
9. A gamma ray has a period of 10^{-24} sec. (a) What is the frequency of the gamma ray? (b) What is the wavelength of the gamma ray in meters? (A gamma ray is an electromagnetic wave. It travels through space at a speed of 3.0×10^8 m/sec.)

The Nature of Light

Light has influenced and intrigued man throughout the ages. Early man hunted by daylight and hid at night. Superstition involving sunlight and eclipses is known to have influenced the outcome of wars in ancient times. The type of eclipse of the sun pictured above was never observed by ancient man. This is a solar eclipse as viewed from the moon by the Apollo astronauts. Can you draw a diagram to indicate the corresponding positions of the earth, moon and sun?

18:1 Light — An Electromagnetic Wave

Light is emitted from an incandescent source by radiation. The sun is a source of huge quantities of radiation. On a smaller scale there are incandescent lamps, carbon-arc lamps, fluorescent lamps and the radiation that is emitted by flames. Some of the radiation that comes from these sources is capable of stimulating the retina of the human eye. This is called light. Much of the radiation that comes from incandescent bodies does not stimulate the retina of the eye and has other names than light. Infrared waves, ultraviolet waves, and even radio waves are emitted by hot bodies, but are not detected by the eye. These waves are detected by other means.

A luminous body is any body that emits light waves. A luminous body is distinguished from an illuminated body which reflects light waves. The sun is a luminous body. The moon is an illuminated body. A body need not be luminous to emit radiation. The word luminous refers to a body that emits light waves. All warm bodies emit radiation, but not necessarily as visible light. The radiation a hot stove gives out cannot be seen but it can be detected by other means.

Mechanical waves require a medium. For example, water waves and waves along a spring studied in Chapter 17 are mechanical waves. Light waves are electromagnetic waves that can travel through empty space. Electromagnetic waves require no medium. Light waves represent only one small portion of known electromagnetic radiations. Figure 18-1 shows the entire known spectrum (array) of electromagnetic waves. Notice that light waves account for only a small portion of the electromagnetic spectrum.

Figure 18-1. A chart of the electromagnetic spectrum. Electromagnetic waves of different frequencies are detected by different means. Notice that the visible spectrum is only a very small portion of the electromagnetic spectrum.

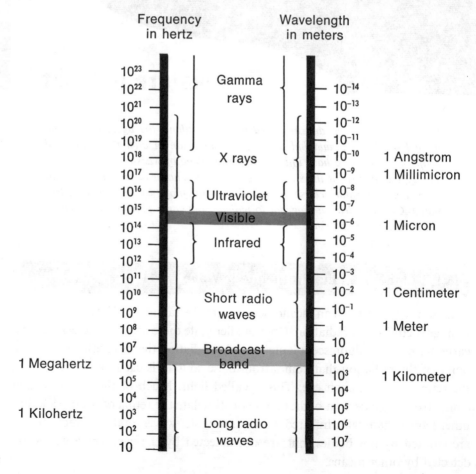

Electromagnetic waves can be called a large family of waves. All electromagnetic waves travel at the same speed in space. They differ in frequency, and therefore, differ in wavelengths. Figure 18-1 shows some frequencies and wavelengths of various electromagnetic waves.

An electromagnetic wave exhibits both electric and magnetic properties. An electric field and a magnetic field are associated with the wave. These fields vibrate in planes perpendicular to each other.

18:2 Transmission and Absorption of Light

Many materials transmit light without causing a noticeable distortion of the rays. Some of these materials are glass, quartz, air, and some plastics. Objects are visible through these materials. For that reason, they are called transparent media. Other matter transmits light but distorts the rays during the transmission. Smoked-glass windows do this. They are said to be translucent rather than transparent. Materials such as brick walls absorb or reflect all light that falls on them. They are opaque.

18:3 Color and Light

Let sunlight or a beam of white light from a lamp fall on a glass prism. The light is dispersed into an array of different wavelengths. The light is then seen to consist of many different colors. White light is a combination of many colors of light. Light waves that pass through a prism are electromagnetic waves. They differ from one another chiefly in their wavelengths. Red light waves have the longest wavelengths. Violet light waves have the shortest wavelengths. Notice in Figure 18-2 that red and violet light are at opposite ends of the spectrum.

Color is a property of light. A red dress is red because it reflects red light. When white light falls on the dress, the pigments of the dye in the dress absorb most

Figure 18-2. Dispersion of white light as produced by a prism.

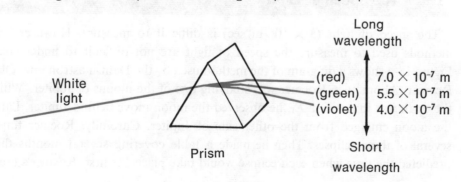

of the light. However, they do not tend to absorb those wavelengths that are in the red region of visible light. These are reflected to the eye and the dress appears to be red. Suppose monochromatic blue light was the only light to fall on the red dress. The pigments in the dye would absorb all the light. No light would be reflected from the dress and it would appear to be black. Black is the absence of color or light.

Figure 18-3. A scientist measures the maturity of tomatoes with a Multiple Wavelength Difference Meter. The color which is a function of the wavelength of light reflected from the tomato is analyzed more accurately than by eye.

USDA Photo

18:4   The Speed of Light

The speed of light (3×10^8 m/sec) is difficult to measure. However, the methods used to measure the speed of light are not difficult to understand. Figure 18-4 shows a diagram of the method used by the Danish astronomer Olaf Roemer. About 1676 Roemer was studying one of the moons of Jupiter. While the earth was in position E_1, he observed the moon move behind Jupiter. Later the moon emerged from the other side of Jupiter. Carefully, Roemer timed several of these eclipses. Then he made a table covering several months that predicted the time when each eclipse would take place. At first, Roemer's table was fairly accurate. But as the months went by, a larger and larger error appeared. The eclipses occurred later and later than predicted. After six months, the error in the time each eclipse began became less and less until the table was accurate once again. Roemer immediately understood the source of the time

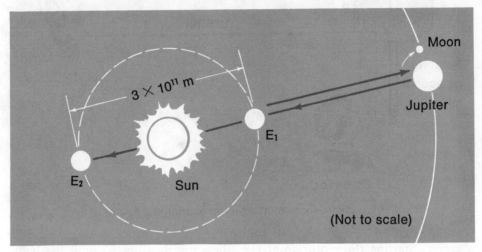

Figure 18-4

discrepancy. He had made his table while the earth was at position E_1 of Figure 18-4. As the earth followed its orbit around the sun, it moved farther and farther away from Jupiter. Jupiter, however, moved only a relatively short distance along its orbit. The error occurred because the light had to travel a greater distance to reach the observer on earth as the months went by. At position E_2, the earth is twice 1.5×10^{11} m or 3×10^{11} m farther from Jupiter than it was at position E_1. The apparent error in the time the eclipse began at this position, according to Roemer's table, was about 1000 seconds. Assuming this to be the extra time needed for the light coming from Jupiter's moon to traverse the diameter of the earth's orbit the speed of light, must be:

$$v = \frac{s}{t} = \frac{3 \times 10^{11} \text{ m}}{1000 \text{ sec}} = 3 \times 10^8 \text{ m/sec}$$

The first accurate terrestrial measurement of the speed of light was made by the American scientist Albert Michelson. Michelson used a rotating octagonal mirror. (Figure 18-5.) The apparatus sent a pulse of light from the source S to the mirror A. The light then traveled the path shown. For the observer O to see the pulse, mirror B must move into the exact position of mirror C in just the time it takes the light to travel the path. The mirror has eight sides. Therefore, the time required for B to move into position C is just one-eighth of the time needed for one revolution of the octagonal mirror. In practice, the octagonal mirror is spun by an electric motor. The speed of the motor is adjusted by the

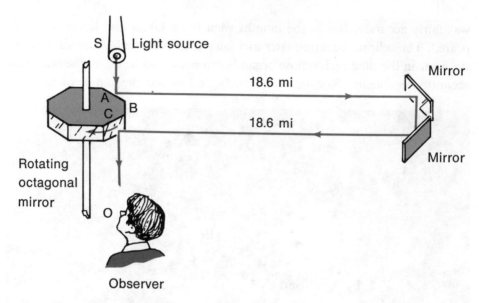

Figure 18-5.   Michelson's method of measuring the speed of light.

observer. Starting the motor from rest, the speed is adjusted until the light reflected from *C* is at maximum brightness. Then, the rate of rotation of the mirror is determined and the speed of light calculated. Study the following problems to help understand the reasoning behind Michelson's method of measuring the speed of light.

Problems

1. The octagonal mirror in Figure 18-5 makes 625 rev/sec. What time is required for one revolution?
2. Calculate (a) one-eighth the time determined in Problem one (b) the total distance the light travels while mirror *B* moves into position *C*.
3. Use the solutions to Problem 2 to determine the speed of light.
4. The octagonal mirror happens to be rotating at the rate of 1250 rev/sec. Would an observer see the pulse of light? Explain.
5. What steps can an observer take to be sure that the octagonal mirror does not rotate at some multiple of the proper number of rev/sec?

18:5   Light Travels in a Straight Line

Sometimes the air contains enough dust to make a flashlight beam visible. The dust particles reflect some of the light waves from the beam to the eye and the path of the beam is seen. Such an observation makes it apparent that light travels in a straight line.

Official U.S. Coast Guard Photo

Figure 18-6. The fact that light travels in straight lines may be observed in beams of light reflected from fog and dust in the air. How is this property of light used to guide ships away from rocks?

Even a small beam or "pencil" of light consists of an almost infinite number of individual waves of many different wavelengths. All the waves travel together in a straight line. This knowledge helps to explain much of the behavior of light. Since light does travel in straight lines in the direction of the waves, lines can be used to represent the direction of the light waves. The lines are called rays. To study light in this way is called ray optics.

Figure 18-7. A ray shows the direction of propagation of a wave. Circular waves propagate from a common center (a). Rays for circular waves are perpendicular to the wave fronts. Thus, the rays of circular waves are along radii of the circles and extend out from the wave front. Straight waves (b) move in a direction that is perpendicular to the wave front. Rays are drawn in the direction the wave front moves. Rays are useful for describing the geometric behavior of light.

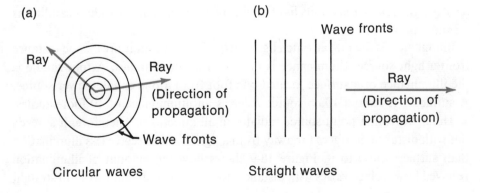

(a)

Ray

Ray
(Direction of propagation)

Wave fronts

Circular waves

(b)

Wave fronts

Ray
(Direction of propagation)

Straight waves

18:6 Illumination by a Point Source

Light from a point source obeys the inverse square law. The illumination that is given to any surface by a point source of light varies inversely as the square of the distance between the surface and the source.

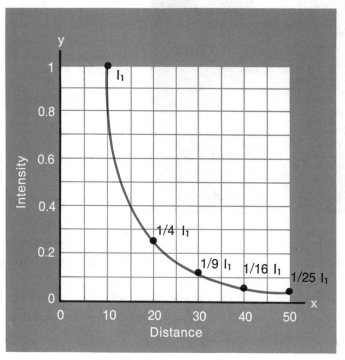

Figure 18-8. The graph of distance from a lamp versus the lamp's intensity illustrates the inverse square law.

The intensity of a light source is measured by comparing it with the international unit, the standard candle. The standard candle is a special candle made to exact specifications. A standard candle has an intensity of one candle-power (cp). A light source that emits light at five times the rate of a standard candle has a candle-power of 5.

Illuminance is the rate at which light energy falls on a unit area some distance from a light source. Illuminance is measured in foot-candles. A foot-candle is the illuminance of a surface located one foot from a one candle-power source. A surface 1 ft from a 10 cp source receives an illuminance of 10 foot-candles.

The light from a point source radiates in all directions. Therefore, it spreads out with distance. Surfaces far away from a light source receive less illumination than surfaces close to it. Figure 18-9 shows how the amount of illumination received by a surface varies with distance. Remember that light travels in straight lines. Therefore, the light energy that falls on a square foot of surface one foot away from the source spreads out to cover an area of 4 ft² on a second screen 2 ft away from the source. Hence the illumination of the screen 2 ft away is $\frac{1}{4}$ the illumination of the screen 1 ft away from the source. Likewise, a screen 3 ft from the source receives $\frac{1}{9}$ the illumination of a screen 1 ft from the source.

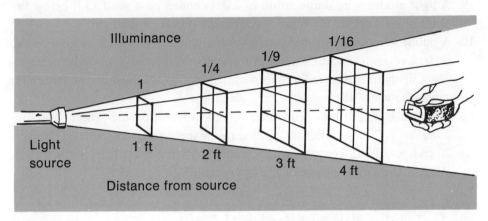

Figure 18-9.　The illuminance of a surface varies inversely as the square of its distance from a light source.

To increase the illuminance of a surface some distance from a light source, the intensity of the source must be increased. Doubling the intensity of the source doubles the illuminance on a surface. The illuminance of a surface varies directly as the intensity of the light source. Also the illuminance of a surface decreases as the square of its distance from the source (Figure 18-9). Let I represent the luminous intensity of the source in candle-power; let E represent the illuminance of the surface in foot-candles; then the illuminance of a surface is expressed algebraically as,

$$E = \frac{I}{d^2}$$

Sample Problem 1

A student's desk top is five feet below a 150 cp incandescent lamp. What is the illumination of the desk top?

Solution:

$$E = \frac{I}{d^2}$$
$$= \frac{150 \text{ cp}}{(5\text{ft})^2}$$
$$= 6 \text{ ft-cdls}$$

Problems

6. Determine the illumination of a surface 4 ft below a 32 cp light source.

7. A lamp is moved from 1 ft to 3 ft above the pages of a book. How does the illumination of the book compare before and after the lamp is moved?

8. The intensity of illumination on a surface 3 ft below a 150-watt incandescent lamp is 10 ft-candles. What is the intensity of the lamp in candle-power?

9. A light produces an illumination of 2.0 ft-candles on a road 15 ft below the point of its suspension. What is the candle-power of the light?

10. A public school law requires a minimum illumination of 20 ft-candles on the surface of each student's desk. An architect's specifications call for classroom lights to be located 6 ft above the desks. What must be the minimum candle power of the lights?

11. A screen is placed between two lamps of different candle-power. The illumination is 20 ft-candles on both sides of the screen. The smaller lamp is 20 cp located 1 ft from the screen. The larger lamp is 2.5 ft from the screen. What is the candle-power of the larger lamp?

18:7 Light — Waves or Particles?

During Newton's lifetime a controversy arose concerning the fundamental nature of light. Newton held that light consists of minute particles. The Dutch scientist Christian Huygens proposed that light consists of waves. Both of these theories had strong arguments in their favor. They are included in the more complex quantum theory.

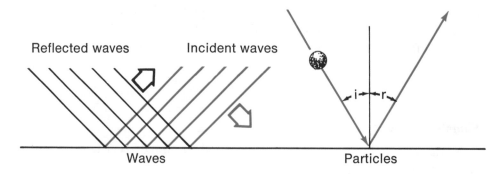

Figure 18-10.   The law of reflection applies equally to waves and to particles. In both, the angle of incidence equals the angle of reflection.

Newton reasoned that light consists of particles because of the way light reflects from a surface. Newton knew that when a beam of light strikes a surface the angle of reflection is equal to the angle of approach (Figure 18-10) in the same way a particle is reflected. Huygens, however, was just as aware that when waves reflect from a surface, they behave in a like manner. Therefore, the way in which a light beam is reflected is not conclusive evidence that light consists of either particles or waves.

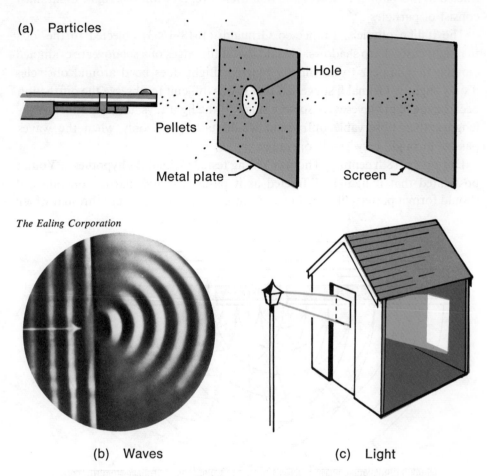

(a) Particles

Hole

Pellets

Metal plate

Screen

The Ealing Corporation

(b)   Waves   (c)   Light

Figure 18-11.   (a) Particles do not diffract as they pass through openings. (b) Waves do diffract at openings. (c) Light does not seem to diffract at large openings.

Diffraction is the bending of a wave around barriers placed in its path. Because waves bend around the edges of obstacles, they behave as shown in Figure 18-11 (b). The wave passes through at an opening in the barrier. As it passes through, the wave bends around the two edges and forms a new, more circular wave. The wave spreads out to the left and right of the opening. Particles do not seem to act this way. In Figure 18-11 (a) compressed air gun shoots pellets at a steel plate. The plate has a small circular opening in its center. The pellets cut a sharp, well defined image of the opening on a paper screen some distance from the plate. The pellets travel straight through the hole. No bending takes place around the edges. Figure 18-11 (c) shows that light apparently behaves in a manner like the pellets and unlike the waves. A street lamp casts a sharp image of a window onto the wall of a room. From this it appears that light is not diffracted in the manner of waves and that therefore, Newton was right. Light must consist of particles.

The Italian physicist Francesco Grimaldi (1618–1663) objected to the idea that light casts sharp shadows. He said that if the edges of a shadow are examined closely, they appear to be slightly blurred. Light does bend around obstacles if only slightly. Grimaldi suggested that it was difficult to observe the diffraction because the light waves were so very small. If the light rays had very short wavelengths, then observable diffraction would take place only when the waves passed through very small openings.

During the 18th century, Thomas Young tested Grimaldi's hypothesis. Young postulated that if light is diffracted as it passes through narrow openings, it should form a pattern like the one in Figure 18-12. The openings through which

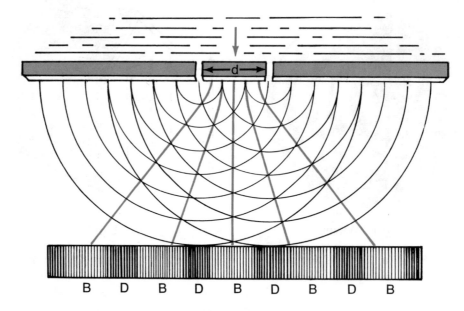

Figure 18-12.   If the slits are small compared to the wavelength of the waves, a diffraction pattern is observed.

he passed the light were very small. This was done by making two narrow slits in a screen. The pattern formed was very similar to the interference pattern formed by the diffraction of water waves. Lines of constructive interference in this case resulted in bright spots on a screen some distance from the narrow slits. Between these bright spots were dark spots on the screen where destructive interference

Double slit diffraction from single-concept film by Franklin Miller, Jr.

Figure 18-13. Interference pattern produced by a pair of very narrow slits. Note the equal spacing between the bright bands.

caused the light waves to cancel. Young concluded that since light exhibited interference it must be some form of waves.

To repeat Young's experiment, blacken a small piece of glass, such as a microscope slide, in the flame of a candle. Break a double-edged razor blade in half and place the edges of the blade together. Quickly draw two lines across the glass. The result is two narrow slits. Look at a light source through these slits to observe an interference pattern very similar to that of Figure 18-13.

18:8 The Interference of Light Falling on Thin Films

The diffraction of light is not the only evidence in favor of the wave theory of light. Another is the colorful pattern often seen in soap films, soap bubbles, and oil-slicks. The weight of a soap film held vertically makes it thicker at the bottom than at the top. In fact, the film varies in thickness rather smoothly

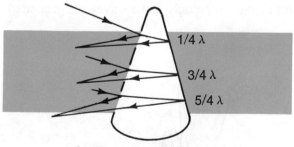

1/4 λ

3/4 λ

5/4 λ

Cross section of soap film

Figure 18-14. Each color will be reinforced where the soap film is ¼, ¾, 5/4 of the wavelength for that color. Since each color has a different wavelength, a series of color bands are seen reflected from the soap film.

from top to bottom. A light wave striking the film is partially reflected and partially transmitted in accordance with the rules of wave behavior. The transmitted wave travels through the film to the opposite boundary. Here it is partially reflected again. If the thickness of the film is $\frac{1}{4}$ of the wavelength of the wave, the path length of the transmitted wave in the film is $\frac{1}{2}\lambda$. This is because the wave must go over and back. It would appear at first that the wave returning from the inner surface would arrive back at the outersurface just one-half wavelength out of phase with the first reflected wave and that the two waves would cancel. However, when a wave is reflected from a more dense medium it undergoes inversion. The first reflected wave is inverted upon reflection, while the second reflected wave is not. The wave returning from the inner surface arrives back at the first surface completely in phase with the first reflected wave. Thus reinforcement rather than cancellation occurs.

Different colors of light have different wavelengths. The thickness of the film meets the $\frac{1}{4}\lambda$ requirement for different colors at intervals down the film. This is because the thickness of the film changes. Thus a progression of different colors are reinforced. The result is a rainbow of color if white light is falling on the film. Eventually, a point is reached where the thickness is $\frac{3}{4}\lambda$ for the first color. This again suits the $\frac{1}{2}\lambda$ path difference, and the color reappears at that point. Any odd multiple of quarter wavelengths such as $\frac{1}{4}\lambda$, $\frac{3}{4}\lambda$, or $\frac{5}{4}\lambda$ satisfies the conditions for a given color. If the film is $\frac{1}{2}\lambda$ thick, or any multiple thereof, the returning wave cancels the wave reflected from the outer surface. There is no reflected wave for the wavelength at that point.

18:9   The Polarization of Light

In Figure 18-15, waves sent along a rope pass through a slot. Under these circumstances, waves can be sent along a rope only if the waves are generated

Figure 18-15

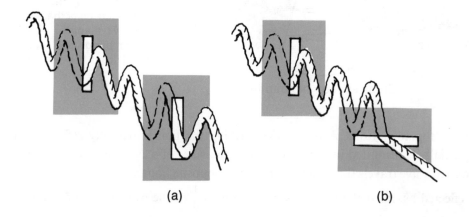

(a)   (b)

in the plane that allows passage through the slot. Each slot permits only those waves that are oriented to a particular plane to pass through. The waves are said to be polarized to a particular plane, or *plane polarized.*

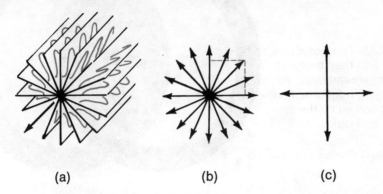

(a)   (b)   (c)

Figure 18-16.   Unpolarized light consists of waves vibrating in many planes along the path of the ray (a). (b) shows an end-on representation of (a). The vectors resolve into vertical and horizontal components (c).

A beam of light waves contains an infinite number of waves vibrating in every possible plane. Mathematically, this averages out as if one-half of the waves vibrate vertically and one-half vibrate horizontally. This is because all the waves can be resolved into vertical and horizontal components. If a filter

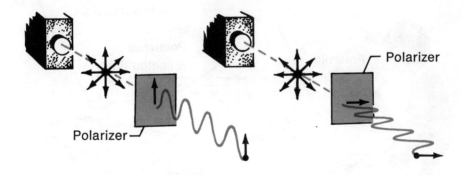

Figure 18-17.   Plane polarized light vibrates in only one plane.

(polarizer) such as polaroid material, is placed in front of the beam of light, half of the light is eliminated. Only those waves that vibrate parallel with the permitted plane pass through. Suppose a second sheet of polaroid material (analyzer) is placed in the path of the polarized light in such a way that it presents its favored plane perpendicularly to the remaining polarized light. Almost no light will pass through.

Figure 18-18. Two polarizers are held with their transmitting axes perpendicular. Polarized light from the first disk is absorbed by the second disk.

Bruce Charlton

Light can be polarized by reflection. Suspend a lamp above a tank of water. Look at the reflected light through a piece of polaroid. Rotate the polaroid and continue to observe the reflected light. Notice that the light brightens and dims. Try various angles of reflection. There will be one angle at which the light from the bulb is completely absorbed by the polaroid. This is the angle of polarization. At this angle the light which is reflected from the water is completely polarized.

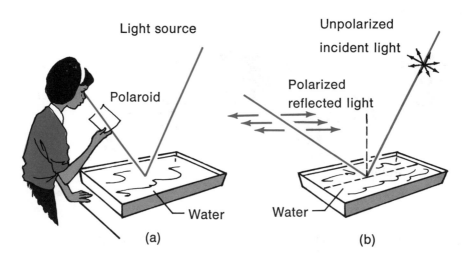

Figure 18-19.   (a) Observing the polarization of light reflected from water. Rotate the polaroid until the reflected light disappears. (b) The water reflects light vibrating in one plane and absorbs the other rays.

Light can be polarized by three methods: by reflection, by scattering, and by passing through special crystals and polymers in which the waves travel at different speeds in different directions. Polaroid is a plastic material which has its molecules aligned in the same direction. The molecules all absorb light of the same polarization.

The fact that light can be polarized supports two ideas. First, light consists of waves because particles would be unaffected by a polarizer. Second, light waves are transverse waves. Longitudinal waves would be largely uninterupted by a polarizer. For example, sound waves cannot be polarized.

18:10 The Photoelectric Effect

Beyond all doubt, the diffraction, interference, and polarization of light demonstrate the wave properties of light. Now consider an effect that demonstrates just as clearly that light consists of particles.

Light which falls on a metal surface, such as zinc or cesium, ejects electrons from the metal. Furthermore, these electrons leave the metal with a kinetic energy that cannot be accounted for by assuming the energy of light incident on the metal is distributed evenly over the entire wave front. This means that light energy is not distributed evenly. Instead, it is concentrated in little packages or bundles of energy called quanta, or photons. This is definitely not a property of waves.

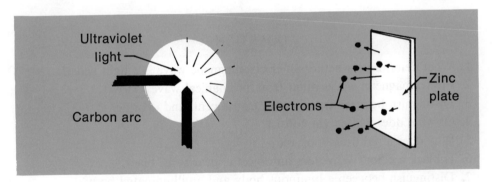

Figure 18-20. Apparatus to demonstrate the photoelectric effect.

The question still remains. Is light a form of wave motion or is it particles? The answer is, light cannot be expected to behave wholly either as waves or as particles. Light is a fundamental phenomenon of nature. The behavior of light cannot be judged in terms of observable macroscopic properties of matter.

18:11 The Quantum Theory

The quantum theory of light was proposed by Max Planck and fostered by Neils Bohr and Albert Einstein. This theory attempts to account for the dual nature of light. According to the quantum theory, light is emitted from a source in tiny discrete packages. These packages are quanta of energy called *photons*. Each photon is associated with a light wave of specific frequency. The energy associated with a photon is proportional to its wave frequency in accordance with the formula proposed by Max Planck, $E = hf$. In the equation, E represents the energy in joules; h is Planck's constant 6.6×10^{-34} joule-sec; and f is the frequency of the photon.

The quantum theory provides for both the wave-like and particle-like behavior of light. The laser (Section 22:7) makes use of both the wave and particle properties of light.

Sample Problem 2

A photon of red light has a frequency of 5.0×10^{14} hertz. What energy is associated with this photon?

Solution:

$$E = hf$$
$$= (6.6 \times 10^{-34} \text{ joule-sec})(5.0 \times 10^{14} \text{ hertz})$$
$$= 3.3 \times 10^{-19} \text{ joules}$$

QUESTIONS

1. What determines whether an electromagnetic wave is a light wave?
2. Electromagnetic waves differ from mechanical waves. How?
3. Distinguish between transparent, translucent, and opaque.
4. Of what does white light consist?
5. Why does a red dress look red?
6. Is black a color? Why does an object appear to be black?
7. Distinguish between a luminous body and an illuminated body.
8. In what unit is the intensity of a light source measured?
9. In what unit is the illumination of a surface measured?
10. To what is the illumination of a surface by a light source directly proportional? To what is it inversely proportional?
11. Explain why the reflection of light cannot be used as evidence that light is either waves or particles.
12. What theory of light does the diffraction of light support?
13. What theory of light does the polarization of light support?
14. The polarization of light indicates that light waves are what kind of waves?
15. The photoelectric effect supports what theory of light?
16. To what is the energy possessed by a photon proportional?

PROBLEMS

1. An observer uses a 10-sided mirror to measure the speed of light. The mirror is rotating at 2000 rev/sec when the observer observes maximum brightness. The total path of the light pulse is 15 km. What is the speed of light?

2. An observer uses an octagonal mirror to measure the speed of light. He obtains a spot of maximum brightness when the mirror is rotating at the rate of 3126 rev/sec. The total path of the light between mirrors is 12 km. What is the speed of light?

3. Assume that the sun is 1.5×10^8 km from the earth. Calculate the time required for light to travel from the sun to the earth.

4. A radar signal is reflected from the moon. It is detected after a 2.58 sec time lapse between sending and receiving. How far away is the moon?

5. The light year is a unit of distance used by astronomers. It is the distance light travels in one year. (a) Calculate this distance in miles. (b) The nearest star is approximately four light years away. How far in miles is this star from the earth?

6. A 64-cp point source of light is 6 ft above the surface of a desk. What is the intensity of the illumination on the desk?

7. A 100-cp point source of light is 2 ft from screen A and 4 ft from screen B. How does the intensity of illumination on screen B compare with the intensity of illumination on screen A?

8. The illumination on a tabletop is 20 ft-candles. The lamp providing the illumination is 4 ft above the table. What is its candle power?

9. Two lamps illuminate a screen equally. The first lamp is 100 cp and is 5 ft from the screen. The second lamp is 3 ft from the screen. What is its candle power?

10. A polaroid plate is placed over the light detecting surface of a light meter. Then the meter is exposed to the sun on a clear day. The meter reads 500 foot-candles. What actual illumination falls on the meter?

11. If the sun is 9.3×10^7 mi away, what is the candle power of the sun? (Use the answer to Problem 10 and scientific notation. Let one mile equal 5.3×10^3 ft.)

12. (a) Calculate the intensity of illumination that falls on a movable screen when it is located at these distances from a 400 cp light source: 5 ft, 10 ft, 15 ft, 20 ft, 25 ft (b) Make a table to show the distances in the first column and the corresponding intensities of illumination in the second column. (c) Use graph paper to plot the intensities of illumination versus distance. Draw the curve that best fits these points. Plot the distances horizontally.

13. A radio wave has a frequency of 10^8 hertz. Planck's constant is 6.6×10^{-34} j-sec. What energy is associated with the radio wave's photons?

14. A gamma-ray photon has a frequency of 10^{20}/sec. What energy is associated with this photon?

15. Which has more energy, the radio wave or the gamma ray?

16. The speed of light is 3.0×10^{10} cm/sec. (a) What is the wavelength of a light wave of frequency 10^{15} hertz? (b) An Angstrom unit is 10^{-8} cm. How many angstrom units does the solution to part (a) represent? (c) How thick is the first point near the top of a soap-film wedge that reinforces this wavelength?

Reflection and Refraction

Our eyes are often said to play tricks on us. A puddle may appear to exist at some distance down the highway on a hot summer day. You may have great difficulty finding your way out of a maze of mirrors at a carnival. A coin dropped in a swimming pool may not be located exactly where you think it is. These are examples of reflection and refraction. What examples of reflection and refraction do you find in the above photograph?

19:1 The Law of Reflection

When a light ray is incident upon a surface, *the angle of incidence is equal to the angle of reflection.* Both the angle of incidence and the angle of reflection are measured from a normal (perpendicular) to the surface at the point of incidence. The incident ray, the reflected ray, and the normal all lie in the same plane.

229

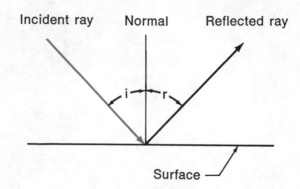

Figure 19-1. The law of reflection. The incident ray, the reflected ray, and the normal to the surface at the point of reflection, all lie in the same plane. The angle of incidence and the angle of reflection are measured from the normal.

19:2 Diffuse and Regular Reflection

When a beam of light strikes most surfaces, the light rays reflect in many different directions. Because most surfaces are not smooth, they do not reflect light in a regular manner. A painted wall or a page of a book appears to be smooth. Actually their surfaces consist of many very small projections and irregularities. Rays of light strike different parts of these projections. Each ray reflects according to the law of reflection and the rays are scattered in many different directions.

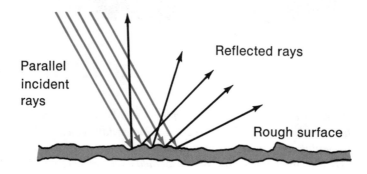

Figure 19-2. Diffuse reflection results when light strikes an uneven surface. There are many uses for surfaces which scatter light in this manner. Explain how such a surface might be useful.

If light rays fall upon an extremely smooth surface, the rays reflect in a regular way. Figure 19-3 shows a beam of parallel rays reflecting from a smooth, flat surface. Since each ray follows the law of reflection, the reflected rays remain parallel. The rays are arranged in the same order after they leave a smooth surface as they were before they approached the surface.

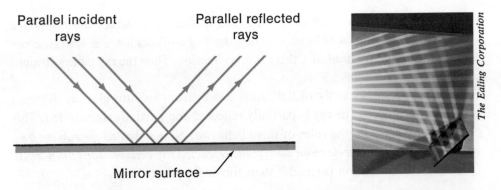

Figure 19-3. Regular reflection from a mirror surface. (a) Parallel rays are reflected in the same plane in which they are incident. (b) A mirror reflects pencils of light. How is this property of plane mirrors put to use?

19:3 Refraction of Light

Refraction is the bending of light at the boundary between two media. Refraction occurs because the speed of light in a medium is less than the speed of light in a vacuum. The speed of light varies with different media as well. Refraction can take place between the surfaces of different media.

An incident ray is a ray that falls on the boundary between two media. Once the ray enters a new medium, it is a refracted ray. The angle between the incident ray and a normal to the surface at the point of incidence is the angle of incidence. The angle between the refracted ray and the same normal is the angle of re-

Figure 19-4. Comparison of the refraction of light at a boundary to the deflection of a car at the boundary of mud and pavement. (a) Incidence angle is 90° with the boundary. Angle of incidence is increased (b) and (c).

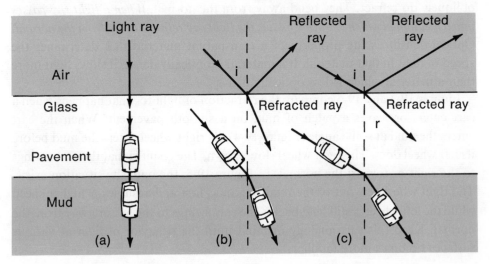

fraction. Refraction occurs only when the incident ray strikes the boundary between the two media obliquely. When the angle of incidence is zero (the ray strikes the boundary head on), there is no refraction. Then the ray passes straight into the new medium.

Figure 19-4 shows a ray of light as it passes from air into glass at different angles of incidence. The ray is partially reflected and partially transmitted. This is in accordance with the rules of wave behavior. Notice that *as the ray enters a medium in which it travels more slowly, the refracted ray bends toward the normal.* The angle of refraction is smaller than the angle of incidence.

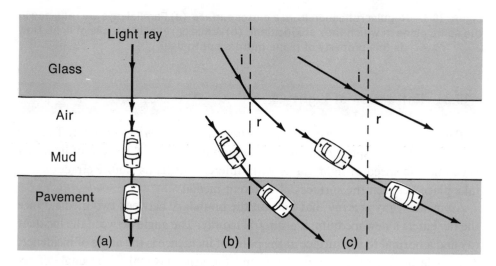

Figure 19-5.   Refraction away from the normal as a less dense medium is entered.

In Figure 19-5 a light ray passes from glass into air at different angles. A ray perpendicular to the surface does not refract. The rays that strike the surface obliquely do refract. They bend away from the normal. *When a light ray passes into a medium in which it travels faster, the light ray refracts away from the normal.* Optical density is the property of a transparent material that determines the speed of light in that material. If a material is optically dense, it slows light more than a material which is less optically dense.

Figures 19-4 and 19-5 compare the refraction of light to what happens when a cart enters or leaves a patch of mud on a smooth pavement. When the cart enters the mud at some angle (Figure 19-4), its right wheel enters the mud before its left wheel does. The right wheel slows down. The result is that the cart swings to the right or toward the normal. In Figure 19-5, the opposite situation exists. The right wheel gets out of the retarding mud first and resumes a higher speed while the left wheel is still held back. The cart swings to the left or away from the normal. Keep this cart analogy in mind until the behavior of light at various surfaces becomes more familiar.

Problem

1. Determine the path of the incident light ray through and beyond the medium in each case.

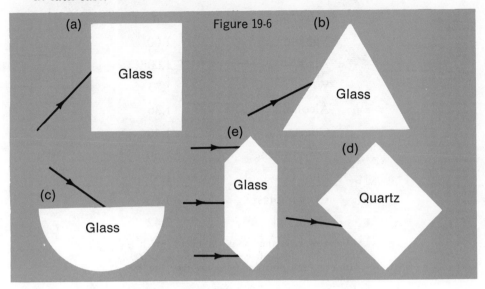

Figure 19-6

19:4 Snell's Law

Rays of light that travel from air into glass, or any other medium more optically dense than air, are refracted toward the normal. As the angle of incidence increases, the angle of refraction increases (Figure 19-4). The increase in the angle of refraction does not vary directly as the increase in the angle of incidence. That is, doubling the angle of incidence does not double the angle of refraction. Still, the way in which the angle of refraction becomes larger as the angle of incidence is made larger suggests that some definite relationship does exist.

The relationship between the angle of incidence and the angle of refraction was discovered first by the Dutch scientist Willibrod Snell. This is what Snell found. *Whenever a ray of light passes from air into a more optically dense medium at some angle, the ray is bent in such a way that the ratio of the sine of the angle of incidence to the sine of the angle of refraction is a constant.* (Snell's law).

The constant for a light ray passing from a vacuum into a given medium is the index of refraction (n) for that medium. Symbolically Snell's law is represented as

$$n_s = \frac{\sin i}{\sin r}$$

where i is the angle of incidence, r is the angle of refraction, and n_s is the index of refraction of the substance.

Table 19–1

INDICES OF REFRACTION

Medium	n
Vacuum	1.00
Air	1.00*
Water	1.33
Alcohol	1.36
Quartz	1.46
Polyethylene	1.50
Flint Glass	1.61
Crown Glass	1.52
Diamond	2.42

*Index of refraction of air is 1.0003 which is higher than that of vacuum which is 1.0000. However, for practical purposes they are the same.

Sample Problem 1

A ray of light traveling through air is incident upon the surface of a sheet of crown glass at an angle of 30°. What is the angle of refraction?

Solution:

Find the index of refraction from Table 19-1. Find the sine of 30° from Table A-2 in the Appendix.

$$n = \frac{\sin i}{\sin r}$$

$$\sin r = \frac{\sin i}{n}$$

$$= \frac{0.5}{1.52}$$

$$= 0.32$$

$$r = 19° \quad \text{(taken from Table A-2 to the nearest degree)}$$

Problems

2. Light is incident upon a piece of crown glass at an angle of 45°. What is the angle of refraction to the nearest degree?

3. A ray of light passes from air into water at an angle of 30°. Find the angle of refraction to the nearest degree.

4. Light is incident upon a piece of quartz at an angle of 45°. What is the angle of refraction to the nearest degree?

5. A ray of light is incident upon a diamond at 45°. (a) What is the angle of refraction? (b) Compare this solution to the solution for Problem 2. Which medium bends light more, glass or diamond?

6. A ray of light travels from air into a transparent liquid. The ray is incident upon the liquid at an angle of 30°. The angle of refraction is 22°. (a) What is the index of refraction of the liquid? (b) Look at Table 19-1. What might be the liquid?

7. In Sample Problem 1 on page 234, a ray of light is incident upon crown glass at 30°. The angle of refraction is 19°. Assume the glass is rectangular in shape. Construct a diagram to show the incident ray, the refracted ray, and the normal. Continue the ray through the glass until it reaches the opposite edge. (a) Construct a normal at this point. Measure the angle at which the refracted ray is incident upon the opposite edge of the glass. (b) Did you measure this angle or use a geometric proof to find its value? (c) Assume the material outside the opposite edge is air. What is the angle at which the ray leaves the glass? (d) Is the ray refracted away from the normal or toward the normal?

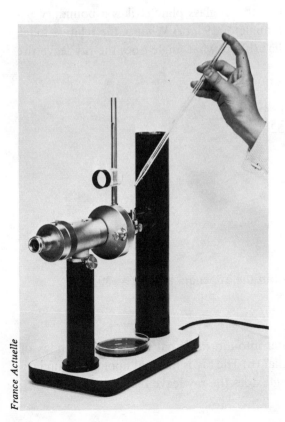

Figure 19-7. This refractometer is used to measure the amount of sugar in honey. The index of refraction of honey changes with varying amounts of dissolved sugar.

19:5   Relative Indices of Refraction

A light ray does not have to travel from air into a more dense substance. Conversely, it may travel from a dense substance into air. It is also possible for a light ray to travel obliquely from a substance such as kerosene into water. Or it may travel from one transparent substance into another transparent substance.

In such cases, a relative index of refraction is used to find angles of refraction. Let n_2 and n_1 represent the indices of refraction of the second and first media respectively. The index of refraction between the first medium and the second medium $(n_1 - n_2)$ is the ratio of the two indices of refraction or $n_{1-2} = n_2/n_1$.

The index of refraction of air is 1.000. Thus, a ray traveling from air into a medium $\dfrac{n_2}{n_1} = \dfrac{n_2}{1.000} = n_2$. On the other hand, the index of refraction for a ray traveling from a medium other than air into air becomes $n_2/n_1 = 1/n_1$. Hence the index of refraction from any medium into air is the reciprocal of the index of refraction of the medium.

Sample Problem 2

A ray of light traveling through a crown glass plate strikes a boundary between the glass plate and air at an angle of 19°. (a) What is the relative index of refraction between the two media? (b) At what angle does the ray leave the glass?

Solution:

$$(a) \quad n_{g-a} = \frac{n_a}{n_g} = \frac{1}{1.52} = 0.66$$

$$(b) \quad n_{g-a} = \frac{\sin i}{\sin r}$$

$$0.66 = \frac{\sin 19°}{\sin r}$$

$$\sin r = \frac{0.326}{0.66}$$

$$\sin r = 0.5$$

From Table A-2 in the appendix angle $r = 30°$

Problems

8. A ray of light passes from water into air. (a) What is the relative index of refraction between the two media? (b) The ray is incident upon the boundary at an angle of 40°. At what angle does the ray leave the water?

9. A ray of light passes from water into flint glass. (a) What is the index of refraction? (b) The ray strikes the glass at 30°. What is the angle of refraction?

10. A ray of light passes from flint glass into water. (a) What is the index of refraction? (b) The ray of light is incident upon the surface of the water at an angle of 24°. What is the angle of refraction?

19:6   Index of Refraction and the Speed of Light

Figure 19-8 illustrates the behavior of two parallel rays of light that are incident upon a glass plate. The rays are refracted toward the normal. Consider the wave front CB as it approaches the glass plate. After a time interval, the wave front reaches position DA. Since the speed of the wave is slower in the glass, point C on ray y travels only distance CD. Point B on ray x travels distance BA. This causes the wave front to turn.

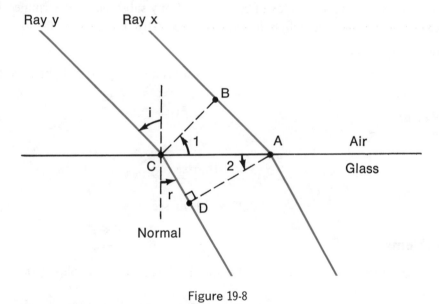

Figure 19-8

Point B on ray x travels to A in the same time that point C on ray y travels to D. Therefore, the ratio of BA to CD is the same as the ratio of the speed of light in vacuum v_v to the speed of light in glass v_g.

$$\frac{BA}{CD} = \frac{v_v}{v_g}$$

Angle 1 in Figure 19-8 is equal to the angle of incidence of the ray. Angle 2 is equal to the angle of refraction of the ray (corresponding sides mutually perpendicular). The sine of angle 1 is BA/CA. The sine of angle 2 is CD/CA. Using Snell's Law, the index of refraction is

$$n_{\text{vacuum-glass}} = \frac{\sin i}{\sin r} = \frac{\sin_1}{\sin_2} = \frac{BA}{CD} = \frac{v_{\text{vacuum}}}{v_{\text{glass}}}$$

and the index of refraction of any substance is the speed of light in vacuum divided by the speed of light in the medium. Actual experiments that measure the speed of light in a vacuum and in various substances confirm this relationship.

The speed of light in air is assumed to be the same as the speed of light in a vacuum. Because this speed has a special significance, it is assigned the symbol c. The index of refraction for any substance is,

$$n = \frac{c}{v}$$

where v represents the speed of light in the medium.

It is possible to calculate the speed of light in any medium if the index of refraction is known. The index of refraction of any substance is determined by measurement. The speed of light in a vacuum is 3×10^8 m/sec or 186 000 mi/sec.

Sample Problem 3

The index of refraction of water is 1.33. Calculate the speed of light in water in m/sec.

Solution:

$$v = \frac{c}{n}$$

$$= \frac{3 \times 10^8 \text{ m/sec}}{1.33}$$

$$= 2.25 \times 20^8 \text{ m/sec}$$

Problems

11. Use Table 19-1 to determine the speed of light in (a) alcohol (b) quartz (c) polyethylene.
12. The speed of light in a plastic plate is 2.0×10^8 m/sec. What is the index of refraction of the plastic?
13. The speed of light in a glass plate is 122 370 mi/sec. Determine the index of refraction of the glass.

19:7   Total Internal Reflection

When a ray of light passes from a dense medium into air, it is refracted away from the normal. This means that the angle of refraction is larger than the

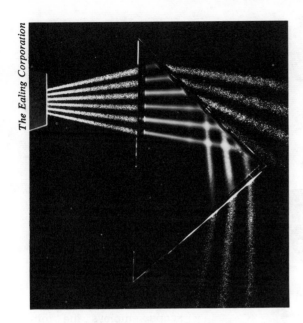

Figure 19-9. Total internal reflection in a glass prism. Notice that part of each pencil of light is transmitted and part is reflected.

angle of incidence. The requirement that the angle of refraction be larger than the angle of incidence leads to an interesting phenomenon. This phenomenon is known as total internal reflection. Figure 19-10 shows how total internal reflection takes place. Ray 1 is incident upon the surface of the water at angle i_1. Ray 1 produces the larger angle of refraction, r_1. Ray 2 is incident at such a large angle that the only way the angle of refraction can be larger is for it to lie right along the surface of the water. The angle of refraction is 90°. Any ray introduced

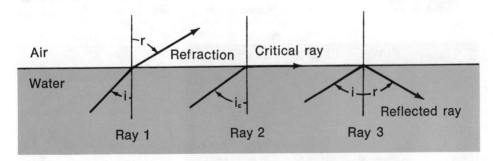

Figure 19-10

to the surface at an angle greater than the angle at which ray 1 strikes the surface cannot be refracted. The incident angle which causes the refracted ray to lie right along the boundary of the substance (angle i_c) is peculiar to the substance. It is the *critical angle* of that substance. A ray which falls upon the surface of the water at an angle greater than the critical angle (ray 3) cannot be refracted. It is totally reflected.

(a)

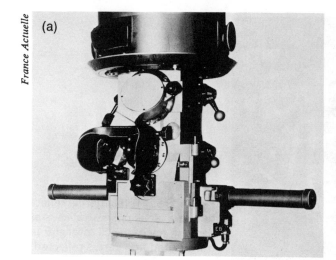

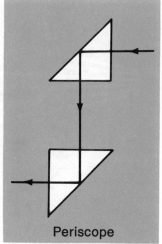

Periscope

(b)

Figure 19-11. (a) The periscope employs the total internal reflection of light by glass prisms to make objects above the water observable from a submarine. (b) Binoculars use a system of prisms to produce an erect image.

(c) Fiber optics use the total internal reflection of light in Lucite to "pipe light" to the area in which it is needed.

(c)

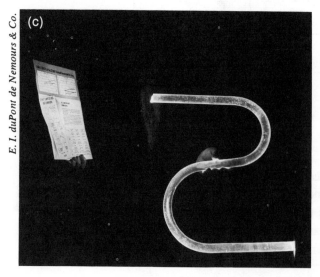

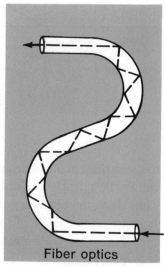

Fiber optics

19:8   Effects of Refraction

Many seemingly curious effects relate to the refraction of light. Such effects as the puddle-effect, the apparent shift in the position of objects immersed in liquids, and the lengthening of the day are examples.

The puddle-effect is commonly observed along highways in summer. A driver looking down the road sees what looks like a puddle of water, but the puddle disappears as the car approaches. This effect results from the fact that the air next to the surface of the road is heated sooner than the air above and expands. The air above the road therefore gradually becomes cooler as the distance above the road increases. As a result, the density of the air gradually increases. Therefore, the index of refraction of the air also increases with distance above the road. As a ray of light approaches the road it passes through air of increasingly lower index of refraction. The ray bends in the manner shown in Figure 19-12. To an observer, the refracted light looks like light reflected from a puddle.

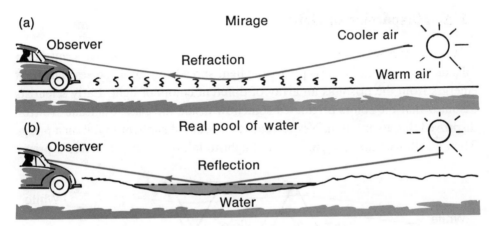

Figure 19-12.   (a) Refraction of light in air of differing densities produces the same effect as (b) reflection of light from a pool of water.

An object viewed in a liquid is not where it appears to be. As a result of the refraction of light, the object in Figure 19-13 seems to be closer to the surface of the liquid than it actually is. This is the same effect that causes a pencil or stick placed in a glass of water to appear to be broken.

Light travels at a slightly slower speed in air than it does in the near vacuum conditions of outer space. Consequently, sunlight is refracted by the atmosphere. In the morning, this causes sunlight to reach the earth before the sun actually comes up. In the evening, the sunlight is bent over the horizon after the sun has actually set. The result is the lengthening of daylight beyond its astronomic maximum.

Image

Object

Figure 19-13.   The image of a fish as seen by an observer above the water.

19:9   Dispersion of Light

When a narrow beam of light from the sun or from an incandescent lamp falls on the surface of a glass prism, the light spreads out or disperses. The light emerges from the prism as an array of different colors of light. Early scientists assumed that the colors originated somehow inside the glass. Sir Isaac Newton disproved this assumption. Newton caused a beam of sunlight to fall on a prism. Then he allowed the emerging colored light to fall on a second, inverted prism.

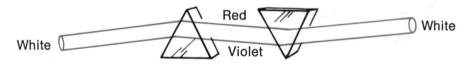

Figure 19-14.   Newton showed that white light can be dispersed into a spectrum of colors and that the white light can be reconstituted by sending the dispersed light through a second prism.

The colored light rays recombined to form white light once again. Newton was the first person to understand that white light is a mixture of many colors of light.

All electromagnetic waves travel through space at the speed of light, but electromagnetic waves travel more slowly in material media. Furthermore, while passing through the material, waves of different frequencies travel at slightly different speeds. Glass or water mediums have a slightly different index of refraction for each wavelength of light. When white light falls on a prism, the waves of each color bend by different amounts and the light disperses. If the waves are projected upon a screen, they produce a "rainbow" of colors.

As light emerges from a prism, the various colors are in a distinct arrangement. Red light is refracted the least by the prism which has the lowest index of refraction for red light. Red light has the fastest speed in the glass. Violet light always is refracted the most. Violet light has the slowest speed in the glass.

19:10 Spectra

The array of different colors of light produced by a prism is a spectrum. (The plural of spectrum is spectra). Light from an incandescent solid or liquid produces a continuous spectrum. A continuous spectrum consists of many different colors. The refracted rays merge together to make a solid array of color. Sunlight passing through a prism produces a continuous spectrum. Sunlight passing through raindrops produces a continuous spectrum. This continuous spectrum forms a rainbow.

When a small amount of an element in a gaseous state is contained in a glass tube, the molecules of the gas can be made to emit light. This is done by sending an electric current through the tube. For example, a glass tube equipped with an electrode in each end is evacuated with a vacuum pump. A small amount of neon gas is admitted to the tube. Then the tube is sealed and a high voltage is applied to the electrodes of the tube. High velocity electrons travel through the tube and cause the neon gas to emit light. The tube gives out red light. There is an interesting fact about using gaseous forms of the elements. The light emitted is characteristic of the particular element. The spectrum produced is an emission spectrum. To illustrate, when the light from neon is sent through a prism, it does not form a continuous spectrum. Instead, neon produces a few definite lines of light. This is a line spectrum. The spectrum of neon is always the same and is identified by the positions of its lines.

It is possible to observe the spectra of the elements that are not ordinarily found as gases (iron, zinc, etc.). A small sample of the element is placed on the end of a carbon rod. A second carbon rod is brought close to the first rod, and a very high voltage is applied to the two rods. The resulting electric arc has a temperature of over 3000°K and vaporizes the solid element. The light emitted by gaseous forms of solids is sent through a prism and photographed. Each element is found to have a characteristic spectrum.

Because each element emits a characteristic spectrum, it is possible to determine the exact nature of an unknown material. This is done by spectroscopic analysis. A spectroscope has these features: it contains a means to vaporize the material; it has a prism or other means to disperse the light; and it has a telescope

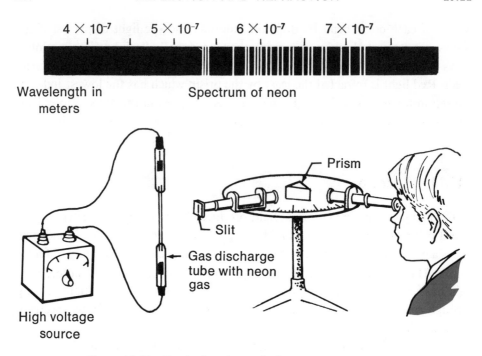

Wavelength in meters

Spectrum of neon

4×10^{-7} 5×10^{-7} 6×10^{-7} 7×10^{-7}

Prism

Slit

Gas discharge tube with neon gas

High voltage source

Figure 19-15.   Producing the emission spectrum of neon.

to observe the resulting spectra. Frequently a photographic plate is used to photograph the spectrum. Then it can be examined at a later time. The larger the amount of any given element in a material examined, the stronger are the lines on the photographic plate that correspond to the characteristic wavelengths of that element. By comparing the intensity of the lines on the plate, the relative amounts of each element in a substance are detected and the substance is thoroughly analyzed.

19:11   Absorption Spectra

Another method to detect the nature of a substance is use of absorption spectra. To obtain an absorption spectrum, white light, such as from the sun or any incandescent solid, is sent through a gas and then into a prism. Careful analysis of the continuous spectrum that results reveals several dark lines along its length. This indicates that certain wavelengths are missing from the continuous spectrum. A comparison of the emission spectrum of the gas with the dark lines on the continuous spectrum reveals that the lines of the emission spectrum of the gas and the dark lines occur at the same wavelengths. Gaseous elements absorb the same wavelengths that they emit naturally. To analyze a gas, white light is sent through it and then through a prism. The resulting continuous spectrum is then inspected for missing lines.

(a)

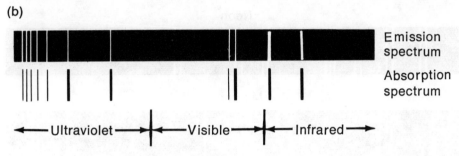

(b)

Figure 19-16. (a) Producing an absorption spectrum for sodium. (b) Comparison of the line absorption spectra of sodium.

The absorption lines in a continuous spectrum were noticed first by the German scientist, Fraunhofer. While examining the spectrum of sunlight, Fraunhofer noticed some unusual dark lines. The dark lines he found in the sun's spectrum are known as Fraunhofer lines. To account for dark absorption lines in the sun's spectrum, assume that the sun has an atmosphere of hot gaseous elements. As light leaves the sun, it passes through these gases. As a result, the gases absorb the light's characteristic wavelengths and these wavelengths are missing from the sun's spectrum. By comparing the missing lines with the known lines of the various elements, the makeup of the sun is determined. The sun contains all of the elements known on earth.

Figure 19-17. Clouds of atoms in space make their presence known by their effect upon transmitted light. They absorb small amounts of energy from the starlight passing through them, thereby producing absorption lines in the spectra of the most distant stars. The bottom of the photograph shows some absorption lines for sodium in the spectrum of a star.

Mount Wilson and Palomar Observatories

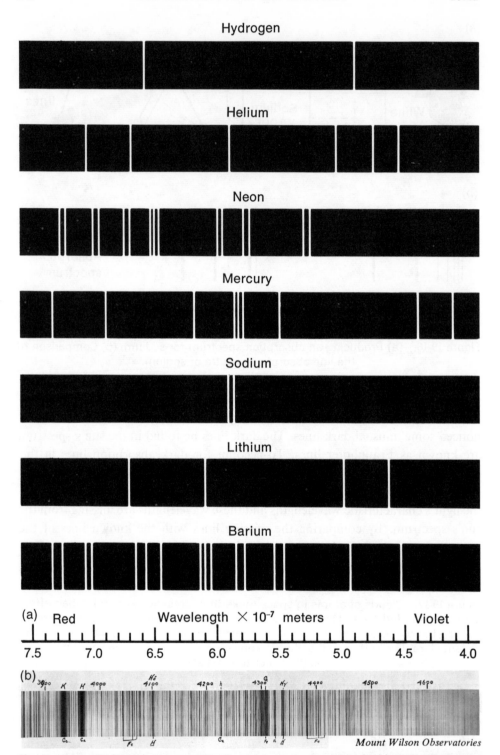

(a)

Figure 19-18. (a) The major emission lines for some elements. (b) A photograph of a portion of solar spectrum. Wavelength is $\times 10^{-10}$ meters.

Official U.S. Navy Photo

Figure 19-19. Dr. George R. Carruthers became the first to detect molecules in outer space. His observations of stellar spectral lines showed the absorption spectrum of molecular hydrogen. The hydrogen absorbed characteristic lines from the light of stars.

QUESTIONS

1. How does regular reflection differ from diffuse reflection?
2. If a light does not undergo refraction at a boundary between two media, what is its angle of incidence?
3. How does the angle of incidence compare with the angle of refraction when a light ray passes obliquely from air into glass?
4. How does the angle of incidence compare with the angle of refraction when a light ray leaves glass and enters air?
5. State Snell's law.
6. Use two different sets of symbols to write two equations for finding the index of refraction of a medium.
7. What is the "critical angle" of incidence?
8. Explain the "puddle-effect."
9. Explain how white light is dispersed by a prism.
10. Which travels fastest in glass: red light, green light, or blue light?
11. What type of spectrum is the spectrum of sunlight?
12. What type of spectrum is emitted by a gaseous element?
13. What are absorption spectra?
14. See the absorption lines in the sun's spectrum in Figure 19-18. Compare these dark lines with the spectra of some of the elements shown. List three substances that might exist on the sun.

PROBLEMS

1. A ray of light incident upon a mirror makes an angle of 36° with the mirror. What is the angle between the incident ray and the reflected ray?

2. In the diagram, a ray of light is incident upon the surface of a glass prism. Trace the diagram on a separate sheet of paper. Extend the ray to show how it travels through the prism and beyond. Follow the same procedure for the glass objects in problems 3, 4, and 5.

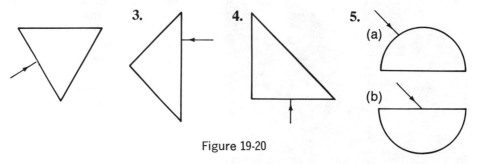

Figure 19-20

6. A ray of light is incident at an angle of 60° upon the surface of a piece of glass ($n = 1.5$). What is the angle of refraction?

7. A light ray strikes the surface of a pond at an angle of 36°. At what angle, to the nearest degree, is the ray refracted?

8. Light is incident at an angle of 60° on the surface of a diamond. Calculate the angle of refraction.

9. A light ray is incident at an angle of 45° on one surface of a 10-cm glass cube ($n_g = 1.5$). At what angle with the normal does the ray emerge from the other side of the cube?

10. By what amount is the emergent ray of Problem 9 shifted from its original path?

11. A ray of light leaves air and enters water at an angle of 42°. (a) What is the angle of refraction? (b) The light ray then passes through the water and reaches a thick glass plate. At what angle does the ray strike the glass plate? (c) The index of refraction of the glass is 1.5. At what angle does the ray refract into the glass?

12. The index of refraction of water is 1.33. What is the speed of light in water?

13. What is the speed of light in diamond?

14. The speed of light in a clear plastic is 1.90×10^8 m/sec. A ray of light enters the plastic at an angle of 22°. At what angle is the ray refracted?

15. The speed of light in medium A is 2.26×10^8 m/sec. The speed of light in medium B is 2.58×10^8 m/sec. (a) What is the index of refraction of medium A? (b) What is the index of refraction of medium B? (c) What is the index of refraction for a ray passing from medium A into medium B?

Mirrors and Lenses

Mirrors reflect light. In contrast, lenses transmit light. They both produce images. Mirrors and lenses may be flat or curved. The shape of the mirror or lens determines the nature of the image which you see. Thus, the image may be right side up or inverted, or it may be larger or smaller than the object used to produce the image. In what ways do you use mirrors and lenses in everyday life?

20:1 Plane Mirrors

Regular reflection accounts for our ability to see images of objects in mirrors. In Figure 20-1, object *A* is illuminated by a source of light. A large number of the rays that fall on object *A* are reflected in all directions. This permits *A* to be seen from any direction. Each part of object *A* reflects different amounts of light and also slightly different colors of light. This depends upon the characteristics of the particular location from which the light is reflected. Object *A* is recognized because of the difference between the amount of light and the colors of light reflected from each part of *A*.

Rays that leave A fall on a mirror and reflect in the same order in which they approach the mirror. Therefore, to look at the mirror produces the same effect as to look at A. Since the path of the rays is changed, the observer gets the impression that object A is at A' and not at A. Also notice that the order of the rays is reversed. The first ray to leave A on the left becomes the first ray to

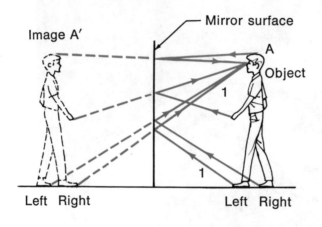

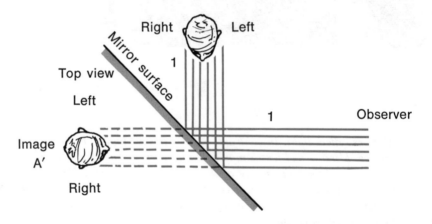

Figure 20-1. Production of an image in a plane mirror. Rays leave all parts of the object and strike the mirror. However, only those rays which reach the eye of the observer are seen to produce the image. The image appears to be the same size as the object, the same distance behind the mirror as the object is in front, erect, but reversed right for left.

approach the observer on the right. This apparently reverses the image from left to right in the mirror. The right ear of A becomes the left ear of his image A'. To verify this, look in a mirror and pull your left ear. Your image will pull its right ear.

Suppose an object is located at point P (Figure 20-2). Light rays are drawn in every direction from point P. The rays that strike the mirror at points M_1 and M_2

are reflected to the eye of an observer. By continuing the two reflected rays behind the mirror, point P' is located. Triangles PBM and $P'BM$ are congruent. Point P' appears to be as far in back of the mirror as point P is in front of the mirror. Use the same method to locate a second point next to P. The eye interprets the image to be the same size as the object.

In summary, *the image observed in a plane mirror is the same size as the object. It is as far in back of the mirror as the object is in front of the mirror. And it appears to be reversed from left to right.*

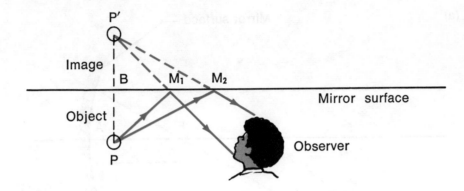

Figure 20-2. Ray diagram for finding an image in a plane mirror. Two rays from the object are traced to the point behind the mirror at which they intersect.

20:2 Convergent Mirrors

Figure 20-3 represents a number of small plane mirrors. They are arranged to form a portion of a circle. The parallel beams of light sent to the mirrors follow the law of reflection. They converge at the point F. In this way curved mirrors focus light rays at a point F, the focal point.

Figure 20-3. Each ray striking a mirror follows the law of reflection. If the mirrors are arranged in the proper curve, all the rays intersect at a single point called the focus.

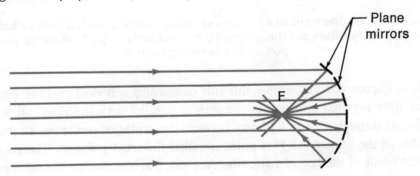

Figure 20-4 shows a spherical mirror. Three dimensions are needed to show a curved mirror at its best. However, you should mentally picture it as spherical rather than circular. The inner reflecting surface is part of a sphere, so the mirror is a spherical concave mirror. Think of it as an infinite number of plane mirrors arranged in a spherical fashion.

Since it is a portion of a sphere, a spherical mirror has a geometric center or vertex, *A* (Figure 20-4). A radius perpendicular to this point passes back to the center of curvature of the mirror, *C*, (Figure 20-4) and is called the principal axis.

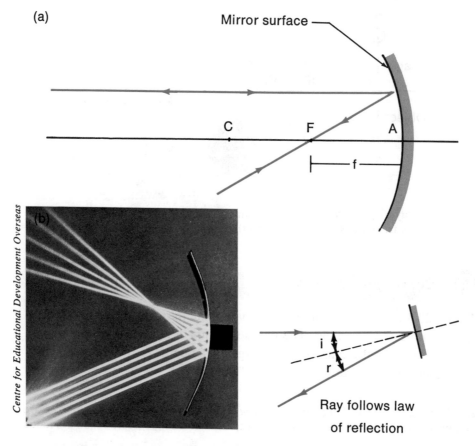

Figure 20-4. (a) The focus of a concave spherical mirror is located halfway between the center of curvature and the center of the mirror surface. (b) Rays are focused by a portion of a cylindrical mirror.

It is important to remember this rule concerning spherical concave mirrors. Any light ray that approaches the mirror parallel with the principal axis is reflected through a point half-way between the center of curvature, *C*, and the vertex of the mirror, *A*. This point is called the focal point, *F*. The rule is a direct result of the law of reflection. Any ray that approaches the mirror on a path that leads it through F will, upon reflection, leave the mirror in a direction parallel with the principal axis.

If the principal axis of a small concave mirror is pointed at the sun, all rays that fall on the mirror are parallel with one another and with the principal axis. Rays from the sun travel 93 000 000 mi to reach the mirror. Any rays that leave the sun which are not parallel with the principal axis would be far from the mirror by the time they travel this distance. To quickly determine the focal point of any concave mirror, point it at the sun or any fairly distant light source. Use a screen or piece of paper to find the sharpest point of focus. This is the focal point. The distance from the focal point to the vertex of the mirror is the focal length (f) of the mirror.

20:3   Spherical Aberration

In a truly spherical mirror all rays that approach the mirror parallel with the principal axis do not reflect through F. Those rays that strike the mirror along its outer edge slightly miss F. This defect of spherical mirrors, again a consequence of the law of reflection, is called spherical aberration. To avoid spherical aberration, a slightly parabolic mirror is used rather than a spherical mirror.

Figure 20-5.   (a) In a spherical mirror, the rays close to the principal axis focus at one point and rays farther from the principal axis focus at other points along the axis. This causes the light to form a diffuse cone rather than a sharp point at the focus. (b) A parabolic mirror focuses all rays at a sharp point. However, parabolic surfaces are much more difficult to produce than spherical surfaces.

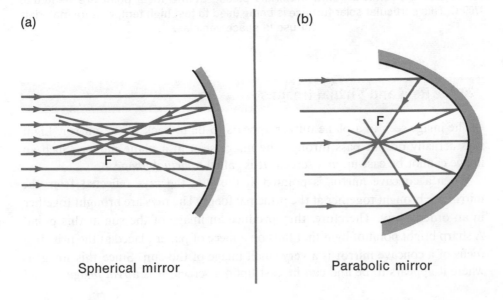

(a)

(b)

Spherical mirror   Parabolic mirror

Fuel is scarce in India so parabolic mirrors are used to some extent as a means of cooking. A large concave mirror is pointed at the sun and a cooking pot placed at *F*. The concentrated sunlight provides an intense source of heat. Another use of parabolic mirrors is to place a light source at *F*. The light rays that leave *F* reflect from the mirror as a parallel beam of light. This is how a flashlight or automobile headlight sends out a parallel beam of light.

Figure 20-6. The "solar furnace" used here is a large parabolic mirror which focuses the rays of the sun to a point. Materials placed at the focal point are heated to 4700°C. This particular solar furnace is being used to test high temperature materials for use in space vehicles.

20:4   Real and Virtual Images

The image seen in a plane mirror appears to be in back of the mirror. Light rays actually do not pass through the image seen in a plane mirror. Such an image cannot be cast upon a screen. It is called a *virtual image*.

When a concave mirror is pointed at the sun, the rays reflected from the mirror are brought together at the principal focus. The rays are brought together in an orderly way. Therefore, they produce an image of the sun at this point. A sharp bright point of light that falls on a piece of paper placed at the principal focus of a concave mirror is a very small image of the sun. Since this image is where it appears to be and can be cast upon a screen, it is a *real image*.

20:5   Images Formed by Concave Mirrors

Figure 20-7 shows how a concave mirror forms an image. An arrow is located some distance greater than C from the mirror. The object (arrow) is said to be "beyond C." An illuminated object reflects a great number of light rays in all directions. The construction of rays from an object to the mirror in any direction can be done in full confidence that rays do travel in that direction.

To construct a ray diagram, first select a point on the object P_1. Draw two principal rays from this point to the mirror. Draw ray 1 to the mirror parallel with the principal axis. Ray 1, therefore, reflects through F. Draw ray 2 from

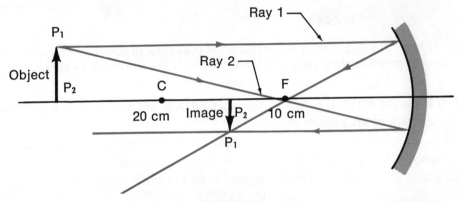

Figure 20-7.   Method of finding the real image produced by a concave mirror. Trace two rays from the top of the object until they intersect at the image.

the same point to the mirror. Let it pass through F on its way. This ray reflects parallel with the principal axis. The two rays from P_1 converge some distance beyond F. If two rays are drawn from point P_2 in the same way, they converge at point P_2 on the image. Other points on the object send out rays that converge on corresponding points on the image. In this way, the image is formed. The object is placed with one end on the principal axis where a ray goes straight to the mirror and straight back. This means the bottom of the image also is located on the principal axis.

Figure 20-7 shows an object that is beyond C. The image is between C and F. It is inverted, smaller than the object, and real. Figure 20-7 also illustrates that if an object is placed in the position of the image, its image is formed in the position of the object. Thus, if the object is between C and F, the image will be beyond C. It will be inverted, larger than the object, and real.

As the object is moved in from beyond C, toward C, the image position recedes from F and approaches C. The image and the object meet at C. In this case, the image is inverted, real, and the same size as the object. If the object

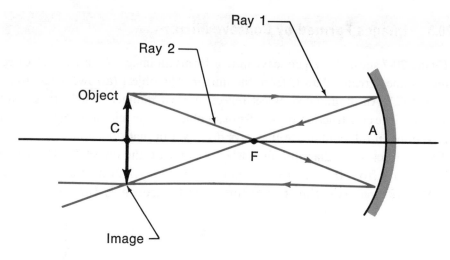

Figure 20-8. The image of an object located at the center of curvature of a spherical concave mirror is at the center of curvature and is the same size as the object.

then is moved between *C* and *F*, the image moves out beyond *C*. Object and image positions are interchangeable. (See Figure 20-12 a, b, c.)

Use the mirror equation to calculate the position of an image or object. Let d_o represent the distance from the object to *A*; d_i represent the distance from the image to *A*; and *f* represent the focal length of the mirror. Then,

$$\frac{1}{d_o} + \frac{1}{d_i} = \frac{1}{f}$$

Also, the size of the image is to the size of the object as the image distance is to the object distance.

$$\frac{d_i}{d_o} = \frac{S_i}{S_o}$$

Sample Problem 1

An object 2 cm high is 30 cm from a concave mirror which has a focal length of 10 cm. (a) What is the location of the image? (b) What is the size of the image?

Solution:

(a) $$\frac{1}{d_o} + \frac{1}{d_i} = \frac{1}{f}$$

$$\frac{1}{30 \text{ cm}} + \frac{1}{d_i} = \frac{1}{10 \text{ cm}}$$

$$\frac{1}{d_i} = \frac{1}{10 \text{ cm}} - \frac{1}{30 \text{ cm}}$$

$$\frac{1}{d_i} = \frac{2}{30 \text{ cm}}$$

$$d_i = 15 \text{ cm}$$

(b) $$\frac{d_i}{d_o} = \frac{S_i}{S_o}$$

$$S_i = \frac{S_o d_i}{d_o}$$

$$= \frac{(15 \text{ cm})(2 \text{ cm})}{30 \text{ cm}}$$

$$= 1 \text{ cm}$$

Problems

Needed: a compass, a metric ruler, a sharp pencil.

1. Use a compass and ruler to solve Sample Problem 1 by constructing a ray diagram. The problem states that the focal length of the mirror is 10 cm. Focal length is always half the radius of curvature, so the radius of the mirror is 20 cm. Scale the diagram down if 30 cm is too long for your paper.

2. An object is 15 cm from a concave spherical mirror of 20 cm radius. Locate the image (a) graphically (b) by use of the mirror equation.

3. An object 3 cm high is 10 cm in front of a concave mirror of 12 cm radius. Locate the image (a) graphically (b) by use of the mirror equation (c) What is the height of the image?

4. An object 1.5 cm in height is 12 cm from a concave mirror of 12 cm radius. Locate the image (a) graphically (b) by use of the mirror equation. (c) What is the height of the image?

5. An object 3 cm high is 12 cm from a concave mirror of 6 cm radius. Locate the image (a) graphically (b) by use of the mirror equation. (c) What is the height of the image?

6. An image of an object is 12 in. from a concave mirror of 8 in. radius. Locate the object.

7. An image of an object is 12 in. from a concave mirror of 8 in. focal length. Locate the object.

20:6   Virtual Images in a Concave Mirror

The object in Figure 20-9 is located between F and the mirror. It is 5 cm in front of a mirror of 10 cm focal length. To locate the image of the object, construct the same two principal rays used in previous examples. Ray 1 leaves the object and follows the path it would have followed had it originated at F. This

Figure 20-9

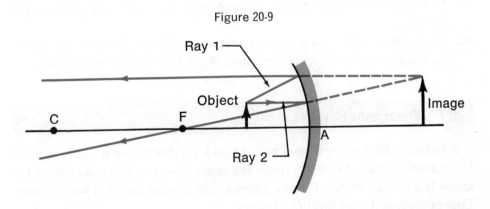

ray is reflected parallel with the principal axis. Ray 2 approaches the mirror parallel with the principal axis. It is reflected through the focal point. Notice that rays 1 and 2 are divergent upon reflection. This means they cannot come together to form a real image. On the other side of the mirror the rays are traced back to their apparent origin. The image is virtual, erect, and on the other side of the mirror. In addition, the image is larger than the object.

When an object is placed between the vertex and the focal point of a concave mirror, the image distance is negative. A negative image distance means that the image is virtual.

Sample Problem 2

Calculate the location of the image in Figure 20-9 if the object is 5 cm in front of a concave mirror of focal length 10 cm.

Solution:

$$d_o = 5 \text{ cm}, f = 10 \text{ cm}$$

$$\frac{1}{d_o} + \frac{1}{d_i} = \frac{1}{f}$$

Solving this equation for d_i yields,

$$d_i = \frac{d_o f}{d_o - f}$$

$$= \frac{(5 \text{ cm})(10 \text{ cm})}{5 \text{ cm} - 10 \text{ cm}}$$

$$= \frac{50 \text{ cm}^2}{-5 \text{ cm}}$$

$$= -10 \text{ cm}$$

Problems

8. An object is 4 cm in front of a concave mirror of 12 cm radius. Locate the image.

9. An object is 6 cm in front of a concave mirror of 10 cm focal length. Find the image.

10. An object is 5 in. from a concave mirror of 8 in. focal length. (a) Locate the image. (b) The object is 2 in. high. What is the height of the image?

20:7 Divergent Mirrors

A convex mirror is a spherical mirror which is reflective on its outer surface. For example, the bowl side of a spoon is a concave mirror. The outer side of the spoon is a convex mirror. Convex mirrors only diverge rays that fall on them. Convex mirrors do not form real images.

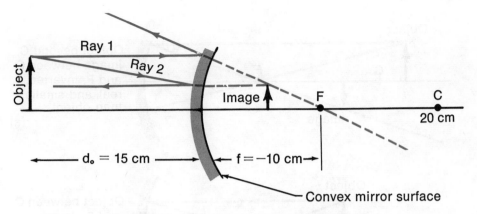

Figure 20-10. Convex mirrors diverge light rays.

The image seen in a convex mirror is always virtual, behind the mirror, erect, and smaller than the object. Figure 20-10 shows how a convex mirror forms a virtual image. Follow the paths of the two principal rays. Ray 1 approaches the mirror parallel to the principal axis and is reflected. The path of the reflected ray, extended behind the mirror (dotted lines), passes through F. Ray 2 approaches the mirror on a path that if extended beyond the mirror would pass through, F. Ray 2's reflected ray is parallel to the principal axis. The two reflected rays when traced back to their point of apparent intersection behind the mirror indicate an erect, smaller, virtual image.

NASA

Figure 20-11. An astronaut during a lunar extravehicular activity. Notice the image of the lunar module reflected in the convex surface of the astronaut's helmet face plate.

Some uses of divergent mirrors are to observe for shoplifters in stores, as rear-view mirrors on cars and trucks, or for other purposes which require a large field of view.

Use the mirror equation to locate the image in a divergent mirror. The focal point is located behind the mirror and so the focal length is considered negative.

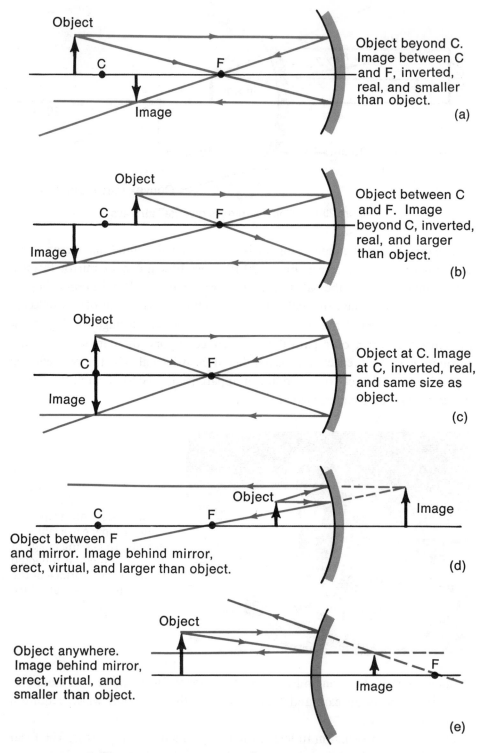

Object beyond C. Image between C and F, inverted, real, and smaller than object. (a)

Object between C and F. Image beyond C, inverted, real, and larger than object. (b)

Object at C. Image at C, inverted, real, and same size as object. (c)

Object between F and mirror. Image behind mirror, erect, virtual, and larger than object. (d)

Object anywhere. Image behind mirror, erect, virtual, and smaller than object. (e)

Figure 20-12. The formation of images in curved mirrors.

Sample Problem 3

Calculate the position of the image in Figure 20-10.

Solution:

$$d_o = 15 \text{ cm}, \quad f = -10 \text{ cm}$$

$$\frac{1}{d_o} + \frac{1}{d_i} = \frac{1}{f}$$

$$d_i = \frac{d_o\,(f)}{d_o - f}$$

$$= \frac{(15 \text{ cm})(-10 \text{ cm})}{15 \text{ cm} - (-10 \text{ cm})}$$

$$= \frac{-150 \text{ cm}^2}{25 \text{ cm}}$$

$$= -6 \text{ cm}$$

Problems

11. An object is 20 cm in front of a convex mirror of −15 cm focal length. Locate the image.

12. A convex mirror has a focal length of −12 cm. An object is placed 60 cm in front of the mirror. Locate the image.

13. A mirror used to observe for shoplifters in a department store has a focal length of —18 in. A person stands in an aisle 20 ft from the mirror. Locate his image.

14. Shiny lawn spheres placed on pedestals are convex mirrors. One such sphere has a focal length of −8 in. A robin perches in a tree 30 ft from the sphere. Locate the robin's image.

20:8 Lenses

Lenses are an essential part of telescopes, eyeglasses, cameras, microscopes, and other optical instruments. A lens is usually made of glass although some are made of transparent plastics. Many precision optical instruments use quartz lenses.

Figure 20-13. Converging and diverging lenses.

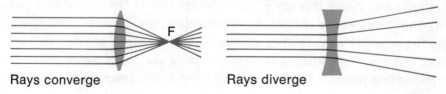

Rays converge   Rays diverge

The two main types of lenses are converging lenses and diverging lenses. A converging lens is thickest at its middle and becomes thinner toward its edges. A diverging lens is thinnest at its middle and becomes thicker toward its edges. Figure 20-13 shows cross sections of some converging and diverging lenses. Because the surfaces of converging lenses are convex, frequently they are called convex lenses. Likewise, diverging lenses are called concave lenses because their surfaces are concave. A converging lens refracts light rays so that they converge. A diverging lens refracts light rays so that they diverge.

20:9   Converging Lenses

The principal axis of a lens is an imaginary perpendicular to the exact geometric center of the lens. All light rays that approach a converging lens parallel with the principal axis will upon refraction, converge at a point. This point is called the principal focus (F) of the converging lens. The distance from the principal focus to the lens is the focal length (f). The focal length of any given converging lens depends upon two factors. These are the shape of the lens, and the index of refraction of the material from which it is made. An important position along the principal axis of a lens is twice the focal length (2F).

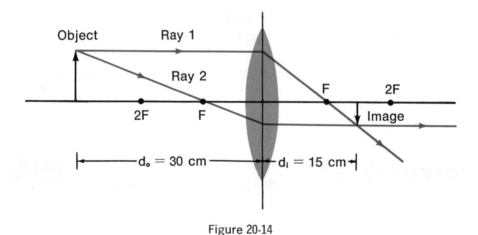

Figure 20-14

In Figure 20-14 an object is placed at a distance greater than 2F. To locate the image, draw two principal rays. Draw ray 1 parallel with the principal axis. It refracts and passes through F on the other side of the lens. Ray 2 passes through F on its way to the lens. Upon refraction, ray 2 leaves the lens parallel with the principal axis. The two rays converge between F and 2F. This is the image location. Rays selected at other points on the object would converge at corresponding points along the image to form a real, inverted, smaller image.

Suppose an object is placed at the image position. The image appears at the old object position because light rays are reversible. Thus, if the object is located between F and $2F$, the image appears beyond $2F$ on the other side of the lens. The image is real, inverted, and larger than the object.

If an object is placed at $2F$, the image appears at $2F$ on the other side of the lens. It is real, inverted, and the same size as the object. An object and image can interchange in lenses the same as they can in mirrors.

It is not necessary to draw a lens to construct graphical diagrams of lens problems. A straight line serves at the point of location of the lens. To determine the size and location of the image mathematically, use these lens equations.

$$\frac{1}{d_o} + \frac{1}{d_i} = \frac{1}{f}$$

$$\frac{S_o}{S_i} = \frac{d_o}{d_i}$$

Notice that these equations are the same as those used with mirrors. The derivations of the equations are on page 264.

Sample Problem 4

In Figure 20-14 the object is 30 cm from a converging lens of 10 cm focal length. Use mathematics to locate the image.

Solutions:

$$\frac{1}{d_o} + \frac{1}{d_i} = \frac{1}{f}$$

$$d_i = \frac{d_o f}{d_o - f}$$

$$= \frac{(30 \text{ cm})(10 \text{ cm})}{30 \text{ cm} - 10 \text{ cm}}$$

$$= 15 \text{ cm}$$

Problems

15. Use the graphical method to find the image position of an object 30 cm from a convex lens of 10 cm focal length. (Let 1 cm equal 2 cm.)
16. An object 1 cm high is 15 cm from a convex lens of 10 cm focal length. Find the distance and size of the image (a) graphically (b) mathematically.
17. An object 3 cm high is 10 cm in front of a convex lens of 6 cm focal length. Find the image distance and height (a) graphically (b) mathematically.
18. An object 1.5 cm high is 12 cm from a convex lens of 6 cm focal length. Find the height and position of the image (a) graphically (b) mathematically.
19. An object 3 cm high is 12 cm from a convex lens of 3 cm focal length. Locate the image.

20. An image of an object is 12 cm from a convex lens of 4 cm focal length. Locate the object.

21. An image of an object is 10 in. from a convex lens of 8 in. focal length. Locate the object.

Derivation of Lens Equation

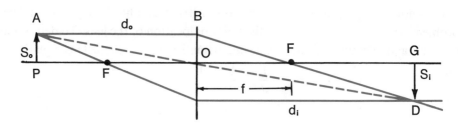

Figure 20-15

Triangles APO and ODG are similar triangles, therefore,

$$\frac{S_o}{S_i} = \frac{AP}{GD} = \frac{PO}{OG} = \frac{d_o}{d_i}$$

and,

$$\frac{S_o}{S_i} = \frac{d_o}{d_i}$$

Also, triangles GDF and BOF are similar triangles and BO is equal to AP as well. Hence: $\dfrac{BO}{GD} = \dfrac{d_o}{d_i}$ and $\dfrac{OF}{FG} = \dfrac{BO}{GD}$, so $\dfrac{OF}{FG} = \dfrac{d_o}{d_i}$.

Since, $OF = f$ and $FG = d_i$ then,

$$\frac{f}{d_i - f} = \frac{d_o}{d_i}$$

which simplifies to $\qquad fd_i + fd_o = d_i\, d_o$

Dividing both sides of this equation by fd_od_i yields,

$$\frac{1}{d_o} + \frac{1}{d_i} = \frac{1}{f}$$

20:10   Virtual Images Produced by a Converging Lens

If an object is placed between a converging lens and its focal point, the image does not appear on the other side of the lens. Instead, the image appears on the same side of the lens as the object. As Figure 20-16 shows, the image is erect, larger, and virtual.

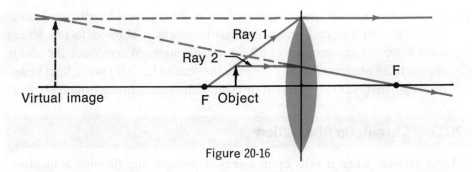

Figure 20-16

To understand how a converging lens forms a virtual image, look at rays 1 and 2 in Figure 20-16. Ray 1 is drawn from the tip of the object to the lens. It follows the same path it would have followed had it originated at F. Therefore, ray 1 is refracted in such a way that it leaves the other side of the lens parallel with the principal axis. Ray 2 is drawn toward the lens parallel with the principal axis. Upon refraction, ray 2 travels through the focal point on the other side of the lens. Notice that when rays 1 and 2 leave the other side of the lens they are divergent. This means they cannot join to form a real image. However, if the two rays are traced back to their apparent origin, a magnified virtual image is seen on the same side of the lens as the object. A convex lens used in this way is a magnifier.

Either a diagram or mathematics can be used to find the location of the virtual image formed by an object placed between a converging lens and its focal point.

Sample Problem 5

An object is 4 cm from a converging lens of 6 cm focal length. (a) Locate the image of the object. (b) What kind of image is formed?

Solution: (a) $\dfrac{1}{d_o} + \dfrac{1}{d_i} = \dfrac{1}{f}$ $\qquad\qquad$ $d = \dfrac{d_o f}{d_o - f}$

$\qquad\qquad d = \dfrac{(4\text{ cm})(6\text{ cm})}{4\text{ cm} - 6\text{ cm}} \qquad = -12\text{ cm}$

(b) Since the image distance is negative, the image is virtual. It is on the same side of the lens as the object.

Problems

22. The focal length of a convex lens is 20 cm. A newspaper is 6 cm from the lens. Calculate the image distance.

23. A magnifying glass has a focal length of 12 in. An object is placed 4 in. from the lens. (a) Locate the image. (b) The object is 2 in. high. How high is the image?

24. An object is 8 cm from a lens. What focal length must the lens have to produce a virtual, erect image 16 cm from the lens?

25. An object is 100 cm from a convex lens of 20 cm focal length. (a) Locate the image. (b) The real image the lens produces is allowed to fall 10 cm from a second convex lens of 12 cm focal length. Where does the image appear to an observer looking through the second lens? (c) Is the final image real or virtual? (d) Is it inverted or erect with respect to the original object?

20:11   Chromatic Aberration

Light refracts when it falls upon a lens. Upon passing through a medium, such as glass, different wavelengths of light refract at slightly different angles. The light that passes through a lens is slightly dispersed. Therefore, the image of any object observed through a lens appears ringed with color. This inherent defect of lenses is called chromatic aberration. Chromatic aberration is particularly noticeable in less expensive optical instruments. Chromatic aberration also limits the sharpness of an image upon the film of a camera.

Although chromatic aberration cannot be eliminated from a lens, it can be corrected. This is done by coating a lens with a material of a different index of refraction than the lens. The new material disperses light but in a way opposite to that of the lens itself. Hence the dispersion caused by the lens is cancelled. A lens prepared in this way is called an achromatic lens. Such lenses are difficult to make and are expensive. That is why telescopes and cameras equipped with achromatic lenses cost more than others.

France Actuelle

Figure 20-17. This precision zoom lens system was used on the TV cameras used on the Apollo missions. The lens system is equipped with achromatic lenses.

20:12   Diverging Lenses

All images seen through diverging lenses are virtual and erect. Figure 20-18 shows how a concave lens forms these images. Ray 1 approaches the lens parallel with the principal axis. Upon refraction, ray 1 appears to originate at the focal point. Ray 2 passes through the center of the lens. Ray 2 is refracted first above the center of the lens as it enters the lens. It is refracted again below the center of the lens as it leaves the lens. The two refractions cancel and ray 2, in effect, passes straight through. Notice that the two rays are divergent and appear to originate at *i*.

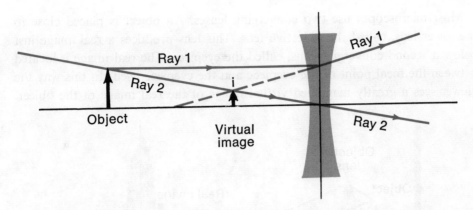

Figure 20-18.   Formation of a virtual image by a diverging lens.

20:13   Optical Devices

Eyeglasses, microscopes, telescopes, and cameras are only a few of the devices that depend upon the proper use of lenses.

The shape of eyeglass lenses depends upon the eyes of the person being fitted. If someone is farsighted, the lens of the eye focuses the image of objects behind the retina. The retina is at the rear of the eye. The image of objects outside the eye must fall directly on the retina if the brain is to interpret them correctly. To correct a farsighted eye, a converging lens is placed in front of it. This causes light rays to converge sooner. Therefore, the image falls on the retina.

A nearsighted eye has the opposite problem. The lens focuses an image in front of the retina rather than upon it. This defect is corrected by a diverging lens which causes a delay in the focusing of an image. Then the image is focused squarely on the retina.

Figure 20-19.   Eye defects that lenses can correct.

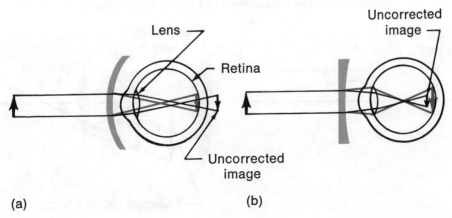

(a)   (b)

Most microscopes use two converging lenses. An object is placed close to the lower lens, called the objective lens. This lens produces a real image just below a second converging lens, called the eyepiece. The real image is located between the focal point of the eyepiece and the eyepiece itself. In this way the viewer sees a greatly magnified virtual image of the real image of the object.

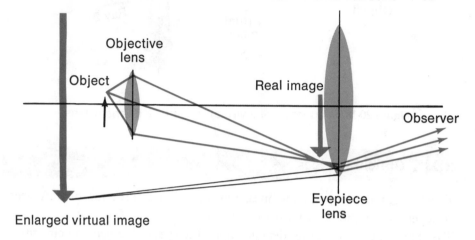

Figure 20-20.   The compound microscope employs an objective lens of short focal length to form the first real image. The eyepiece lens of longer focal length forms a virtual image of the first real image.

A refracting telescope also employs two converging lenses. However, the objective lens of a telescope has a longer focal length than does the objective lens of a microscope. As in the microscope, the objective lens of a telescope forms a real, inverted image of a star or other distant object between the focal point of the eyepiece and the eyepiece itself. The viewer sees an enlarged, virtual, and inverted image of the object.

Figure 20-21.   The lens system of a refracting telescope.

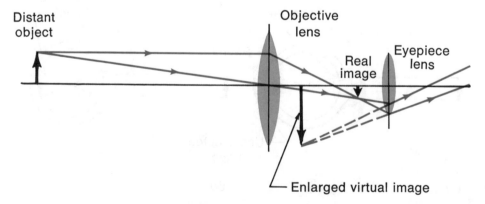

QUESTIONS

1. Describe the image of an object seen in a plane mirror.
2. An object is located beyond the center of curvature of a spherical concave mirror. Locate and describe the image of the object.
3. Locate and describe the image produced by a concave mirror when the object is located at the center of curvature.
4. An object is located between the center of curvature, C and the principal focus, F of a concave mirror. Locate and describe the image of the object.
5. How does a virtual image differ from a real image?
6. An object produces a virtual image in a concave mirror. Where is it located?
7. Describe the image seen in a convex mirror.
8. Describe the properties of a virtual image.
9. What factor, other than the curvature of a lens, determines the location of its focal point?
10. Locate and describe the image produced by a convex lens of an object placed some distance beyond 2F.
11. Name an inherent defect of a concave spherical mirror.
12. Name an inherent defect convex lenses.
13. To achieve the image produced by a movie camera on a screen, the film is placed between F and 2F of a converging lens. This produces an inverted image. Why do the actors appear to be erect when the film is viewed?

PROBLEMS

1. An object is 20 cm from a concave mirror of 8 cm focal length (16 cm radius). Locate the image (a) graphically (b) mathematically.
2. An object 3 cm high is placed 25 cm from a concave mirror of 15 cm focal length. Find the location and height of the image (a) graphically (b) mathematically.
3. An object is 30 cm from a concave mirror of 15 cm focal length. (a) Locate the image. (b) The object is 1.8 cm high. How high is the image?
4. An object is 8 cm from a concave mirror of 12 cm focal length. Locate the image.
5. A convex mirror has a focal length of -8 in. How far behind the mirror does the image of a man 6 ft away appear?
6. An object is 4 in. in front of a concave mirror of 15 in. focal length. Locate the image.
7. How far behind the surface of a convex mirror of -6 cm focal length does an object 10 m from the mirror appear?

8. A convex lens has a focal length of 25 cm. An object is placed 40 cm from the lens. Where is the image?

9. An object is 40 cm from a convex lens of 10 cm focal length. Find the position of the image (a) graphically (b) mathematically. (c) The object is 3 cm high. How high is the image?

10. An object is 25 cm from a convex lens of 12.5 cm focal length. Locate the image.

11. To develop a sharp image on a screen, a projectionist moves the convex lens of the projector to a point which places the film 21 cm from the lens. The focal length of the projector lens is 20 cm. (a) How far is the screen from the lens? (b) How many times larger is the image on the screen than the picture on the film?

Diffraction of Light

Light, like other waves, can bend around obstacles. This bending of light around edges may result in blurred edges of shadows. In the case of a number of obstacles closely spaced side by side, an interference pattern consisting of alternating light and dark areas may result. X rays exhibit this property of diffraction and thus are useful in the determination of crystal structure. Why has the study of crystal structure become very important?

21:1 Diffraction and Interference

Light waves are diffracted as they pass through narrow slits. Figure 21-1 shows the arrangement used by Thomas Young to demonstrate that light waves exhibit diffraction in much the same way as water waves. The arrangement used for light waves differs from that used for water waves because the wave generator in the ripple-tank sends very regular straight waves toward the double slit. Light sources, with the exception of lasers, cannot do this. Instead, different parts of the source emit waves at random. These waves fall on the slits at different times and at different angles. The result is an incoherent pattern. Young remedied

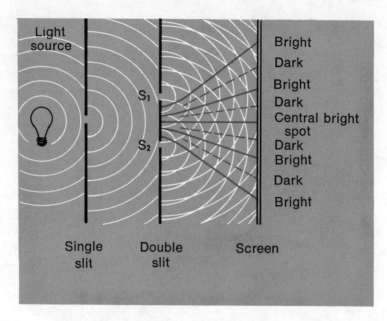

Figure 21-1.   Formation of a diffraction pattern from an incandescent light source. The double slit produces the interference. Each bright spot is edged by a continuous spectrum since each wavelength produces its own pattern.

this situation by placing a single slit in front of the source. Any wave that leaves the source and falls on this narrow slit is diffracted. The single slit, then, acts as a source of uniform new waves which strike the double slit simultaneously. The double slit in turn acts as two sources of new waves. The waves interfere constructively at points where crests overlap and destructively where crests and troughs fall together. In Figure 21-1, the semicircles represent wave crests moving outward from the sources. Midway between the crests are the troughs. The solid lines in the diagram pass through points of constructive interference where crests lie on crests. These antinodal lines are lines of maximum amplitude. At points where antinodal lines fall on a screen, bright bars of light appear since the light is coming from a slit. The dotted lines in Figure 21-1 pass through points of destructive interference. Nodal lines appear where crests and troughs coincide. Dark spots appear at points where nodal lines fall upon the screen. Figure 21-1 shows a bright spot of light directly opposite the midpoint between the two slits appears on the screen some distance from the slits. On either side of this central bright spot are spots of light corresponding to the other lines of reinforcement.

When white light is used as the source for a double slit diffraction pattern, the light is dispersed into a continuous spectrum. A white light source does not emit a single wavelength of light. Several hundreds of wavelengths approach the slits simultaneously. However, one of the basic rules of wave behavior is that

Double slit diffraction from single-concept film by Franklin Miller, Jr.

Figure 21-2. Double-slit interference pattern. Notice the even spacing of the bright bands.

waves can pass right through one another without permanently distorting each other. Each wavelength of light produces its own interference pattern completely unaffected by the other patterns around it.

Each wavelength produces a bright line at the center of the pattern. The addition of all wavelengths at the central bright line produces a line of white light. To either side of the central bright line the lines of reinforcement for each color do not fall in exactly the same places. Each wavelength produces a pattern that is slightly different from that of neighboring wavelengths. The effect is the separation of white light into a continuous array of colors on each side of the central bright line.

21:2 Measuring the Wavelength of a Light Wave

Interference may be used to measure the wavelengths of light waves. Examine Figure 21-1 carefully. Figure 21-1 represents the pattern produced by one wavelength from a source of light. Choose a line of reinforcement other than the central line. Select any point along one of these lines where the two crests come together and count the waves back to S_1. Then from the same point count the waves back to S_2. The difference is always a whole number of wavelengths. For the first line of reinforcement to the right or the left of the central line, the path difference is just one wavelength. For the second line of reinforcement, the path difference is two wavelengths, for the third line, three wavelengths, and so on. Any point selected along a line of reinforcement is always a whole number of wavelengths farther from one slit than the other. Thus, waves arrive at that point in phase and reinforce each other.

Along the first line of reinforcement, the path difference is always one wavelength and this difference is consistent all along the line. It follows that the distance from S_1 to the bright line where this wavelength falls on the screen is just one wavelength longer than the distance from S_2 to that spot. The geometry

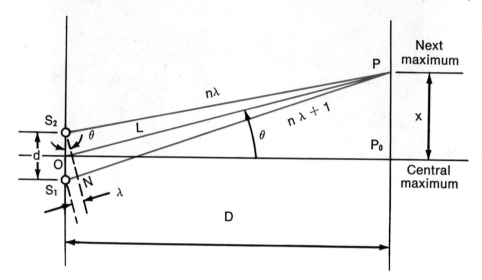

Figure 21-3.   Schematic diagram for analysis of interference.

of the situation is shown in Figure 21-3. In this diagram, L is the distance from the center of the two slits to P , the point where the bright line of light appears on the screen. P_0 is the central bright line and x is the distance from the central bright line to P . During an actual trial, a collection of bright spots or lines, one for each wavelength of light emitted by the source, would appear. These are called first-order lines. First-order lines are also visible to the right of the central bright line. A considerable distance away, second-order lines caused by secondary lines of interference would appear.

The distance between the two slits is measurable and is marked d in Figure 21-3. The distance from the central line to the bright line of reinforcement is x. The distance from S_1 to P is one wavelength longer than the distance from S_2 to P so in right triangle $S_2 S_1 N$ the base, $S_1 N$, equals the wavelength, λ. This triangle is similar to triangle $P P_0 O$ (corresponding sides are mutually perpendicular). Therefore, since the ratios of corresponding sides of similar triangles are equal,

$$\frac{x}{L} = \frac{\lambda}{d}$$

And from this

$$\lambda = \frac{xd}{L}$$

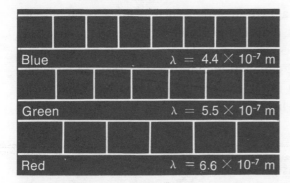

Blue $\lambda = 4.4 \times 10^{-7}$ m

Green $\lambda = 5.5 \times 10^{-7}$ m

Red $\lambda = 6.6 \times 10^{-7}$ m

Figure 21-4. Band pattern produced by means of the same slits
and the same slit-screen distance, but with different wavelengths of light at the slits. The
separation between bands is
proportional to the wavelength.

Sample Problem 1

When red light falls on two small slits 1.9×10^{-4} cm apart, a first-order line appears 22.1 cm to the left of the central bright line on a screen opposite the slits. The distance from the center of the slits to the first-order line is 60 cm. What is the wavelength of the red light?

Solution:

$$x = 22.1 \text{ cm}, d = 1.9 \times 10^{-4} \text{ cm}, L = 60 \text{ cm}$$

$$\lambda = \frac{xd}{L}$$

$$\lambda = \frac{(22.1 \text{ cm})(1.9 \times 10^{-4} \text{ cm})}{(60 \text{ cm})}$$

$$\lambda = 7.0 \times 10^{-5} \text{ cm}$$

Problems

1. Violet light falls on the same pair of slits described in Sample Problem 1 ($d = 1.9 \times 10^{-4}$ cm). A first-order line appears 13.2 cm from the central bright spot. The distance from the center of the slits to the first-order violet line is 60 cm. What is the wavelength of the violet light in cm?

2. Yellow light of wavelength 6.0×10^{-5} cm is substituted for the violet light of Problem 1. The distance from the center of the slits to the first-order line for the yellow light is measured and found to be 58 cm. How far from the central bright spot on the screen is the first-order yellow line?

3. Green light falls on a pair of slits 1.9×10^{-4} cm apart. A first-order line appears 28.4 cm to the left of the central bright line. The distance between the center of the slits and the first-order line is 100 cm. What is the wave-length of the light?

4. Blue light falls on a pair of slits that are spaced 0.02 cm apart. A first-order line appears 0.184 cm from the central bright line on a screen opposite the slits. The distance from the midpoint between the slits to the first-order line is 80 cm. What is the wavelength of the blue light?

5. By replacing the screen of a two-slit arrangement with a photographic plate, electromagnetic waves outside the visible region may be detected. An ultraviolet source produces a line on the film 0.072 cm from the central bright line. The slits are 0.02 cm apart and arranged so that the midpoint between them is 40 cm from the line appearing on the plate. What is the wavelength of the ultraviolet light?

21:3   Frequencies of Light Waves

By using interference patterns, the wavelengths of light waves can be measured with considerable accuracy. It is not unusual for wavelength measurements to be accurate to six digits. In addition to wavelengths, the speed of light is also known. Frequencies of light waves are then calculated by using the relationship

$$c = f\lambda$$

Sample Problem 2

What is the frequency of the yellow light emitted by a sodium vapor lamp if the wavelength of the yellow light is 5.9×10^{-5} cm in air?

Solution:

First, express the wavelength in meters.

$$10^{-5} \text{ cm} = 10^{-7} \text{ m}$$

Then, $$c = f\lambda$$

So, $$f = \frac{c}{\lambda}$$

$$f = \frac{3.0 \times 10^8 \text{ m/sec}}{5.9 \times 10^{-7} \text{ m}}$$

$$f = 5.1 \times 10^{14} \text{ Hz}$$

One thousand cycles per second is a kilohertz (kHz). The solution to the sample problem can be written as,

$$5.1 \times 10^{14} \text{ Hz} = 5.1 \times 10^{11} \text{ kHz}$$

Problems

6. Calculate the frequency of red light of wavelength 6.6×10^{-5} cm in air.
7. What is the frequency of green light of wavelength 5.4×10^{-5} cm in air?
8. The frequency of an X ray is 3×10^{18} Hz. What is the wavelength of this ray in air?
9. Calculate the wavelength of blue light of frequency 7.2×10^{14} Hz in cm.
10. What is the wavelength of yellow light of frequency 5.0×10^{14} Hz?

21:4 Single-Slit Diffraction

When light passes through one narrow slit, a diffraction pattern appears on a distant screen. This single-slit diffraction pattern differs considerably from the double-slit pattern. The spacing between the bright lines lacks the regularity associated with double-slit diffraction pattern. Also, the central bright band is much larger and brighter than when two slits are used.

Single slit diffraction from single-concept film by Franklin Miller, Jr.

Figure 21-5. A diffraction pattern formed by a single slit. Compare this pattern to the pattern in Figure 21-2.

To observe single-slit diffraction, fold a small piece of paper and make a cut in its folded edge with a pair of scissors. Unfold the paper and peer through the slit at a light source. You will see a diffraction pattern. You can vary the width of the slit by pulling on opposite edges of the paper. Observe the effect of the change in slit width on the diffraction pattern.

Figure 21-6 shows how a single slit can cause dark cancellation lines. Here monochromatic light falls on a slit. Because the slit is very narrow, all points of the wave along the slit are in phase. The diffraction pattern falls on a screen located a considerable distance from the slit. At P_0 a wide, bright band of light is observed because the distance L is so large compared to w that all rays falling on w are essentially equidistant from P_0 and arrive there in phase. Point P, however, is exactly one wavelength farther from point $6'$ on the slit than it is from point 1 on the slit. This places point P one-half a wavelength farther from $1'$ than it is from 1. Hence, waves from 1 and $1'$ arrive at point P 180° out of phase and cancel. The same is true for points 2 and $2'$, 3 and $3'$, and so on down the slit. Therefore, no light is observed at P. Notice that although we used only six points along the slit, in reality there are an infinite number of points acting in this fashion.

In Figure 21-6, triangles ADC and BP_0P are similar. Because L is so large when compared to w, you can approximate the corresponding sides of similar triangles. That is, $\overline{BP}$ and L are, within the limits of a very small error, equal. So instead of $\dfrac{\overline{BP}}{y} = \dfrac{w}{\lambda}$, substitute L for BP so that

$$\frac{L}{y} = \frac{w}{\lambda}$$

$$\lambda = \frac{yw}{L}$$

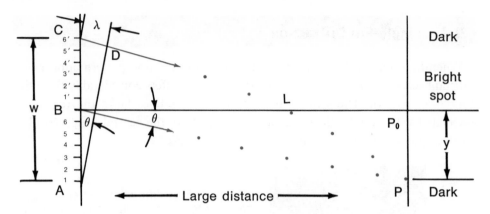

Figure 21-6.   Schematic diagram for analysis of single-slit diffraction pattern.

If w is very small, the bright central band will be larger. If w is one wavelength, then $\lambda/w = 1$. In the language of trigonometry, this means that $\sin \theta = 1$ and θ is 90°. The bright band would then spread over 180° and no dark lines would be observable.

With other slit dimensions, second-order dark bands will appear below point P_0 and below point P. In keeping with our explanation of the first-order dark bands, second-order bands appear where angle θ is wide enough to cause $\overline{CD}$ to equal 2λ. When $\overline{CD}$ is equal to 3λ, or some other multiple of λ, another dark band will appear.

Sample Problem 3

Monochromatic orange light falls upon a single slit of width 0.01 cm located 100 cm from a screen. If a first-order dark band is observed 0.6 cm from the center of the central bright band, what is the wavelength of the orange light?

Solution:

$$\lambda = \frac{yw}{L}$$

$$\lambda = \frac{(6.0 \times 10^{-1} \text{ cm})(1 \times 10^{-2} \text{ cm})}{1 \times 10^2 \text{ cm}}$$

$$\lambda = 6.0 \times 10^{-5} \text{ cm}$$

Problems

11. Determine the wavelength of the monochromatic green light that falls on a slit 0.01 cm wide and produces a first-order dark band 0.55 cm from the center of the central bright band on a screen 100 cm away.

12. Violet light of wavelength 4×10^{-5} cm falls on a slit 0.015 cm wide. The screen is located 80 cm from the slit. How far from the central band will the first-order dark band appear?

13. Yellow light from a sodium vapor lamp falls upon a single slit 0.0295 cm wide. A screen 60 cm away reveals a first-order dark band located 0.120 cm from the center of the bright central band. What is the wavelength of the yellow light?

14. Light of wavelength 4.8×10^{-5} cm passes through a single slit and falls on a screen 120 cm away. What is the width of the slit if the center of the first-order dark band is 0.5 cm away from the center of the bright central band?

21:5   Resolving Power of Lenses

When light from two sources that are close together falls on a lens, the light is diffracted. The lens acts in the same way as a slit. It causes the diffracted light from the two sources to overlap. As a result, the width of a lens limits its ability to distinguish between the two images. To reduce the effects of diffraction, a wide lens must be used. In the case of the objective lens of a microscope, this is not possible. In a microscope, diffraction is reduced by using light of a shorter wavelength. This produces the same effect as a wider lens. For this reason, biology classes often use blue or violet lamps when working with microscopes.

QUESTIONS

1. Explain why the central bright line resulting from the diffraction of light by a double slit cannot be used to measure the wavelength of light waves.

2. Using a compass and a ruler, construct a diagram of the interference pattern that results when waves 1 cm in length fall on a pair of slits 2 cm apart. The slits may be represented by two dots spaced 2 cm apart and kept to one side of the paper. Draw a line through the central line of reinforcement and through all other lines of reinforcement. Draw dotted lines where crests falling in troughs will produce nodal lines.

3. If you are using light of a known wavelength during a double slit experiment, can you determine the distance between the slits? How?

4. More accurate measurements of light waves can be made if the lines obtained for each wavelength are as far apart as possible. Since $\lambda = \dfrac{xd}{L}$ how can the value of x be increased?

5. How does the measurement of the wavelength of a light wave allow us to determine its frequency as well?

6. How does a single-slit diffraction pattern differ from the pattern obtained by using two slits?

7. What happens to a single-slit diffraction pattern when the width of the slit approaches the wavelength of the light falling on it?

8. Why do lenses make it difficult to distinguish between two point sources of light that are very close together?

PROBLEMS

1. Light falls on a pair of slits 1.9×10^{-4} cm apart. The slits are 80 cm from a first-order line which is 19 cm from the central bright line. What is the wavelength of the light?

2. Two slits 5.0×10^{-4} cm apart form a first-order bright line 11.2 cm from the central bright line on a screen opposite the slits. The distance from the center of the slits to the first-order line is 100 cm. What is the wavelength of the light falling on the slits?

3. Light of wavelength 4×10^{-5} cm falls on a pair of slits and first-order bright lines appear 4.0 cm from the central bright line. The first-order lines are 200 cm from the center of the slits. How far apart are the slits?

4. In practice two slits are seldom used to measure the wavelengths of light waves because two slits do not allow very much light to pass onto a screen or photographic plate. Usually glass plates having thousands of openings or lines per centimeter are used. These plates are called gratings. To illustrate that several slits produce the same interference pattern as two slits, use a piece of paper and a compass. Make two points on the paper near the center of one side of the paper about a centimeter apart. Using the compass, draw semicircles that represent waves leaving the slits. Make $\frac{1}{2}$ cm divisions between waves. Draw several waves for each point across the paper. Mark the central line of reinforcement and the first-and second-order lines of reinforcement for this wavelength. Now make a third point 1 cm to the side of the original pair of points and repeat the process. (a) Do the points of reinforcement fall in the same places? (b) Would several points or slits develop the same pattern as just two?

5. A good diffraction grating has 2500 lines per centimeter. What is the distance, d, between two lines in the grating?

6. Using the grating of Problem 5, a red line appears 16.5 cm from the central bright spot on a screen opposite the grating. The distance from the center of the grating to the red line is 100 cm. What is the wavelength of the red light?

7. What is the frequency of light waves of wavelength 4.6×10^{-5} cm?

8. Calculate the wavelength of a gamma ray of frequency 6.0×10^{24} Hz.
9. Light of frequency 6.0×10^{14} Hz falls on a pair of slits that are 2.0×10^{-4} cm apart. The center of the slits is 50 cm from the screen. How far from the central bright line will the first-order bright lines appear?
10. Calculate the wavelength of light that falls on a single-slit 0.01 cm wide and develops a first-order dark band 0.59 cm from the center of the central bright band on a screen 100 cm away.
11. Light that falls on the slit described in Problem 10 develops a first-order dark band 0.48 cm from the bright central band. (a) Calculate the wavelength of the light. (b) Compare the distance between the central bright band and the first-order dark band with the wavelength of the light in this problem and in Problem 10 as well. What relationship exists? Can the wavelengths of the light waves be read directly from the screen in an arrangement of this sort?
12. When light of wavelength 4.0×10^{-5} cm falls on a single slit, the two first-order dark bands are located 0.043 cm from the bright central band. If the slit is 86 cm from the screen, what is its width?
13. Sound waves of frequency 550 Hz fall on a window 4 ft wide. The window is in the exact center of one wall of a theater 80 ft $\times$ 40 ft. The window is 40 ft from the opposite wall along which are a row of seats filled with people. The theater is acoustically prepared to prevent the reflection of sound waves and the speed of sound is 1100 ft/sec. Two people in the row along the wall hear no sound. Where are they sitting?

22

The Origin of Light

Light from luminous objects can be classified as either natural or artificial. Most of the natural light comes from our sun. Other natural sources are stars such as those pictured in the galaxy above. Some sources of artificial light are incandescent and fluorescent lamps, neon signs, heating coils in stoves and toasters, bonfires and even fireworks. Why does the color of the light from these various sources vary? What do these light sources have in common?

22:1 Charged Particles Generate Electromagnetic Waves

Discoveries by Michael Faraday and other scientists helped James Clerk Maxwell to demonstrate mathematically that whenever a charged particle is accelerated, an electromagnetic wave originates about the charged particle. The wave propagates through space at the speed of light. Heinrich Hertz verified Maxwell's prediction by creating a circuit in which electrons accelerated back and forth in a wire loop. Hertz demonstrated that detectable radio waves came from the loop in which the electrons were accelerated. Radio waves are electromagnetic waves. They differ from light waves only in their wavelengths and frequencies.

Today Maxwell's theory includes all electromagnetic waves. Electromagnetic waves, including light waves, are generated by the acceleration of charged particles. Light waves usually are generated by the acceleration of electrons within an atom.

22:2   The Excitation of Atoms

When an electron is ejected from an atom, the atom becomes an ion. An electron also can be given energy without leaving an atom. An electron can be raised from a lower energy level within the atom to a higher energy level within the same atom. When this happens, the atom is excited. An excited atom differs from an ionized atom which has lost an electron completely. Excited atoms remain excited for only a very small fraction of a second. Then the electron

Figure 22-1. Photons are emitted from atoms which have gained energy. The three means of exciting atoms in order to produce light: (a) electron excitation (b) photon excitation (c) thermal excitation.

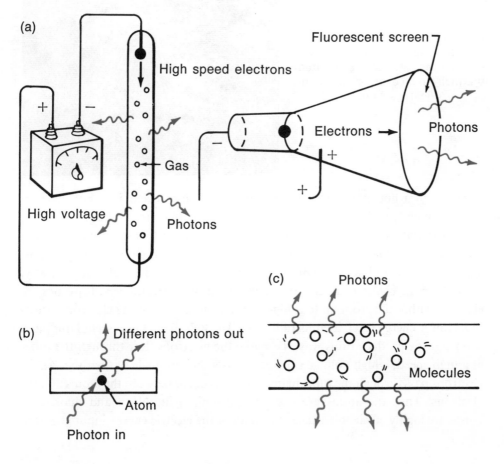

drops from the higher energy level where it does not belong and returns to its normal energy level. However, energy is absorbed by the atom when its electron is raised to a higher energy level. By the law of conservation of energy, this energy, must be accounted for. If the electron returns to its lower energy level, the atom emits light or electromagnetic radiation. The energy content of the radiation is exactly equal to the energy absorbed by the atom when its electron was raised to a higher energy level. This is the origin of light waves.

22:3   Means by Which Atoms are Excited

The three means to excite an atom are by thermal excitation, electron collision, or photon collision. *Thermal excitation* occurs when atoms collide. As a fast moving atom collides with another atom, it imparts energy to that atom. The added energy raises an electron within the atom to a higher energy level.

Figure 22-2. Brilliant fireworks light the night sky. Photons are emitted as atoms are excited thermally in an exothermic chemical reaction.

Courtesy of S. D. Warren Co.

Atoms in a hot material move very fast. Collisions occur in a hot material more frequently and more energetically than in a cool material. Because of this, a hot material emits more noticeable light as a result of thermal excitation than does a cool material. To heat a material often causes it to glow or give off light. The filament of an incandescent lamp and glowing coal give out light this way.

In *electronic collision*, an electron strikes an atom a certain way. It pushes the electron within the atom up to a higher energy level. When the electron returns to its lower energy level, it emits radiation. The light from fluorescent lamps and neon signs is produced this way. To make the electrons flow through the tubes at a high speed, a high voltage is placed across the terminals of the tube. As the electrons pass through the tube, many collisions occur between the atoms and the electrons. Thus the atoms are excited and emit light. Neon and fluorescent lamps are highly efficient because almost all of the electric energy input goes into generating light. On the other hand, incandescent lamps generate more heat than light. A 30-watt fluorescent lamp produces more light than a 100-watt incandescent lamp.

In *photon collision*, a photon of radiation enters an atom and its energy is absorbed. The energy of the photon raises an electron to a higher energy level. The photon disappears. When the electron returns to its normal energy level, one or more photons leave the atom. Consider a red sticker on an automobile bumper. The sticker materials contain atoms which are easily excited by photons. When light from another automobile shines on the sticker, photons of radiation fall on the material and excite some of its atoms. These excited atoms emit red light and the sticker glows.

22:4 Fluorescence and Phosphorescence

Atoms are easily excited in fluorescent and phosphorescent substances. Many minerals are fluorescent. A fluorescent substance differs from a phosphorescent substance. The difference is in the time it takes for excited atoms within the material to return electrons to normal energy levels. Most electrons in energy levels higher than normal are highly unstable in their new positions. They return immediately to their normal levels. Fluorescent materials emit light only while being excited. The red bumper sticker gives out light only while it is being flooded with external light. The sticker is fluorescent. A fluorescent lamp emits light only while electrons pass through the lamp. After the current passing through the lamp is shut off, a fluorescent lamp no longer glows.

A television screen and a doctor's fluoroscope are coated with fluorescent materials. In the TV picture tube, electrons are shot at the fluorescent screen. Wherever an electron strikes, excitation causes the atoms to emit light. The amount of light that comes from any part of the screen is governed by the number of electrons that come from the negative electrode (electron gun) in a picture tube. In turn, the number and energy of the electrons that come from the gun are governed by the signal received from the set. The gun forms a picture on the tube by varying the amount of light emitted from every spot on the surface of the tube.

A doctor's fluoroscope works the same way as the TV picture tube with one exception. The fluorescence uses X rays instead of electrons to bombard the screen. The X rays pass through the person being examined and fall on the fluorescent screen. Because fewer X rays get through bones than flesh, the result is a picture of only the bone structure.

Phosphorescent materials contain atoms that lend greater stability to electrons in higher than normal energy levels. After excitation occurs, excited phosphorescent atoms return electrons to their normal levels at once, within several minutes, or it may take up to several hours. If a small doll or statuette is held under a lamp for a short time and glows for a long time afterward, it contains phosphorescent substances.

22:5   Allowed Transitions

The absorption of energy by electrons within an atom is discrete. This means the energy given to the electron must be exactly the proper amount of energy for it to move from one energy level to another. Otherwise it will not change energy levels. This is somewhat like a boy trying to throw a baseball straight up and after being released, having the ball refuse to leave his hand because he failed to give it the right amount of energy to raise it to the intended height. An examination of the nature of energy reveals that it is quantized, or comes in packages.

The electronic structure of every element differs from the electronic structure of every other element. The energy levels within each atom also are peculiar to that atom. Figure 22-3 represents a group of energy levels for a typical atom as E_1, E_2, E_3, and so on.

Figure 22-3.   Each line represents an energy transition from one level to another.

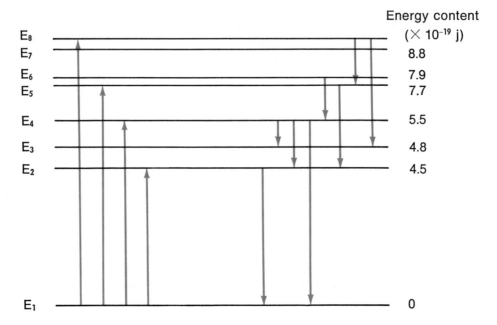

	Energy content ($\times 10^{-19}$ j)
E_8	
E_7	8.8
E_6	7.9
E_5	7.7
E_4	5.5
E_3	4.8
E_2	4.5
E_1	0

The electrons within an atom make only certain transitions between energy levels. These are allowed transitions. To understand why electrons occupy only certain levels, a wave model of the atom is helpful. The model assumes that as an electron travels about the atomic nucleus, it follows a path that is a whole multiple of its wavelength. The electron is then continually reinforcing itself and keeping its energy constant. At any other level, the path would lead the wave to interfere with itself. As a result, its energy would dissipate. Theory and experiment strongly indicate that an electron occupies just the correct energy level it needs to keep a constant energy. Thus, when an electron moves from one energy level to another in an atom, it moves only between exact levels.

When an electron returns from a higher energy level to a lower energy level, once again it is only allowed to make certain transitions. As Figure 22-3 indicates, these transitions need not be the same transitions as those that increased the energy level. This explains how a fluorescent material is flooded with light of one color and emits light of a different color. TV color screens are excited by electron collision. However, the color the screen gives out depends upon the favored down-transitions made by electrons of the material on the screen.

Each element has its own set of allowed transitions. Therefore, under normal conditions, each element emits only certain wavelengths of light. This is why every element has its own spectrum.

22:6   Fraunhofer Lines

When absorbing energy, an atom favors energy carried by photons that have the same wavelengths that the atom can emit. These wavelengths contain just the right amount of energy to excite the atom. An atom that emits blue light absorbs blue light easily. This also explains several observable phenomena. The Fraunhofer lines, for example, are dark lines that appear in the solar spec-

Figure 22-4. The Fraunhofer dark lines in the visible part of the solar spectrum; only a few of the most prominent lines are represented. The two yellow "D" lines are characteristic of the element sodium.

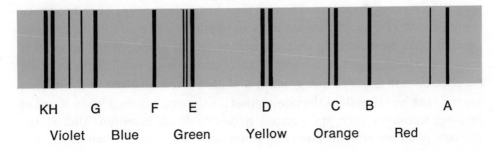

trum. The lines indicate that certain wavelengths are missing from the spectrum. The absence of these lines is accounted for by assuming that the sun is surrounded by hot layers of gases which absorb these wavelengths and reemit them in new directions. Thus, certain wavelengths of light which leave the sun in the direction of the earth are absorbed and reemitted in new directions. The sunlight is redirected and never reaches the earth. Consequently, these wavelengths are missing from the solar spectrum.

22:7   Lasers and Masers

Light emitted by atoms of an incandescent source is highly random. Each atom emits light of different wavelengths at different times and in different directions. Such light is incoherent light. Once scientists thought that the nature of matter would not permit the development of a coherent light source. *Coherent light consists of light waves of the same wavelength joined together in phase to produce a highly intense beam of light.* Today the laser produces coherent light.

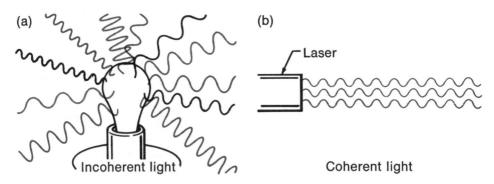

Figure 22-5.   (a) Incandescent light sources give out light of varying wavelength and random phase. (b) Lasers produce coherent light of a single wavelength and the waves are all in phase.

The word laser is an acronym. It represents *L*ight *A*mplification by the *St*imulated *E*mission of *R*adiation. The first laser was a short ruby (Al_2O_3) rod containing about 0.1% chromium atoms as an impurity. The operation of the laser depends upon an interesting characteristic of excited atoms. When an atom is excited an electron goes to a higher than normal energy level. Suppose while the electron is in this high energy state, a photon enters an atom. If the photon has the same wavelength as the photon that the electron will emit when it makes its down-transition, then, the electron makes its down-transition. That is, the presence of a photon in the atom that is the same as the photon that the excited atom will emit stimulates the atom to emit that photon. What is more, the two photons leave the atom completely in phase. This is what is meant by coherent light.

It is not unusual for the right photon to enter an atom at the right time to stimulate emission of radiation. A small bit of material contains many excited atoms that are at the same energy level. They emit the same photons having just the proper energy to stimulate down-transitions. Usually the effect is not large enough to be noticeable. A photon that has been amplified by stimulating one atom can lose its excess energy to the next atom. This occurs if the next atom is not in the excited state. A large majority of the atoms in a laser are in the excited state. The photons increase their energy each time they enter a new atom. This produces a highly intense beam of coherent light.

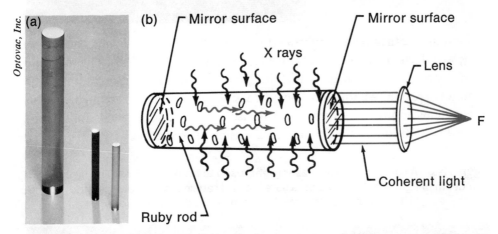

Figure 22-6. (a) The photograph shows ruby rods with reflective ends used to make lasers. (b) The ruby rod is flooded with X rays. Atoms begin emitting photons which in turn trigger more photons of the same wavelength.

Figure 22-6 shows one laser arrangement. A ruby rod is flooded with X rays which are high-energy photons. The flooding of the rod is *pumping*. Pumping excites a great number of atoms in the rod. A mirror is placed at each end of the rod. The mirror on one end partially transmits and partially reflects. When a photon enters an excited atom, it stimulates the electron to make its down-transition. Thus, the photon is amplified. This takes place in many atoms at once. The amplified photons pass on to other excited atoms. This continues to increase their intensities. The photons on a line between the two mirrors are reflected. They repeat the process back and forth between the two mirrors. In a short time, the entire process results in an avalanche of down-transitions. A short burst of highly intense, coherent light emanates from the end of the ruby rod. This beam may be diffracted by a pair of slits. The diffraction pattern shows that laser light is coherent. The laser beam may be focused with a lens to provide an even more intense and accurately placed spot of coherent light.

Figure 22-7. Ruby laser beam piercing a sheet of tantalum. The beam a million times brighter than the sun melts the metal at 5500°C.

Hughes Aircraft Co.

Substances other than ruby can be made to "lase." Several solids and gases work well. Helium and neon gas can emit continuous laser beams. The radiation emitted does not have to be in the visible region. Masers emit radiation in the microwave region. Although beyond the visible region, masers are highly useful in communications. The word maser is also an acronym. It stands for *M*icrowave *A*mplification by the *S*timulated *E*mission of *R*adiation.

Figure 22-8.   A camera and ruby laser (right) used to track satellites. The laser fires a thin beam of light that bounces off a satellite and returns to a receiver on the ground. The distance to the satellite is measured very precisely.

NASA

Figure 22-9. The hologram is a photographic recording of tiny interference fringes. These recorded fringes contain all the optical information about a 3-dimensional scene. When the hologram is properly illuminated by a laser beam, the fringes diffract and alter the beam until a virtual image of the 3-dimensional scene is reconstructed in space. The virtual image exhibits all the optical properties of the original scene, including parallax. The photograph shows the virtual image reconstructed from a hologram.

QUESTIONS

1. How does an excited atom differ from an ionized atom?
2. Name three different methods by which an atom may be excited.
3. Why does a hot substance emit light?
4. A TV picture tube is coated with a fluorescent material rather than a phosphorescent material. Explain why.
5. The electrons within an atom absorb energy only in discrete amounts. Explain why electrons make transitions between specific energy levels only.
6. Make a diagram of a laser. Explain its operation.

Static Electricity

Static electricity is familiar to you as the shock you receive when you touch an object after having shuffled your feet across a carpet. A rubber balloon when rubbed with wool cloth clings to a wall because of static electricity. A build-up of negatively charged particles on substances is responsible for these phenomena. Do you see any resemblance between the electric arcs produced by the electrostatic generator above and a certain weather phenomenon?

23:1 Micro-structure of Matter

Atom models have the relatively dense protons and neutrons in the center or nucleus of the atom. The protons bear a net positive electric charge. The charge is exactly the same on each proton. Neutrons are neutral and bear no electric charge. Located outside the nucleus of the atom is a "cloud" of electrons. Each electron bears a net negative charge equal in magnitude but opposite in sign to the charge on a proton. The mass of an electron is negligible compared

to the mass of a proton. An electron has $\frac{1}{1837}$ of the mass of a proton. The

magnitude of the charge is the same on all electrons and protons. The basic
charge on an electron or proton is the elementary unit of charge. Under ordinary
circumstances, an atom contains as many electrons as protons. Therefore, it is
electrically neutral. Electric phenomena become evident when this balance is
disturbed.

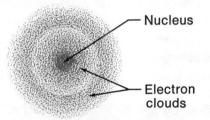

Nucleus

Electron
clouds

Figure 23-1. The essentially
spherical atom is diagramed
to indicate its dense nucleus
with two electron clouds
surrounding it.

In most cases, the proton is firmly "locked" in the nucleus of the atom. It is
dislodged only by methods encountered in nuclear physics. All electric phenomena are due to the movements of electrons. The electron is the mobile
particle of the atom.

23:2 Charging Bodies Electrically

The electron is the only electrically charged particle within an atom that is
moved easily. Its mobility is sufficient to produce negative and positive charges
on objects. A neutral body contains as many electrons as protons. Because

Figure 23-2. Charges are acquired by an object through a gain or loss of electrons.
(a) The neutral object has equal numbers of electrons and protons. (b) The negative
object has excess electrons. (c) The positive object is deficient in electrons.

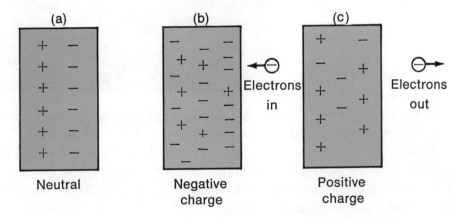

electrons are easy to move, it is possible to add electrons to a neutral body. Electrons are then in excess, and the body bears a net negative charge. On the other hand, removal of electrons from a neutral body causes the body to gain a net positive charge. The body then contains an excess of protons. In either case, the protons remain in the nucleus and the electrons move. When a body is charged by the addition or subtraction of electrons, the charge resides on the body, at least temporarily. The body bears a static charge. Static means "at rest."

To illustrate, rub a glass rod with a piece of silk. The glass rod donates electrons to the silk. The glass rod then bears a net positive charge while the silk bears a negative charge. Rubbing the glass vigorously with the silk increases the intensity of the charge on the glass. Rubbing the silk and the glass together only increases the contact area. This causes more electrons to leave the glass and move onto the silk.

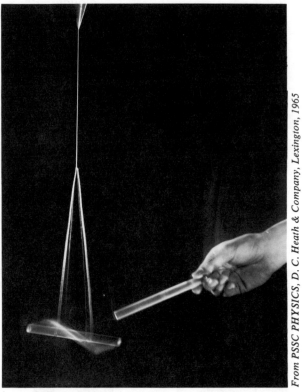

Figure 23-3. An electrically charged rod, when brought close to another rod which is suspended in a manner allowing free rotation, will attract or repel the suspended rod depending on the nature of the charges involved. Two neutral rods will not affect one another.

From PSSC PHYSICS, D. C. Heath & Company, Lexington, 1965

If two glass rods are rubbed with a silk cloth and charged positively, one of the rods may be suspended and the second glass rod brought close to it. The suspended rod will be repelled. Thus, two positively charged bodies repel one another. Likewise, two rubber rods are charged negatively by rubbing them with fur or wool. If one of the rubber rods is suspended, it is repelled by the second rubber rod. Thus, two negatively charged bodies repel one another. However, if the negatively charged rubber rod is brought close to the suspended, positively charged rod, attraction occurs. There are three important facts concerning static electric charges:

1. Like charges repel one another. Unlike charges attract one another.
2. Bodies bearing electric charges exert forces on other bodies through a distance.
3. Electric charges are of two distinct kinds, positive and negative.

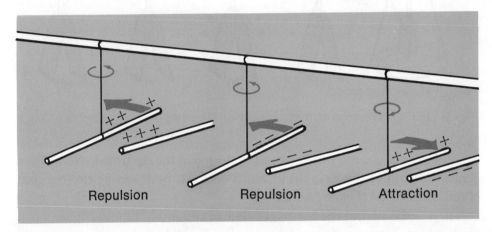

Figure 23-4.   Rods which are both positively charged repel one another. Rods which are both negatively charged repel one another. A negative rod and a positive rod exhibit mutual attraction.

23:3   Electrostatic Demonstrations

Many demonstrations support the theory that static charges are due to the transfer of electrons. The device in Figure 23-5 is an electroscope. It has a metal rod insulated from the ground by a glass support. Attached to the metal rod are two leaves of silver or aluminum foil. When either a negatively or positively charged rod is brought close to the top of the electroscope, the leaves diverge. The negatively charged rod repels the free-to-move electrons down into the leaves, charging both negatively. The leaves repel one another. A positively charged rod attracts the electrons up into the top of the electroscope. This causes both leaves to bear a net positive charge. Again repulsion takes place (Figure 23-5 b). When either rod is removed, the electrons at once redistribute themselves and the leaves fall.

A negatively charged rod touched to the top of the electroscope repels electrons from the top of the electroscope down into the leaves. The positive top of the electroscope then draws electrons from the negative rod. This causes the electroscope to gain an over-all excess negative charge. When the negative rod is removed, the leaves remain in diverged position for some time (Figure 23-5 c).

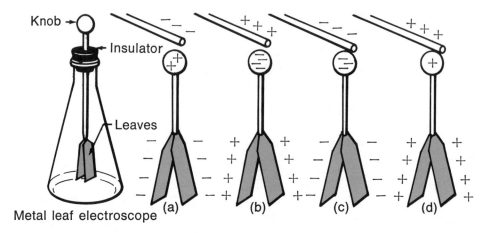

Figure 23-5.   Electroscope with accompanying diagrams of possible distributions.

A positively charged rod when touched to the top of the electroscope develops a permanent positive charge in the leaves. It does this by attracting electrons out of the electroscope (Figure 23-5 d).

A negatively charged rod is brought close to two insulated metal spheres that are touching. Negative electrons are repelled from the sphere nearest the rod into the sphere farthest away. If the spheres then are separated, one is charged negatively and the other positively. Either sphere brought close to the knob of an electroscope causes the leaves to diverge. The two spheres are charged equally

Figure 23-6.   Metal spheres used to transfer charges by conduction or induction.

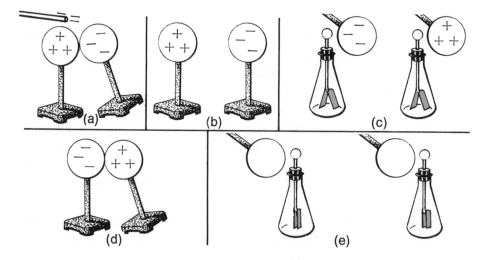

and oppositely. To demonstrate this, touch them together. The excess electrons flow from the negative sphere into the positive sphere. The result is a neutralization of charge on both spheres. To show that the spheres no longer bear a charge, bring them close again to the knob of an electroscope. The uncharged spheres do not affect the leaves.

23:4   Charged Bodies Attract Neutral Bodies

During demonstrations of static electricity, usually rubber rods or glass rods are used. This leads to the incorrect impression that static charges are induced only on glass or rubber. All substances contain electrons, and all substances can be charged electrostatically. A charged rubber rod held near a stream of water pulls the stream to one side. The negative rod repels electrons from the side of the stream closest to it to the other side of the stream. This makes the surface of the stream nearest the rod positive. Then the positive water is attracted to the

Figure 23-7

negative rod. The stream of water bends. Similarly, a comb run through hair gains a negative charge. It can be used to pick up small bits of paper even though the paper is neutral. The negatively charged comb repels electrons from the side of the paper closest to it. This side of the paper is then positive, and the negative comb attracts it. The paper is drawn to the comb. Almost at once the paper is violently repelled by the comb as the negative comb feeds electrons into the positive side of the paper. Soon the paper itself becomes negative. The negative paper and comb then repel. In this way, a charged body attracts a neutral body.

Figure 23-8. (a) A comb with a negative charge attracts paper. (b) The negatively charged comb now repels the paper which acquired a negative charge from it.

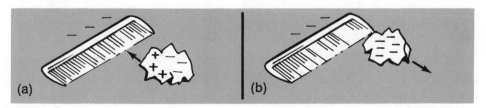

23:5   Grounding

Suppose an insulated metal sphere is charged negatively and then touched to a second sphere. As in the case of the paper and comb, the charged sphere repels electrons from the surface it is touching. Then it feeds electrons into the now positive side of the second sphere. What happens to the charge on the first sphere? This depends upon the size of what it is touching. If the metal sphere is touched to a second sphere of equal size, the charge is shared equally. Both spheres indicate they are charged when held near an electroscope. But they do not indicate as intense a charge as the one originally possessed by the first sphere. If the sphere is touched to a much larger sphere, it does not stop feeding the charge into the larger sphere until both spheres have the same charge per unit of surface area. This means that the intensity of the charge on the small sphere is greatly reduced. An electroscope is affected only slightly, if at all, by either sphere. Now consider what happens if the sphere is touched to the earth. The sphere tries to share its charge with the earth itself. In effect, this means that the sphere feeds all its charge into the earth and becomes neutral. This is grounding.

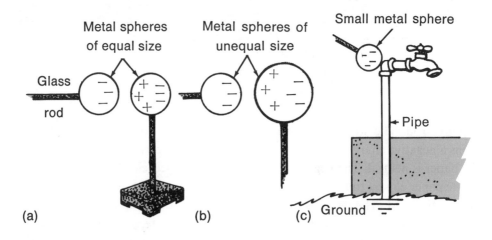

Figure 23-9. (a) A charged sphere and a neutral sphere of equal size share charge equally. (b) A smaller sphere gives much of its charge to a larger neutral sphere. (c) A sphere gives virtually all of its charge to a grounded object.

23:6   Conductors and Insulators

All materials can be charged electrostatically. However, not all substances conduct electrons well. A rubber rod can be charged, but its charge does not move along the rod. This is why rubber or glass rods are used for electrostatic experiments. The reluctance of such materials to conduct electricity makes them good insulators. On the other hand, all metals are good conductors of electricity. Atoms of metallic solids are packed close together. Their outermost electrons are practically as close to the attractive force of the positive nuclei of surrounding atoms as they are to the nuclei to which they belong. Many of these electrons pull free and move through the solid. This is especially true of metals like copper or silver. They only have one electron in their outermost levels. Silver and copper, in that order, are the best commercial conductors of electricity.

A metal rod is charged by rubbing it. As a good conductor, the metal sends its excess charges through the rod to the person's hand holding it and on to ground. The charge does not stay on the rod. A metal sphere or rod held on an insulating glass support, however, can be charged. It maintains the charge for some time.

23:7   Concentration of Charge

Electrons repel electrons. Therefore, any charged body distributes its charge over the outer surface of the body. It is on this outer surface that the electrons can get farthest away from one another. Yet the electrons can distribute themselves in such a way as to bring about equilibrium between individual charges. Any pointed or angular surface of a body must have a high concentration of charge to establish equilibrium. Charge along a pointed surface increases as the body narrows (Figure 23-10). The decrease in surface area along the point

 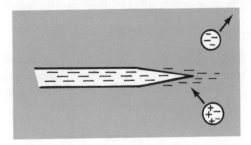

Figures 23-10. Electrons are concentrated around sharper surfaces of an object. They become so concentrated on pointed surfaces that they readily leak off the object.

causes this. More charges are needed in less area to push against the repulsive force of the larger areas and produce equilibrium. The concentration becomes extreme at the tip. An intense charge exists. The charge is so intense that it causes the electrons in the atoms of the air around it to repel to the side farthest away from the point. This polarizes the molecules of the air and leaves the side facing the point charged positively. At once the molecules are attracted to the point where they pick up electrons. They become charged negatively themselves and are violently repelled from the point. A point does this so efficiently that it sets up a vigorous wind of air and accomplishes the rapid discharge of the entire body of which it is a part. This is the discharge from a point. To prevent loss of charge from devices designed to hold static charges, the surfaces are rounded. This accounts for the knob on an electroscope and the use of metal spheres to hold charges.

23:8   Electric Potential Energy

When a mass is raised to a height above the surface of the earth, the earth-mass system has energy it previously did not have. If the mass falls back to earth, the energy can be used to do work. The system has energy because the earth and the mass attract one another. Work is done to separate, or lift, the mass from the surface of the earth against the attractive force. This work is reclaimed as the mass returns to the surface of the earth.

Suppose charges are separated so that one body (plate) has an excess of electrons and another body has a deficiency of electrons. The situation is exactly analogous to the one just described. Electrons are forced away from the positive plate and through some distance onto the negative plate. Work is done to separate the charge. The work is reclaimed when the charge moves back to the positive plate. While on the negative plate, the electrons have potential energy in respect to the positive plate. When the electrons flow from the negative plate to the positive plate, the flow is an electric current. Therefore, electric currents deliver energy.

Figure 23-11.   Electrons flow from an area of higher concentration to an area of lower concentration. They move from a negative to a positive body, from a more negative to a less negative body, or even from a less positive to a more positive body.

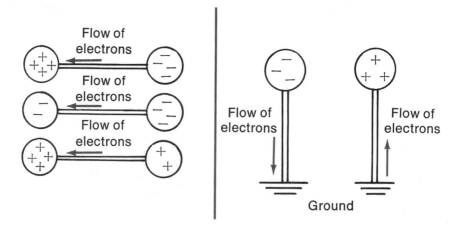

Electric potential energy is more complex than gravitational potential energy. For example, the gravitational force between the earth and a mass some distance above the earth always is attractive. Electric forces are both attractive and repulsive. Also, the gravitational force acting on a unit mass near the surface of the earth is more or less the same everywhere on earth. The electric force acting on a unit charge depends upon the concentration of electrons about the charge. Still, gravitational potential energy and electric potential energy essentially are similar. Work is done to create the potential energy. The same amount of work is realized when the potential energy is utilized.

A negatively charged body and a positively charged body are not both necessary to have electric potential energy. Electrons always flow from areas of a higher concentration to areas of a lower concentration. Thus, if a wire connects two negatively charged bodies, electrons flow from the body of higher electron concentration to the body of lower electron concentration. Likewise, electrons flow from a negatively-charged body to a neutral body or from a neutral body to a positively-charged body. When a wire connects two bodies bearing different concentrations of electrons, electrons flow from the body of higher electron concentration to the body of lower electron concentration.

Bodies that bear different concentrations of electrons have a difference in potential between them. This means that the two bodies constitute a source of potential energy. The energy depends upon the concentration of electrons on each. *This difference in potential is measured in volts.*

Figure 23-12. (a) Electrons flow from the negative to the positive plates. (b) As electrons are pumped from one plate to another, making one plate positive and the other negative, the excess electrons flow back to the positive plate through the other wire producing an electric current. (c) A diagram of an ordinary battery.

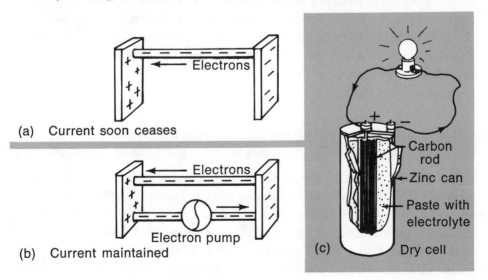

(a)　Current soon ceases

(b)　Current maintained

(c)　Dry cell

23:9   Electric Circuits

An electron flow takes place if two bodies having a difference in potential are connected by a conductor. This flow constitutes an electric current. To be useful, the current must be maintained. The only way to do this is to maintain

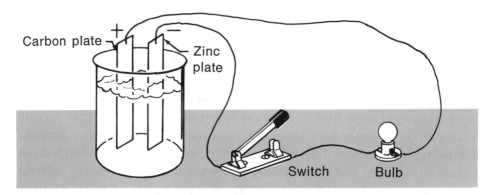

Figure 23-13.   A simple electric circuit which functions because the two electrodes differ in tendency to give up electrons.

the charge on the two bodies that are at different potentials. To maintain a potential difference, some device must pump the electrons back to the body with higher electron concentration as soon as they arrive at the body with lower electron concentration. Several devices can do this. Voltaic cells (batteries) and generators are the most common. The ordinary flashlight battery is actually a single cell consisting of a zinc plate and a carbon rod. They are separated by a paste containing an oxidizing agent. The chemical reaction between the oxidizing agent and the zinc causes the plates to maintain an electric charge. Essentially, this is the same as burning any fuel to provide a source of energy. The actual chemical reaction is not too important. However, remember that devices do exist that use energy sources to provide two constantly charged plates to connect together to form an electric circuit.

23:10   The Coulomb

The quantity of electric charge that exists on a charged body is measured in *coulombs*. This is analogous to measuring water in gallons. A gallon of water may be defined as consisting of so many molecules of water. A coulomb is defined as the electric charge on 6.25×10^{18} electrons or protons. This definition originated in the early days of electrical experimentation. At that time electric charge was measured in terms of the amount of silver deposited on a plate during a silver-plating experiment. Later the existence of electrons and protons was established. It became possible to determine the number of electrons or protons in a coulomb by combining the concepts of the mole and Avogadro's number with the results of the silver-plating experiment.

The coulomb is the charge found on 6.25×10^{18} electrons or protons. Therefore, the charge on a single proton or electron is $\dfrac{1}{6.25 \times 10^{18}}$ or 1.60×10^{-19} coulomb. This is the value of the elementary unit of charge. It is not possible to visualize quantities of these magnitudes. Think of a coulomb as a certain quantity of charge, just as a gallon of water is a certain quantity of water.

23:11 Coulomb's Law

Electric forces are important in holding together the particles that make up atoms and in holding atoms together. The basic behavior of electric forces is the key to understanding atomic structure.

In 1785 Charles Coulomb measured the force between two small charged spheres. He used a very sensitive torsion balance (Figure 23-14). The force required to twist the wire supporting the balance arm through any given angle was first carefully measured. Then the arm balanced by two small spheres was suspended from the wire. A charged sphere, B, was touched to sphere A so that the two spheres, being equal in size, shared the charge equally. By varying the distance, r, between A and B, Coulomb then measured the deflection of A from its rest position. The deflection produced the angle of twist of the wire. This permitted Coulomb to measure the force between the two spheres and relate this

Figure 23-14

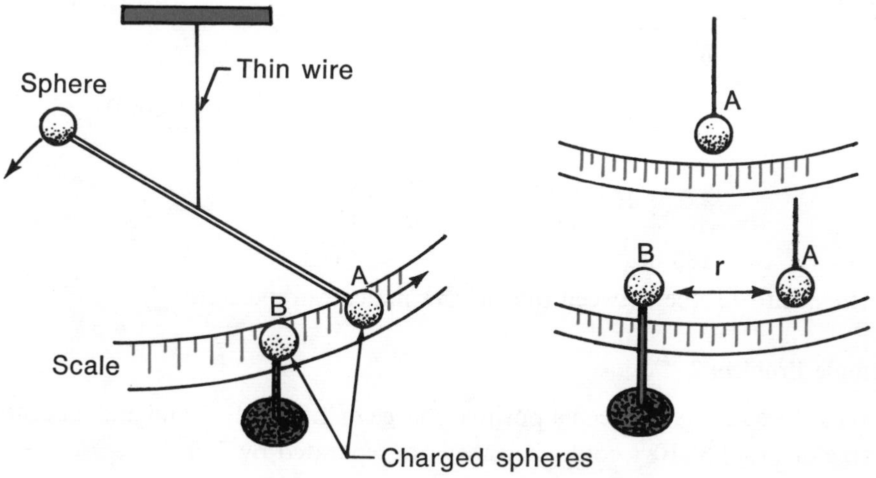

to the distance between them. Coulomb touched A with his finger and grounded it after a series of measurements. Then he touched B to A a second time. The charges on both A and B became half their former charge. He repeated the process. The spheres then had one-fourth their former charge. After a number of careful experiments, Coulomb formed this conclusion: *the force between two charged bodies varies directly as the product of their charges and inversely as the square of the distance between them.* This is expressed

$$F \propto \frac{qq'}{r^2}$$

The charges on the bodies are represented by q and q'; r represents the distance between them. Note the similarity between this expression and the one for gravitational force.

In general, electricity is measured in MKS units. Charge is expressed in coulombs (coul), distance in meters, and force in newtons. Coulombs were not designated with the metric system in mind. This means a constant of proportionality is needed to calculate electric forces in newtons.

$$F = K \frac{qq'}{r^2}$$

The constant K, is found by measuring the force F (in newtons) between two known charges q and q' (in coulombs) that are a known distance (in meters) apart. The constant turns out

$$K = 9.0 \times 10^9 \frac{\text{nt-m}^2}{\text{coul}^2}$$

Sample Problem 1

A positive charge of 6.0×10^{-6} coul is 0.03 m from a second positive charge of 3.0×10^{-6} coul. Calculate the force between the charges.

Solution:

$$F = K \frac{qq'}{r^2}$$

$$= 9.0 \times 10^9 \frac{\text{nt-m}^2}{\text{coul}^2} \frac{(6.0 \times 10^{-6} \text{ coul})(3.0 \times 10^{-6} \text{ coul})}{(0.03 \text{ m})^2}$$

$$= 9.0 \times 10^9 \frac{\text{nt-m}^2}{\text{coul}^2} \frac{(18 \times 10^{-12}) \text{ coul}^2}{9 \times 10^{-4} \text{ m}^2}$$

$$= 180 \text{ nt}$$

The positive force between the charges indicates repulsion.

Sample Problem 2

What force exists between a positive charge of 1.5×10^{-5} coul and a negative charge of -6.0×10^{-6} coul when they are separated by 5 cm?

Solution:

$$F = K\frac{qq'}{r^2}$$

$$= 9.0 \times 10^9 \ \frac{\text{nt-m}^2}{\text{coul}^2} \ \frac{(1.5 \times 10^{-5} \text{ coul})(-6.0 \times 10^{-6} \text{ coul})}{(0.05 \text{ m})^2}$$

$$= \ -324 \text{ nt}$$

The negative force between the charges indicates attraction. Note the large forces involved between electric charges given in millionths of a coulomb. The force in Sample Problem 1 is about 36 lb. The force in Sample Problem 2 is about 64 lb.

Coulomb's Law is useful when working with very small atomic particles. It helps to explain the forces that exist between electrons, protons, and the other particles within the atom, as well as the atom itself. Atomic and sub-atomic particles are very close to point charges. Coulomb's law applies accurately to them. When two charged bodies are fairly large and fairly close, Coulomb's law applies only with modification.

Problems

1. Two positive charges of 6.0×10^{-6} coul are separated by 0.5 m. What force exists between the charges?
2. A negative charge of -2.0×10^{-4} coul and a negative charge of -8.0×10^{-4} coul are separated by 0.3 m. What force exists between the two charges?
3. What is the force between a positive charge of 0.0008 coul and a negative charge of 0.0003 coul separated by 0.7 m?
4. (a) Determine the force between two positive charges of 1 coul each separated by 1 m. (b) One ton is roughly equal to 1×10^4 nt. How many tons of force is this?
5. A negative charge of -6.0×10^{-6} coul exerts an attractive force of 64.8 nt on a second charge 0.05 m away. What is the magnitude of the second charge?
6. A positive charge of 2.0×10^{-6} coul is 0.06 m from a second positive charge of 4.0×10^{-6} coul. Determine the force between the two charges.
7. Suppose the bodies of Problem 6 each have a mass of 5 g (0.005 kg) and are suddenly made free to move in a frictionless medium. What is the instantaneous acceleration of the masses upon release?

23:12   Electric Fields

A charged body can exert a force on a second charged body through a distance with no apparent medium existing between the two. The electric field concept is used to describe the behavior of any charged body when it is near another charged body. The electric field is not, in itself, an explanation of electric force.

To plot an electric field, a small positive test charge is placed at several points in the field. Its behavior is noted. The force acting on the test charge is directed toward a negatively charged body. The force is directed away from a positively charged body. Figure 23-16 shows vectors representing the forces acting on a test charge in two possible situations. In all cases the vectors are perpendicular to the

Figure 23-15. A positive test charge is used to study the electric field around charged objects.

surface of the charged body. For this reason the field around a charged body somtimes is described by drawing lines of force about the body. Although these lines represent the force field, they do not actually exist. The lines get farther apart as the distance from the charged body increases. This indicates a weakening of the field with distance.

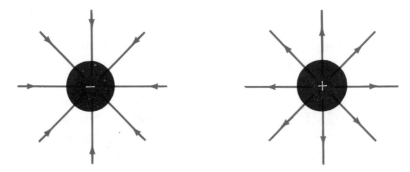

Figure 23-16. Lines of force are drawn perpendicularly away from the positive body and perpendicularly into the negative body.

Figure 23-17 shows the patterns taken by the lines of force when the fields between charged bodies are plotted. Lines of force only serve to describe the behavior of a positively charged test body placed in the field. *The direction of an*

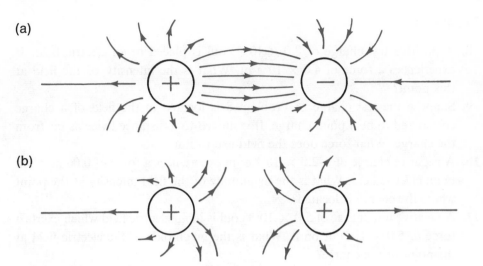

Figure 23-17.   Lines of force between (a) unlike charges, and (b) like charges.

electric field is the direction of the force on a positive charge placed in the field. This is always away from a positive charge and toward a negative charge. For this reason, *electric fields are said to run from positive to negative.*

23:13   Electric Field Intensity

A positive test charge placed at some point in an electric field experiences a force that is proportional to the product of the field intensity, E, and the magnitude of the charge, $F = Eq$. The intensity of the field at a given location is

$$E = \frac{F}{q}$$

F is in newtons; q is in coulombs; and E is in newtons per coulomb.

Sample Problem 3

A positive test charge of 4.0×10^{-5} coul is placed in an electric field. The force acting on it is 0.6 nt. What is the magnitude of the field intensity at the point where the charge is placed?

Solution:

$$E = \frac{F}{q}$$

$$= \frac{0.6 \text{ nt}}{4.0 \times 10^{-5} \text{ coul}}$$

$$= 1.5 \times 10^4 \text{ nt/coul}$$

Note: If the charge is negative, the field intensity still is measured the same way. However, the charge experiences a force in the opposite direction.

Problems

8. A positive test charge of 8.0×10^{-5} coul is placed in an electric field. It experiences a force of 4.0×10^{-3} nt. What is the intensity of the field at this point?

9. Suppose the test charge of Problem 8 is located in the field of a charge considered to be a point charge. It is moved to a distance twice as far from the charge. What force does the field exert on it?

10. A negative charge of -2.0×10^{-8} coul experiences a force of 0.06 nt when in an electric field. What is the magnitude of the field intensity at the point where the charge is located?

11. A positive test charge of 5.0×10^{-4} coul is in an electric field which exerts a force of 5.0×10^{-4} nt on it. What is the magnitude of the electric field at the point of the charge?

23:14   The Electric Field Between Two Parallel Plates

Point charges are used rarely for practical purposes in electricity. Point charges are used chiefly in the study of the structure of matter. The field that exists

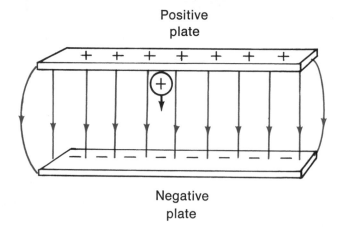

Figure 23-18. Diagram of electric field existing between two parallel plates of opposite charge. Note that the lines of force are drawn from the positive plate to the negative plate.

between two charged parallel plates is of more practical concern. Except at the very edges of the plates, the field is uniform in the region between two such plates. A test charge experiences the same force at any point in the space between the plates.

QUESTIONS

1. List the three major particles of the atom. State the electric charges of each.
2. Explain how a body is charged (a) positively (b) negatively (c) neutrally.
3. Explain how the leaves of an electroscope are made to diverge (a) by the near presence of a rod charged positively (b) by the near presence of a rod charged negatively.
4. A charged body attracts a neutral body. Describe how a negatively charged rod attracts a neutral bit of paper.
5. Why does a charged body lose its charge when it is connected to the ground?
6. A charged rubber rod placed on a table maintains its charge for some time. Why does the charge not "ground" immediately?
7. Name three good conductors of electricity.
8. What shape body is designed to maintain a static charge?
9. Draw a simple electric circuit.
10. Define the coulomb.
11. What is the charge on a single electron or proton?
12. State Coulomb's law.
13. Diagram the field between (a) two like charges (b) two unlike charges
14. How is the direction of an electric field determined?

PROBLEMS

1. A positive charge of 1.8×10^{-6} coul and a negative charge of -1.0×10^{-6} coul are 0.04 m apart. What is the force between the two particles?
2. Two negative charges of -5.0×10^{-5} coul are 0.2 m from each other. What force acts on the particles?
3. A positive charge of 1.5×10^{-5} coul and a negative charge of -1.5×10^{-5} coul are separated by 15 cm (0.15 m). Calculate the force between the two particles.
4. What force exists between two negative charges of 1.2×10^{-3} coul separated by 1 m?
5. The common isotope of hydrogen contains a proton and an electron separated by about 5.0×10^{-11} m. Use 1.6×10^{-19} coul as the elementary unit of charge to determine the force of attraction between the two particles.
6. The mass of a proton is approximately 1.7×10^{-27} kg. The mass of the electron is approximately 9.0×10^{-31} kg. (a) Use Newton's law of universal gravitation to calculate the gravitational force between the electron and proton in the hydrogen atom. (b) Compare this solution to the solution of Problem 5. How many orders of magnitude is the electric force between the two particles greater than the gravitational force between the two particles?

7. Two pith balls 1 g each (0.001 kg) are given equal charges so that $q = q'$. One pith ball is suspended by an insulating thread. The other charge is brought to within 3 cm of it ($r = 0.03$ m). The suspended pith ball is deflected from its rest position so that the thread forms an angle of 30° with

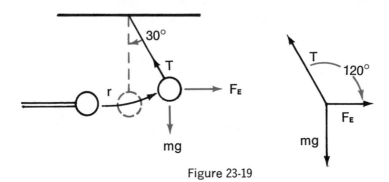

Figure 23-19

the vertical. Equilibrium exists because F_E and mg add vectorially to yield T. Calculate (a) mg (b) F_E (c) the charge on the pith balls.

8.

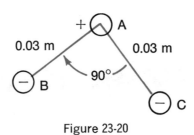

Figure 23-20

Charges of 6.0×10^{-6} coul exist on the three charges in Figure 23-20. Determine the magnitude of the resultant force on A by vector addition.

9. A charge of 2.0×10^{-4} coul is placed in the electric field around a larger body bearing a negative charge. The force acting on the charge is 0.0008 nt. (a) What is the intensity of the electric field at the position of the test charge? (b) Is the field directed toward or away from the larger body?

10. What net force acts on a test charge of 4.0×10^{-3} coul when it is in an electric field at a point where the field intensity is 20 nt/coul?

11. What charge exists on a test charge that experiences a force of 1.0×10^{-8} nt at a point in an electric field where the field intensity is 2.0×10^{-4} nt/coul?

12. A positive test charge of 3.0×10^{-4} coul is placed between a pair of parallel plates. One is positive and the other is negative. The force acting on the test charge is 0.9 nt. (a) What is the intensity of the field at the location of the charge? (b) The charge is moved 2 cm closer to the positive plate. What force acts on it?

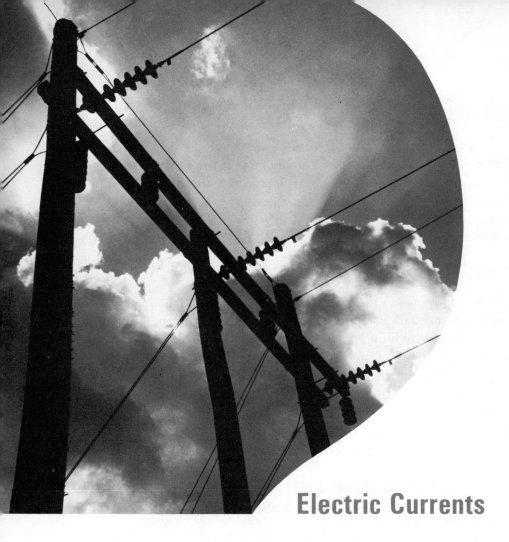

Electric Currents

Current electricity is a flow of electrons through some electrical conductor. Today it takes a power failure to make us realize to what extent we depend on electricity. How is electricity used in industry, in the city, on the farm and in the home?

24:1 The Purpose of Electric Currents

Electric currents transfer energy from one place to another. All electric currents require an energy source. Hydroelectric plants convert the kinetic energy of falling water into electric energy. In dry cells, a chemical reaction provides energy. Coal or oil provides the energy source in many power stations. In each case, electricity transfers energy from a point of supply to a point of use. The great amount of available energy at Niagara Falls means little to a factory one hundred miles away unless the energy can be economically transferred to that factory. Electric currents afford the means to make the transfer. Many other devices, such as radios and lamps, operate by electrical means but exchange energy that is traced back to falling water, burning coal, or some other source.

311

24:2 Difference in Potential

The magnitude and direction of the intensity of any field is measured by placing a standard unit in the field and noting the force that acts upon it. For example, the earth's gravitational field close to the earth has an intensity of 9.8 nt/kg. That is, the earth's gravitational field exerts a force of 9.8 nt on each kilogram of mass near its surface. Other gravitational fields have different intensities. The intensity of the gravitational field on the moon is 1.6 nt/kg or roughly $\frac{1}{6}$ that of the earth's field intensity.

To lift 1 kg of mass 1 m above the surface of the earth requires a force of 9.8 nt acting through a distance of 1 m. This means that 9.8 nt-m or 9.8 j of work are done on the mass to lift it 1 m. We then say that the mass has 9.8 j of potential energy. Another way of saying the same thing is to say that the *difference in potential* between the surface of the earth and a point 1 m above the surface of the earth is 9.8 j/kg. The difference in potential between any two points in a field is the *work* required to move a unit of whatever is affected by the field between the two points. Notice that the potential difference is calculated by multiplying the field intensity by the distance the unit mass is moved.

Potential difference = Field intensity × Distance

9.8 j/kg = 9.8 nt/kg × 1 m

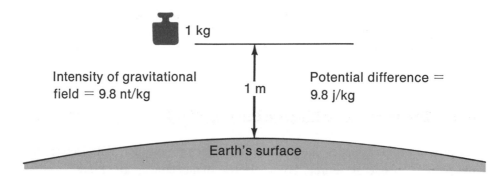

Figure 24-1. Gravitational potential difference is a function of both the distance the object is raised and the existing gravitational field intensity.

Electric fields affect electric charges. To measure the intensity of an electric field we place a standard charge in the field and measure the force acting on it. Thus, we speak of newtons per coulomb when dealing with electric field intensity (Chapter 23).

If a coulomb of charge is placed in an electric field and we find that the field produces a force of 1 nt on the charge we say that the field intensity is 1 nt/coul. If a force of 1 nt is applied to the charge and it is moved a distance of 1 m against the field the work done on the charge is 1 nt-m or 1 joule. But the coulomb of charge then has 1 j of potential energy that it did not have before so we say that

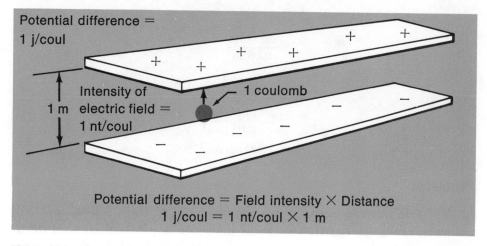

Figure 24-2. Electric potential difference is a function of the distance the charge is moved and the existing electric field intensity.

the *difference in potential* between the two points a meter apart is *a joule per coulomb or in electrical terms one volt*. Note that the potential difference is found by multiplying the field intensity (E) by the distance (d). This is exactly the same method used to calculate gravitational potential difference.

For electric potential difference, $V = Ed$

In practice, electric fields are usually more intense than 1 nt/coul. Also, two parallel plates bearing electric charges are closer together than 1 m. The sample problem illustrates a more realistic situation.

Sample Problem 1

Two parallel plates are 0.03 m apart. The field intensity between them is 3000 nt/coul. What is the difference in potential between the plates?

Solution:

$$V = Ed$$
$$= 3000 \text{ nt/coul} \times 0.03 \text{ m}$$
$$= 90 \text{ nt-m/coul}$$
$$= 90 \text{ j/coul}$$
$$= 90 \text{ volts}$$

Sample Problem 2

A voltmeter shows a difference in potential of 50 volts between two parallel metal plates. The plates are 0.05 m apart. What is the field intensity?

Solution:

$$V = Ed$$
$$E = \frac{V}{d}$$
$$= \frac{50 \text{ volts}}{0.05 \text{ m}}$$
$$= \frac{50 \text{ j/coul}}{0.05 \text{ m}}$$
$$= \frac{50 \text{ nt-m/coul}}{0.05 \text{ m}}$$
$$= 1000 \text{ nt/coul}$$

Problems

1. The field intensity between two charged metal plates is 800 nt/coul. The plates are 0.5 m apart. What is the difference in potential between them?
2. The field intensity between two plates is 2000 nt/coul. What is the difference in potential between one parallel plate and a point half-way to a second parallel plate 0.06 m away?
3. A voltmeter reads 500 volts when placed across two parallel plates. The plates are 0.02 m apart. What is the field intensity between them?
4. Two plates are 0.008 m apart. The difference in potential between them is 200 volts. What is the field intensity between the plates?
5. What voltage is applied to two metal plates 0.05 m apart if the field intensity between them is 2500 nt/coul?

24:3 Work and Energy

A difference in potential of 1 volt between two plates means that 1 j of work is done on 1 coul of charge that is transferred between the plates against the electric field. A volt is 1 j/coul. To transfer 1 coul of charge through a potential difference of 100 volts against the field, 100 j of work are done on the charge. To transfer 2 coul of charge between the 100-volt difference in potential, 200 j of work are done on the charge.

$$W = Vq$$

The work done on the charge is stored as available electric energy. When 1 coul of charge flows back between the plates under the influence of the electric field, it

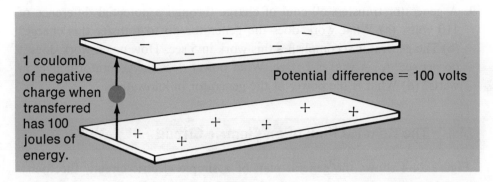

1 coulomb of negative charge when transferred has 100 joules of energy.

Potential difference = 100 volts

Figure 24-3. In moving electrons from a positive plate to a negative plate, work must be done. A corresponding amount of energy is released when the electrons return to the positive plate.

delivers exactly the same energy that was used to move it against the field. Thus, to move 1 coul of charge in electrons through a potential difference of 100 volts, 100 j of work are exerted upon it. When the charge returns through the field, it delivers 100 j of energy. Suppose the charge passes through an electric motor on its return through the field. It would deliver 100 j of energy to the motor, and the motor would be able to do 100 j of work.

Sample Problem 3

(a) What work is done on 5 coul of charge to transfer it through a potential difference of 90 volts? (b) What is the potential energy of the charge as a result of the transfer?

Solution:

$$\text{(a)} \ \ W = Vq$$
$$= 90 \ \text{j/coul} \times 5 \ \text{coul}$$
$$= 450 \ \text{j}$$

(b) By the law of conservation of energy, 450 j

Problems

6. (a) What work does a generator do to transfer 1 coul of charge through a potential difference of 110 volts? (b) What is the potential energy of 1 coul of charge after the transfer takes place?

7. What work is done by the chemical energy of a dry cell to transfer 5 coul of negative charge from its positive plate to its negative plate if the dry cell is rated at 1.5 volts?

8. How much work does the chemical energy of a 90-volt battery do to transfer 30 coul of charge between its plates?

9. A generator transfers 50 coul of charge through a potential difference of 110 volts. (a) What work does the generator do to transfer this charge? (b) The generator accomplishes this work in 5 sec. How much work does it do per sec? (c) A watt is 1 j/sec. What power does the generator deliver in watts? (d) What is the power of the generator in kilowatts?

24:4   The General Plan of an Electric Circuit

Figure 24-4 shows the general plan of a simple electric circuit. Electricity takes advantage of natural sources of energy. A potential difference is created between two plates. Often this is done by an electric generator or by a battery (dry cell). If a wire is connected between the plates, the electric field appears in

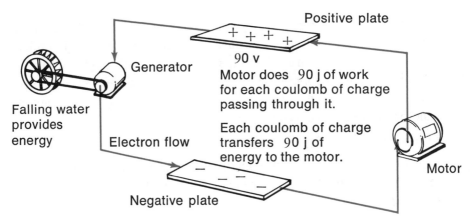

Figure 24-4. Simple diagram of production and use of electric current.

the wire and forces electrons from the negative plate to the positive plate. The charge falls back through the potential difference. As the charge falls back, it delivers energy to devices requiring energy. The process is similar to a mass lifted to a height above the earth and made to do work as it falls.

In Figure 24-4, the quantity of energy delivered to the motor depends upon the quantity of charge that passes through it. If the difference in potential between the two plates is 90 volts, then every coulomb of charge that passes through the motor delivers 90 j of energy to the motor.

24:5   The Ampere and Electric Power

Power is the rate of doing work. It is measured in j/sec. Suppose the current flowing through the motor in Figure 24-4 is 3 coul/sec. Then a potential difference of 90 volts supplies the motor with 90 j/coul × 3 coul/sec, or 270 j/sec, or 270 watts. This is voltage (V) times electron current flow (i). So to find power in electricity, multiply the voltage by the electron current flow. In electric units, a flow of 1 coul/sec is one ampere.

$$P = Vi$$

P is the power in watts; V is the potential difference in volts; i is the current in amperes.

Sample Problem 4

A 6-volt battery delivers 0.5 amp of current to an electric motor connected across its terminals. (a) What is the power of the motor? (b) What energy does the motor use in 5 min?

Solution:

$$\text{(a) } P = Vi$$
$$= 6 \text{ j/coul} \times 0.5 \text{ coul/sec}$$
$$= 3 \text{ j/sec}$$
$$= 3 \text{ watts}$$
$$\text{(b) } 3 \text{ j/sec} \times 300 \text{ sec} = 900 \text{ j}$$

Problems

10. The current through a light bulb connected across the terminals of a 120-volt outlet is 0.5 amp. At what rate does the bulb use electric energy?
11. A 90-volt battery causes a current of 2 amp to flow through a lamp. What is the power of the lamp in watts?
12. A toaster connected to a 120-volt source uses 4 amp of current. What power in watts does the toaster use?
13. A light bulb uses 1.2 amp when connected across a 120-volt source. What is the wattage of the bulb?
14. What current flows through a 75-watt light bulb connected to a 120-volt outlet?
15. The current through a motor connected to a 60-volt battery is 2 amp. What energy in joules does the motor consume in 5 min?
16. A lamp is connected across a 24-volt difference in potential. The current flowing through it is 4 amp. (a) What power does the lamp use? (b) How much electric energy does the lamp use in 10 min?

24:6   Ohm's Law

The German scientist Georg Simon Ohm (1787–1854) discovered that the ratio of the potential difference between the ends of a wire and the current flowing through the wire is a constant. This ratio is the resistance of a wire because it is constant for any metal wire. This relationship is known as Ohm's Law. The current that flows through any given wire varies directly as the applied voltage.

$$i = \frac{V}{R}$$

The electron current flow, i, is in amperes; V is the potential difference in volts; R is the resistance of the conductor in ohms. An ohm is the resistance which permits a current of 1 amp to flow between a potential difference of 1 volt.

A higher voltage causes a greater current flow between the ends of a conductor. To obtain a higher voltage, a more intense charge must be placed on the plates. This results in a greater difference in potential. The electric field between the plates becomes more intense as well. The more intense field moves more electrons per unit time between the plates.

Figure 24-5. Ohm's law.

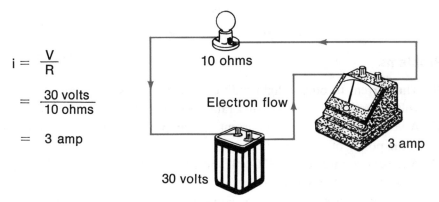

$$i = \frac{V}{R}$$

$$= \frac{30 \text{ volts}}{10 \text{ ohms}}$$

$$= 3 \text{ amp}$$

Sample Problem 5

What current flows between a potential difference of 120 volts through a resistance of 30 ohms?

Solution:

$$i = \frac{V}{R}$$

$$= \frac{120 \text{ volts}}{30 \text{ ohms}}$$

$$= 4 \text{ amp}$$

Problems

17. A resistance of 30 ohms is placed across a 90-volt battery. What current flows in the circuit?

18. A voltage of 75 volts is placed across a 15-ohm resistor. What current flows through the resistor?

19. 0.5 amp flow through an incandescent lamp when it is connected to a 120-volt source. (a) What is the resistance of the lamp? (b) What is the wattage of the lamp?

20. A motor with an operating resistance of 30 ohms is connected to a voltage source. Four amperes of current flow in the circuit. What is the voltage of the source?

21. A transistor radio uses 0.2 amp of current when it is operated by a 3-volt battery. What is the resistance of the radio circuit?

22. A resistance of 60 ohms allows 0.4 amp of current to flow when it is connected across a battery. What is the voltage of the battery?

24:7 Diagramming Electric Circuits

Figure 24-6 (a) shows the arrangement of a simple electric circuit. Figure 24-6 (b) represents the circuit schematically. The jagged line in the circuit represents the resistance, or the electric device being operated. The alternate long and short

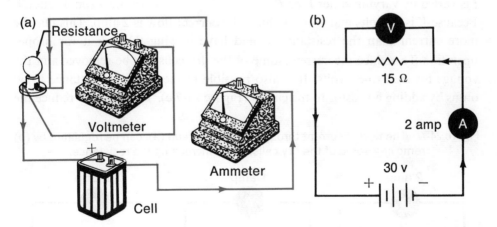

Figure 24-6. (a) Pictorial diagram of simple electric circuit. (b) Schematic diagram of the same simple electric circuit.

lines are the cells of a battery. The short lines indicate negative terminals. The long lines indicate positive terminals. The symbol for the Greek letter omega, Ω, represents ohms.

A voltmeter measures the drop in potential across the resistor. A voltmeter connects to both sides of the resistance and is said to be in parallel with the resistance. An ammeter measures the current flowing in the circuit. It connects directly into the circuit and the entire current flows through it. An ammeter is in series with the resistance.

In Figure 24-6 the resistance in the circuit is a light bulb. Technically, the resistance of the connecting wires should be included as well. But the resistance of such wires usually is low enough to overlook. However, to obtain a fine measurement, the resistance of these wires has to be accounted for.

Problems

23. (a) Draw a diagram to show a circuit that includes a 90-volt battery, an ammeter, and a resistance of 60 ohms. (b) What does the ammeter read?

24. (a) Draw a circuit diagram to include a 60-volt battery, an ammeter, and a resistance of 12.5 ohms. (b) Indicate the ammeter reading.

25. (a) Draw a circuit diagram to include a 16-ohm resistor, a battery, and an ammeter that reads 1.75 amp. (b) Indicate the voltage of the battery.

24:8   Controlling Current in a Circuit

There are two ways to control the current that flows in a circuit. Since $i = \dfrac{V}{R}$, i is varied by varying either V or R, or both. Figure 24-7 shows a simple circuit. Because V is 60 volts and R is 30 ohms, the current flow is 2 amp. This may be more current than the resistance should have flowing through it for proper operation. To reduce the current, some of the dry cells can be removed and the voltage lowered to 30 volts. It is also possible to increase the resistance to 60 ohms by adding a resistor to the circuit (Figure 24-7 c). This will also reduce the

Figure 24-7.   The flow of current through a simple circuit (a), can be regulated by (b) removing some of the dry cells, or (c) increasing the resistance.

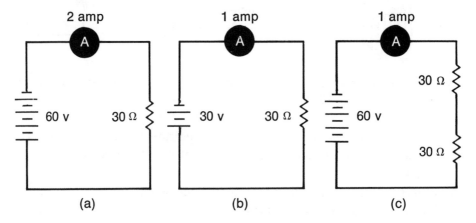

current flowing through the device to 1 amp. Resistors used to control the current flow in electric circuits are control resistors. Control resistors are generally used to send the proper amount of current through circuits or parts of circuits. Radios and other electric circuits use such resistors.

Sometimes it is necessary to vary the current flow through a resistor. The electric motors used on ripple-tanks usually are arranged so that the current through them can be varied. As a result, the motor runs faster or slower. This is done by adding a variable resistor to the circuit (Figure 24-8). The resistor consists of a coil of wire and a sliding contact point. By moving the contact point to various positions along the coil, the amount of wire added to the circuit varies. The more wire placed in the circuit, the higher is the resistance of the circuit. As a result, less current flows in accordance with Ohm's Law. In this way, the speed of the motor is adjusted. The same device controls the speed of electric fans, household electric mixers, and many other appliances.

The resistance of a resistor can change during use. Sometimes the temperature of a resistor increases during use. This can cause its resistance to change. Light bulbs increase in resistance after they have been on for a while. If the resistance of a circuit changes while it operates, the current flow changes accordingly.

Figure 24-8. A variable resistor can be used to regulate the flow of current in a circuit. This type of resistor is desirable because it is easily adjusted.

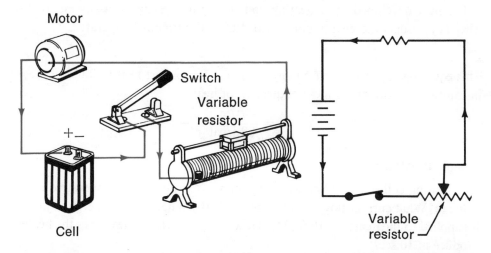

24:9 Heating Effect of Electric Currents

The power (energy/sec) used by an electric circuit is equal to the voltage multiplied by the current.

$$P = Vi$$

From Ohm's Law $\qquad V = iR$

Substituting: $\qquad P = iR \times i$

$$P = i^2 R$$

The power used by a resistor is proportional to the square of the current that passes through it and is proportional to its resistance.

How a resistance uses the power supplied to it depends upon the nature of the device. An electric motor converts electric energy into useful mechanical energy. An electric light generates light energy. However, not all of the electric energy used by a motor or an electric light ends up as work or light. All electric devices also generate some heat. If most of the energy supplied to a device results in heat, the device usually was designed for that purpose.

The total energy supplied to any resistor is the power used by the resistor multiplied by the time of its operation.

$$\text{Energy} = Pt$$

$$= \text{watts} \times \text{sec}$$

$$= \text{j/sec} \times \text{sec}$$

$$= \text{j}$$

The expression for power is $i^2 R$. The total energy supplied to any device, Pt, is $i^2 Rt$.

The heat developed by a heating coil or a pure resistance, assuming 100% efficiency, equals the energy consumed during the time it is operated.

$$H = i^2 Rt$$

This equation expresses heat energy in joules. To convert heat in joules to heat in calories, use the mechanical equivalent of heat.

$$H = \frac{i^2 Rt}{4.2 \text{ j/cal}}$$

Sample Problem 6

A heating coil has a resistance of 10 ohms. It is designed to operate on 120 volts. (a) What current flows through the coil? (b) What electric energy in joules is supplied to the heater in 10 sec? (c) How many calories of heat does the heater produce in 10 sec?

Solution:

$$\text{(a)} \quad i = \frac{V}{R}$$

$$= \frac{120 \text{ volts}}{10 \text{ ohms}}$$

$$= 12 \text{ amp}$$

(b) Energy $= i^2Rt$

$\qquad = (12 \text{ amp})^2 (10 \text{ ohms})(10 \text{ sec})$

$\qquad = 14\ 400 \text{ j}$

(c) $H = \dfrac{i^2Rt}{4.2 \text{ j/cal}}$

$\qquad = \dfrac{14\ 400 \text{ j}}{4.2 \text{ j/cal}}$

$\qquad = 3430 \text{ cal}$

Problems

26. (a) What current flows through a 15-ohm electric heater when it operates on a 120-volt outlet? (b) What energy in joules is used by the heater in 30 sec? (c) What heat in calories is liberated by the heater during this time?

27. (a) What current flows through a 30-ohm resistor connected to a 60-volt battery? (b) The resistor has pure resistance. What energy in joules does it use in 5 min? (c) All of the energy is converted to heat. How many calories are produced during the 5 min?

28. The resistance of an electric stove element at operating temperature is 11 ohms. (a) 220 volts are applied to it. What current flows through the element? (b) What energy in joules does the element use in 30 sec? (c) How much heat in calories does the stove develop in this time?

29. An electric heater is rated at 500 watts. (a) How many joules of energy does the heater use in half an hour? (b) How many calories of heat does the heater generate during this time?

30. A 100-watt incandescent lamp is 20% efficient. (a) How many joules does the lamp convert into heat each minute it is in operation? (b) How many calories of heat does the lamp produce each minute?

24:10 Transmission of Current Over Long Distances

Available energy is not always located near populated areas where electricity is in demand. Electric power often is transmitted over long distances. The wires that transmit electricity are pure resistances and generate heat. This heat serves no useful purpose and represents wasted energy. To keep energy loss to a minimum, $H = i^2Rt$ indicates that it is important to keep the resistance of the lines low. Even more important, the current flowing in the lines needs to be kept low.

Wire of large diameter and of good conductivity lowers the resistance of transmission lines. Such wires provide a wide path for the transmission of electrons and present less resistance to current flow. However, the longer the wire, the greater its resistance. Therefore, transmission lines do have some heat loss.

Generated heat is proportional to the square of the current. This makes it even more essential that the current passing through the lines be as small as possible. Since $P = Vi$, this is done by making the voltage in the lines very high and the current very low. In this way, large amounts of power are transmitted over long distances and energy loss is kept at a minimum.

Figure 24-9.　High voltage transmission lines carry electricity from the power plant to customers miles away.

Edison Electric Institute

24:11　The Electron Volt

The charge carried by a single electron is 1.6×10^{-19} coul. The energy required to move 1 coul of charge through a potential difference of 1 volt is 1 j. Thus, the energy required to move a single electron through a potential difference of 1 volt is 1.6×10^{-19} j. This energy is one electron-volt (*ev*). Often it is used as a unit of energy to deal with extremely low energy values, such as those found in nuclear physics. A million times the energy of an electron-volt is another useful energy unit. It is a million-electron-volts (1 *Mev* = 1.6×10^{-13} j).

QUESTIONS

1. An astronaut on another planet finds that the force on a standard kilogram mass in 16 nt. (a) What value does he record as the intensity of the field of gravity on the planet? (b) How much work does the astronaut do to lift the mass to a height of 2 m? (c) What is the potential energy of the kilogram mass when lifted to 2 m above the surface of the planet? (d) What is the potential difference between the surface of the planet and a point 2 m above the surface?

2. A force of 50 nt is needed to move a test charge of 1 coul when it is placed between two parallel plates. (a) What is the intensity of the electric field between the two plates? (b) How much work is done to move the charge between the two plates if they are 5 cm (0.05 m) apart? (c) What is the potential

energy in joules of the charge after it is moved between the plates? (d) What is the difference in potential between the plates in joules per coulomb (e) What is the difference in potential between the plates in volts?

3. Define a volt in terms of work done against an electric field.
4. What work is done to transfer 5 coul of charge through a difference in potential of 20 volts against the field?
5. Show how multiplying volts times amperes yields watts.
6. A 12-volt battery is connected to a 4-ohm resistor. (a) What current flows in the circuit? (b) State two ways to reduce the current to 1.5 amperes.
7. What quantities are kept low to transmit electric energy over long distances economically?
8. What is the electron-volt? What does it represent?

PROBLEMS

1. The field intensity between two electrically charged plates is 1500 nt/coul. The plates are 0.08 m apart. What is the difference in potential between them in volts?
2. A voltmeter indicates that the difference in potential between two plates is 50 volts. The plates are 0.02 m apart. What field intensity exists between them?
3. What voltage is applied to a pair of parallel plates 0.04 m apart to develop a field intensity of 2500 nt/coul?
4. How much work is done to transfer 1 coul of charge through a potential difference of 220 volts?
5. A generator transfers 20 coul of charge through a potential difference of 90 volts. (a) How much work does the generator perform? (b) The generator accomplishes this transfer in 60 sec. How much work does it do per sec? (c) What power does the generator deliver in watts?
6. A 60-volt battery transfers 22 coul of negative charge from its negative plate to its positive plate. How much work is done?
7. How much work is done to transfer 6 coulombs of charge through a potential difference of 1.5 volts?
8. A 12-volt battery is connected to an electric motor. The current through the motor is 2 amp. (a) How many joules of energy does the battery deliver to the motor each second? (b) What power does the motor use in watts? (c) How much energy does the motor use in 10 min?
9. (a) What power does a 120-volt generator deliver to an electric lamp that draws 0.5 amp? (b) How many joules of energy does the lamp use in 5 min?
10. A resistance of 15 ohms is placed across a 45-volt battery. What current flows through the resistance?

11. A 20-ohm resistor is connected to a 30-volt battery. What current flows through the resistor?

12. What voltage is applied to a 20-ohm resistor if the current through it is 1.5 amp?

13. What is the resistance of a lamp that is connected to a 120-volt source and draws 1.5 amp of current?

14. What current flows through an electric device that is of 15 ohms resistance and designed to operate on 6 volts?

15. The resistance of an electric motor is 7 ohms. The motor operates properly on a voltage of 12 volts. What current does it require?

16. What voltage is placed across a motor of 15 ohms operating resistance to deliver 8 amp of current?

17. A heating coil has a resistance of 4 ohms and operates on 120 volts. (a) What current flows through the coil while it is operating? (b) What energy in joules is supplied to the coil in 5 min? (c) How many calories of heat does the coil provide during the 5 min?

18. (a) What current passes through a 6-ohm resistor connected to a 15-volt battery? (b) The resistance is a pure resistance. What heat does it produce in 10 min?

19. (a) How many joules of energy does a 60-watt incandescent lamp use in half an hour? (b) The lamp is 25% efficient. How many calories of heat does it generate during the half hour?

Series and Parallel Circuits

Series and parallel refer to the manner in which resistors are connected into an electric circuit. The manner in which they are connected determines the total resistance in the circuit and the functioning of electrical devices which are a part of the circuit. Why do some strands of colored lights go out completely when only one bulb burns out, while other strands continue to function when only one bulb burns out?

The arrangement of resistances in a circuit affects the current through each resistor and the voltage drop across each resistor. Resistors are connected in two basic ways: in series or in parallel.

25:1 Series Circuits

In resistors connected in a series, the current travels through each resistor one after the other. Figure 25-1 shows a series curcuit. The electron current in the

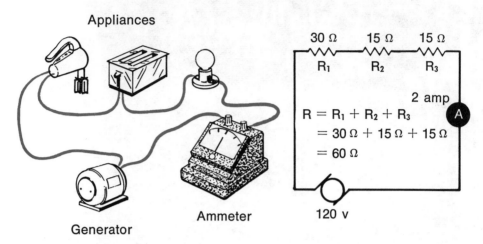

Figure 25-1.   A series circuit represented both pictorially and schematically. The total resistance in a series circuit is equal to the sum of the individual resistances.

circuit passes through each appliance, then through the lamp in succession. *The current in each resistance is exactly the same.* The current flowing in a series circuit is the same everywhere in the circuit.

The current, in turn, encounters resistance by each resistor. Consequently, it is opposed by the sum of the resistances. *The total resistance of a series circuit (R) is equal to the sum of the individual resistances in the circuit.*

$$R = R_1 + R_2 + R_3 \ldots$$

To find the current flowing in the circuit, determine the total resistance of the circuit and apply Ohm's law.

Sample Problem 1

Four 15-ohm resistors are connected in series across a 30-volt battery. What current flows in the circuit?

Solution:

Find the total resistance of the circuit.

$$R = R_1 + R_2 + R_3 + R_4$$
$$= 15 \text{ ohms} + 15 \text{ ohms} + 15 \text{ ohms} + 15 \text{ ohms}$$
$$= 60 \text{ ohms}$$

Then apply Ohm's law to the circuit.

$$i = \frac{V}{R}$$
$$= \frac{30 \text{ volts}}{60 \text{ ohms}}$$
$$= 0.5 \text{ amp}$$

Problems

1. Three 20-ohm resistors are connected in series across a 120-volt generator. (a) What is the total resistance of the circuit? (b) What current flows in the circuit?

2. A 10-ohm resistor, a 15-ohm resistor, and a 5-ohm resistor are connected in series across a 90-volt battery. (a) What is the total resistance of the circuit? (b) What current flows in the circuit?

3. Ten Christmas tree bulbs are of equal resistance. When connected to a 120-volt outlet, a current of 0.5 amp flows through the bulbs. (a) What is the total resistance of the circuit? (b) What is the resistance of each bulb?

4. A 16-ohm resistor, a 14-ohm resistor, and a 30-ohm resistor are connected in series across a 45-volt battery. (a) What is the total resistance of the circuit? (b) What current flows in the circuit?

5. An incandescent lamp of resistance 10-ohms is connected across a 15-volt battery. (a) What current flows through the lamp? (b) What resistance is connected in series with the lamp to reduce the current flowing through it to 0.5 amp?

6. (a) What current flows through a 60-watt bulb when it is connected across a 120-volt outlet? (b) What is the resistance of two 60-watt bulbs connected in series? (c) What current flows through the two bulbs when connected in series and placed across a 120-volt outlet?

25:2 Voltage Drops in a Series Circuit

When resistors are connected in series, each resistance uses a part of the voltage applied to the circuit. The voltage used is proportional to the resistance. To determine the *voltage drop* across each resistor, multiply the current in the circuit by the resistance.

$$V_1 = iR_1 = 2 \text{ amp} \times 10\,\Omega = 20 \text{ v}$$
$$V_2 = iR_2 = 2 \text{ amp} \times 20\,\Omega = 40 \text{ v}$$
$$V_3 = iR_3 = 2 \text{ amp} \times \underline{30\,\Omega = 60} \text{ v}$$
$$V = 120 \text{ v}$$

In Figure 25-2, the total resistance of the circuit is 10 ohms + 20 ohms + 30 ohms, or 60 ohms. By Ohm's law, the current in the circuit is 120 volts/60 ohms = 2 amp. To find the voltage drop across each resistor, apply Ohm's law to that resistor. *Ohm's law may be applied to the entire circuit or to any part of the circuit.* Since $V = iR$, the voltage drop across the first resistor R_1 is iR_1. This is 2 amp × 10 ohms = 20 volts. Use the same method for V_2 and V_3. The

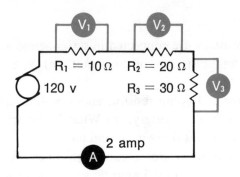

Figure 25-2.   A series circuit diagram showing the voltage drop across the resistance.

voltage drops are 40 volts and 60 volts respectively. The sum of the voltage drops across the resistors is equal to the voltage drop across the entire circuit.

$$V = V_1 + V_2 + V_3$$

Sample Problem 2

A 5-ohm resistor and a 10-ohm resistor are connected in series and placed across a 45-volt difference in potential. (a) What is the total resistance of the circuit? (b) What current flows through the circuit? (c) What is the voltage drop across each resistor? (d) What is the total voltage drop across the circuit?

Solution:

(a) $R = R_1 + R_2$
$ = 5$ ohms $+ 10$ ohms
$ = 15$ ohms

(b) $i = \dfrac{V}{R}$
$ = \dfrac{45 \text{ volts}}{15 \text{ ohms}}$
$ = 3$ amp

(c) The voltage drop across R_1 is
$V_1 = iR_1$
$ = 3$ amp $\times 5$ ohms
$ = 15$ volts
The voltage drop across R_2 is
$V_2 = iR_2$
$ = 3$ amp $\times 10$ ohms
$ = 30$ volts

(d) $V = V_1 + V_2$
$ = 15$ volts $+ 30$ volts
$ = 45$ volts

Problems

7. A 20-ohm resistor and a 30-ohm resistor are connected in series and placed across a 100-volt difference in potential. (a) What is the total resistance of the circuit? (b) What current flows through the circuit? (c) What is the voltage drop across each resistance? (d) What is the total voltage drop across both resistances?

8. Three 30-ohm resistors are connected in series and placed across a difference in potential of 135 volts. Calculate: (a) the total resistance of the circuit (b) the current flowing in the circuit (c) the voltage drop across each resistance (d) the total voltage drop across all three resistors

9. Three resistors of 3 ohms, 5 ohms, and 4 ohms are connected in series across a 12-volt battery. (a) What is the combined resistance of the three resistors? (b) What current flows in the circuit? (c) What is the voltage drop across each resistor? (d) What is the total voltage drop across the circuit?

10. Four resistors of 6 ohms each are connected in series and placed across a voltage source. The current flowing in the circuit is 1.6 amp. (a) What is the total resistance of the circuit? (b) What is the voltage of the source? (c) What is the voltage drop across each of the resistors?

11. A 10-ohm resistance and a variable resistor are connected in series and placed across a 12-volt source. The variable resistor is adjusted until the current flowing in the circuit is 0.6 amp. (a) At what resistance is the variable resistor set? (b) What is the voltage drop across the resistor and the variable resistor?

12. A 40-ohm resistor and a variable resistor are connected in series across a 120-volt outlet. (a) At what resistance is the variable resistor set if a current of 2 amp flows in the circuit? (b) At what value is the variable resistance set if the current in the circuit is 0.5 amp?

25:3   Parallel Circuits

Figure 25-3 illustrates three resistors connected in parallel across a 120-volt generator. This circuit differs markedly from the series circuits in Section 25:1. The wires running from the generator to points A and B are of negligible resistance. They may be considered extensions of the generator terminals. Each line from point A to point B is a complete circuit across the generator and behaves as if the other lines are not present. A 60-ohm resistor across a difference in potential of 120 volts draws 2 amp of current. This is done by each 60-ohm resistor in Figure 25-3. The three 60-ohm resistors together draw three times as much current as would flow if any one of the resistors were the only one across the generator. Therefore, the circuit has a total resistance of only one-third that

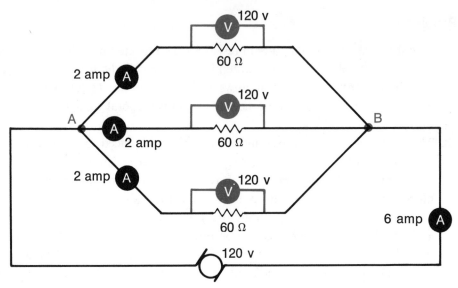

Figure 25-3.   In a parallel circuit the reciprocal of the total resistance is equal to the sum of the reciprocals of the individual resistances.

of any one resistor it contains. Placing resistors in parallel decreases the total resistance of the circuit since each new resistor provides a new path from A to B for the electrons to follow.

To find the total resistance of a parallel circuit,

$$\frac{1}{R} = \frac{1}{R_1} + \frac{1}{R_2} + \frac{1}{R_3} \cdots$$

The total resistance of the circuit of the three 60-ohm resistors in Figure 25-3 is:

$$\frac{1}{R} = \frac{1}{60} + \frac{1}{60} + \frac{1}{60}$$

$$\frac{1}{R} = \frac{3}{60}$$

$$R = 20 \text{ ohms}$$

According to Ohm's law, the current in the circuit is $\frac{V}{R} = \frac{120 \text{ volts}}{20 \text{ ohms}} = 6 \text{ amp.}$

This is the total current when the 2 amp of current in each of the three resistors in the circuit are added together. The total current in a parallel circuit is the sum of the currents in the individual branches.

$$i = i_1 + i_2 + i_3 \cdots$$

The voltage drop across each resistor is the difference in potential between A and B. It is the same across each resistor. The voltage drop in a parallel circuit is the same everywhere. In Figure 25-3, this is the voltage of the generator, or 120 volts.

Sample Problem 3

Three resistors of 60 ohms, 30 ohms, and 20 ohms respectively are connected in parallel across a 90-volt difference in potential. Calculate: (a) the total resistance of the circuit (b) the current flowing in the entire circuit (c) the current flowing through each branch of the circuit.

Solution:

(a) $\dfrac{1}{R} = \dfrac{1}{R_1} + \dfrac{1}{R_2} + \dfrac{1}{R_3}$

$= \dfrac{1}{60} + \dfrac{1}{30} + \dfrac{1}{20}$

$\dfrac{1}{R} = \dfrac{6}{60}$

$R = 10$ ohms

(b) $i = \dfrac{V}{R}$

$= \dfrac{90 \text{ volts}}{10 \text{ ohms}}$

$= 9$ amp

(c) The voltage drop across each resistor is 90 volts.

For R_1, $i_1 = \dfrac{V}{R_1}$

$= \dfrac{90 \text{ volts}}{60 \text{ ohms}}$

$= 1.5$ amp

For R_2, $i_2 = \dfrac{V}{R_2}$

$= \dfrac{90 \text{ volts}}{30 \text{ ohms}}$

$= 3$ amp

For R_3, $i_3 = \dfrac{V}{R_3}$

$= \dfrac{90 \text{ volts}}{20 \text{ ohms}}$

$= 4.5$ amp

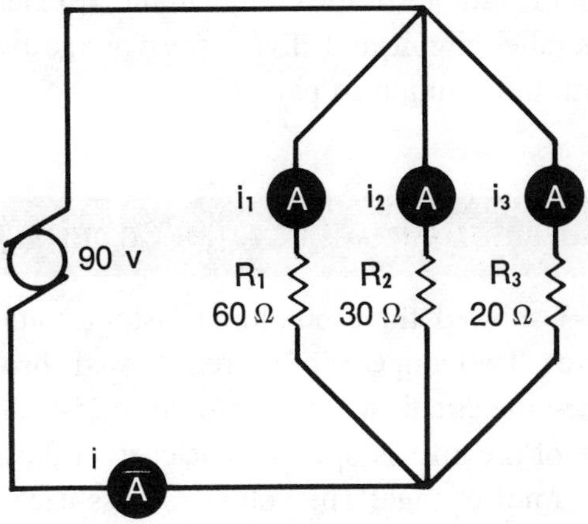

Figure 25-4

The sum of the current in the lines is 9 amp as predicted by part (b). Part (c) could be solved first by adding the currents in the lines and dividing the voltage by the sum of the currents to yield the total resistance of the circuit. This would give the same solution as in part (a).

Problems

13. Three 15-ohm resistors are connected in parallel and placed across a difference in potential of 30 volts. (a) What is the total resistance of the parallel circuit? (b) What current flows through the entire circuit? (c) What current flows through each branch of the circuit?

14. Two 10-ohm resistors are connected in parallel and placed across the terminals of a 15-volt battery. (a) What is the total resistance of the parallel circuit? (b) What current flows in the circuit? (c) What current flows through each branch of the circuit?

15. A 120-ohm resistor, a 60-ohm resistor, and a 40-ohm resistor are connected in parallel and placed across a difference in potential of 120 volts. (a) What is the total resistance of the parallel circuit? (b) What current flows through the entire circuit? (c) What current flows through each branch of the circuit?

16. A 6-ohm resistor, an 18-ohm resistor, and a 9-ohm resistor are connected in parallel and placed across a 36-volt difference in potential. (a) What current flows through each resistor? (b) What total current flows in the circuit? (c) What is the total resistance of the circuit?

17. A 75-ohm heater and a 150-ohm lamp are connected in parallel across a generator supplying a difference in potential of 150 volts. (a) What current flows through the 75-ohm heater? (b) What current flows through the 150-ohm lamp? (c) What current flows through the entire circuit? (d) What is the total resistance of the entire circuit? (e) Determine the total resistance of the parallel circuit and divide the voltage by the resistance. Does this agree with the solution to part (c)?

25:4   Characteristics of Parallel Circuits

Figure 25-3 showed three 60-ohm resistors connected in parallel across a 120-volt source. Two amperes of current flowed through each resistor, and the total current in the circuit was 6 amp. Figure 25-5 shows the same circuit but a switch in one of the lines is opened. The current flowing through the remaining two lines does not change. The voltage across each line is still 120 volts. The current flowing through each line is still 2 amp. The total resistance of the circuit increases from 20 to 30 ohms. This agrees with the 4 amp current requirements of the two remaining resistors. The important characteristic of a parallel circuit is that each resistor can be operated independently of whatever else is going on in the circuit. If one of the lines is opened so no current flows through it, the current flowing in the other parts of the circuit is not affected in any way. When a switch is opened anywhere in a series circuit, or if any one of the resistances

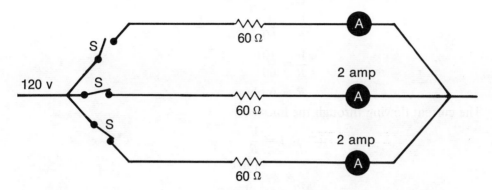

Figure 25-5. Three 60 ohm resistances in parallel but having one switch open. The total resistance of the remaining circuit changes so that the current output in the two resistors is the same as when all three resistances are connected.

burns out, current does not flow anywhere in the circuit. For these reasons, a series circuit is not practical for house wiring. Houses wired in series would require every device to be either on or off simultaneously.

Figure 25-6 shows the general plan of house wiring. Generators at the power stations provide 120 volts. Inside the house, two lines run through the walls to convenient outlets to plug in appliances and lamps. The two wires are much closer together than the diagram indicates.

Figure 25-6. House-wiring diagram indicating the parallel nature of the circuit containing appliances having different resistances. This arrangement permits the use of one or more appliances at a given time; however, one must be careful not to overload the circuit.

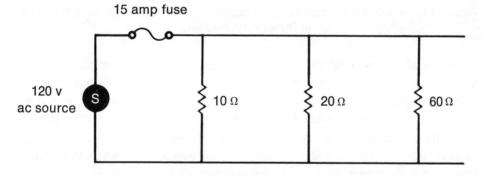

Across the two lines of the diagram are three resistors. One resistor is a 10-ohm heater, another a 20-ohm refrigerator, and the third a 60-ohm lamp. Each device forms a complete circuit across the 120-volt line. Each device operates independently of the others in the circuit. However, if all three devices operate simultaneously, the total resistance is:

$$\frac{1}{R} = \frac{1}{60} + \frac{1}{20} + \frac{1}{10}$$

$$\frac{1}{R} = \frac{10}{60}$$

$$R = 6 \text{ ohms}$$

The current flowing through the lines is,

$$i = \frac{V}{R}$$

$$= \frac{120}{6}$$

$$= 20 \text{ amp}$$

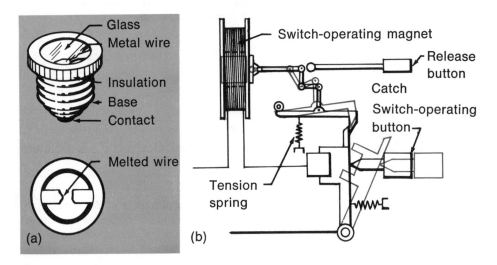

Figure 25-7.   A circuit overload which may result in fire can be prevented by (a) a fuse, or (b) a circuit breaker.

Fuses and circuit breakers in the line act as safety devices to prevent overloading the circuit. A circuit overload occurs when too many appliances are placed across the lines. Each appliance causes more current to flow through these lines. Several appliances placed in the circuit can increase the current flowing in the lines. This current increase may produce a heating effect (i^2R) large enough to cause a fire. A fuse is a short piece of metal which melts when the heating effect of the current reaches a predetermined magnitude. If an overload occurred in Figure 25-6, the fuse would melt and no current would flow anywhere in the circuit. Usually, houses are wired so several separate circuits lead to different parts of the house. This tends to prevent a circuit overload. A circuit breaker is an automatic switch that cuts off current when the circuit is overloaded.

A short circuit occurs when a short piece of low resistance wire is placed across the circuit. This happens if a lamp cord becomes frayed and the wires are brought together accidentally. A short piece of copper wire in the lamp cord might have a resistance of 0.01 ohms. When placed across 120 volts, this resistance draws 120 volts/0.01 ohms, or 12 000 amp. The fuse or circuit breaker immediately blows and prevents the wire from becoming hot and starting a fire.

25:5   Series-Parallel Circuits

Frequently a circuit may consist of series and parallel connections. To determine how the current or the difference in potential is distributed in the various parts of the circuit, Ohm's law is applied to each part of the circuit as well as to the whole circuit.

Sample Problem 4

In Figure 25-8, a 30-ohm resistor is connected in parallel with a 20-ohm resistor. The parallel connection is placed in series with an 8-ohm resistor across a 60-volt difference of potential. (a) What is the total resistance of the parallel portion of the circuit? (b) What is the resistance of the entire circuit? (c) What current flows in the circuit? (d) What is the voltage drop across the 8-ohm resistor? (e) What is the voltage drop across the parallel portion of the circuit? (f) What current flows through each line of the parallel portion of the circuit?

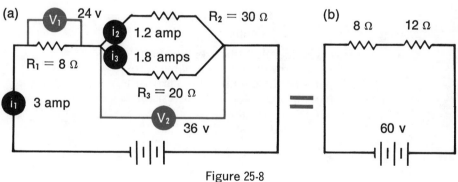

Figure 25-8

Solution:

(a) R_2 and R_3 are connected in parallel. Their combined resistance is

$$\frac{1}{R} = \frac{1}{R_2} + \frac{1}{R_3}$$

$$\frac{1}{R} = \frac{1}{30} + \frac{1}{20}$$

$$\frac{1}{R} = \frac{5}{60}$$

$$R = 12 \text{ ohms}$$

(b)   The circuit is now a series circuit (Figure 25-8, part b) with an 8-ohm resistor and a 12-ohm resistor in series.

$$R = R_1 + R_{2,3}$$
$$= 8 \text{ ohms} + 12 \text{ ohms}$$
$$= 20 \text{ ohms}$$

(c)   The current flowing in the circuit is

$$i = \frac{V}{R}$$
$$= \frac{60 \text{ volts}}{20 \text{ ohms}}$$
$$= 3 \text{ amp}$$

(d)   The voltage drop across the 8-ohm resistor is

$$V = iR_1$$
$$= 3 \text{ amp} \times 8 \text{ ohms}$$
$$= 24 \text{ volts}$$

(e)   The parallel portion of the circuit behaves as a 12-ohm resistor. Therefore, the voltage drop across it is

$$V = iR_{2,3}$$
$$= 3 \text{ amp} \times 12 \text{ ohms}$$
$$= 36 \text{ volts}$$

(f)   The 36-volt drop across the parallel portion of the circuit is the same across all parts of the circuit. This means the current through the 30-ohm resistor is

$$i = \frac{V}{R_2}$$
$$= \frac{36 \text{ volts}}{30 \text{ ohms}}$$
$$= 1.2 \text{ amp}$$

The current through the 20-ohm resistor is

$$i = \frac{V}{R_3}$$
$$= \frac{36 \text{ volts}}{20 \text{ ohms}}$$
$$= 1.8 \text{ amp}$$

The total current through the parallel part of the circuit is 1.2 amp plus 1.8 amp, or 3 amp. This agrees with the current in the circuit as a whole.

Problems

18. Two 60-ohm resistors are connected in parallel. This parallel arrangement is connected in series with a 30-ohm resistor. The entire circuit is then placed across a 120-volt difference in potential. (a) What is the resistance of the parallel portion of the circuit? (b) What is the resistance of the entire circuit? (c) What current flows in the circuit? (d) What is the voltage drop across the 30-ohm resistor? (e) What is the voltage drop across the parallel portion of the circuit? (f) What current flows in each branch of the parallel portion of the circuit?

19. Three 15-ohm resistors are connected in parallel. This arrangement is connected in series with a 10-ohm resistor. The entire circuit is then placed across a 45-volt difference in potential. (a) What is the resistance of the parallel portion of the circuit? (b) What is the resistance of the entire circuit? (c) What current flows in the circuit? (d) What is the voltage drop across the 10-ohm resistor? (e) What is the voltage drop across the parallel portion of the circuit? (f) What current flows in each branch of the parallel portion of the circuit?

20. Three 15-ohm resistors are connected in parallel. They are connected in series to a second set of three 15-ohm resistors, also connected in parallel. The entire circuit is then placed across the terminals of a 12-volt battery. (a) What is the total resistance of the circuit? (b) What current flows through the circuit? (c) What current flows through each resistor?

21. Determine the reading of each ammeter and voltmeter in Figure 25-9.

Figure 25-9

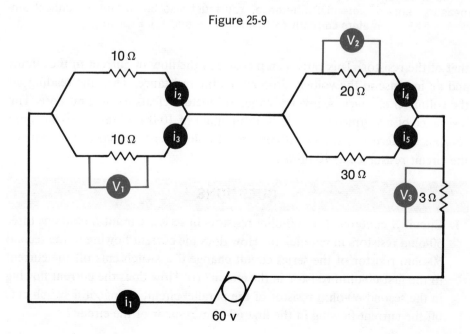

60 v

25:6   Ammeters and Voltmeters

An ammeter is placed in a circuit in series with the resistors. A voltmeter is placed in parallel with the resistor where the voltage drop is measured. The resistance of an ammeter must be extremely low. Otherwise it changes the entire resistance of the circuit in which it is placed. If an ammeter has sufficient resistance to influence the total resistance of the circuit, it changes the current flowing in the circuit and defeats its own purpose.

Conversely, a voltmeter must have a very high resistance. This is necessary so as not to affect the resistance of that portion of the circuit where the difference in potential is being measured. A low resistance voltmeter placed in parallel with a second resistance constitutes a parallel circuit of lower resistance than

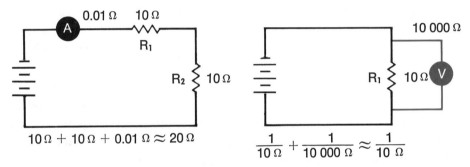

$$10\,\Omega + 10\,\Omega + 0.01\,\Omega \approx 20\,\Omega$$

$$\frac{1}{10\,\Omega} + \frac{1}{10\,000\,\Omega} \approx \frac{1}{10\,\Omega}$$

Figure 25-10. (a) An ammeter is wired in series with the resistor during measurements of current flow. (b) A voltmeter is wired in parallel with the resistor during measurements of potential difference. You must also be careful to connect ammeters correctly as to polarity (+ and −). Explain.

that of the resistor. This causes an increase in the flow of current in the circuit and an increase in the voltage drop across the resistance. Then the reading on the voltmeter changes. A low resistance voltmeter defeats its own purpose. The resistance of a voltmeter usually is a minimum of 10 000 ohms. A 10 000-ohm resistance placed in parallel with another 10-ohm resistance keeps that part of the circuit resistance at 10 ohms.

QUESTIONS

1. Circuit *A* contains three 60-ohm resistors in series. Circuit *B* contains three 60-ohm resistors in parallel. (a) How does the current flowing in the second 60-ohm resistor of the series circuit change if a switch cuts off the current to the first 60-ohm resistor in the circuit? (b) How does the current flowing in the second 60-ohm resistor of the parallel circuit change if a switch cuts off the current flowing in the first 60-ohm resistor of the circuit?

2. What is the difference in resistance between three 60-ohm resistors connected in series and three 60-ohm resistors connected in parallel?

3. A man needs a 10-ohm control resistor and a 15-ohm control resistor. He has only 30-ohm resistors in stock. Must he go buy resistors or can he save himself a trip? Explain.

4. The total current flowing through a parallel circuit is equal to the sum of the current flowing through its branches. $i = i_1 + i_2 + i_3$, and so on. Since the voltage across each branch of a parallel circuit is the same, this equation written in Ohm's law form is $\frac{V}{R} = \frac{V}{R_1} + \frac{V}{R_2} + \frac{V}{R_3}$. Remember that the voltages are all equal. Now rewrite this equation in a more simplified form.

5. For each part of this question, write whichever applies: *series circuit* or *parallel circuit*.
   (a) The current is the same throughout.
   (b) The total resistance is equal to the sum of the individual resistances.
   (c) The total resistance is less than the resistance of the lowest value resistor in the circuit.
   (d) The voltage drop is the same across each resistor.
   (e) The voltage drop is proportional to the resistance.
   (f) Adding a resistor decreases the total resistance.
   (g) Adding a resistor increases the total resistance.
   (h) If one resistor is shut off or broken, no current flows in the entire circuit
   (i) If one resistor is shut off, the current through all other resistors remains the same.
   (j) Suitable for house wiring.

6. Explain the function of a fuse in an electric circuit.

7. Why does an ammeter have a very low resistance?

8. Why does a voltmeter have a very high resistance?

9. What is a short circuit? Why is a short circuit dangerous?

PROBLEMS

1. Two resistors of 5 ohms and 7 ohms are connected in series across a 12-volt battery. (a) What is the total resistance of the circuit? (b) What current flows through the 5-ohm resistor? (c) What current flows through the 7-ohm resistor? (d) What is the voltage drop across each resistor?

2. Two 6-ohm resistors and a 3-ohm resistor are connected in series. A potential difference of 6 volts is applied to the circuit. (a) What is the total resistance of the circuit? (b) What current flows in the circuit? (c) What is the voltage drop across each resistor?

3. A light bulb has a resistance of 2 ohms. It is connected in series with a variable resistor. A difference in potential of 6 volts is applied to the circuit. An ammeter indicates that the current of the circuit is 0.5 amp. At what resistance is the variable resistor set?

4. What resistance is connected in series with an 8-ohm resistor that is connected to a 60-volt generator if the current through the resistors is 4 amp?

5. Ten Christmas tree lights are connected in series. When they are plugged into a 120-volt outlet, the current flowing through the lights is 0.75 amp. What is the resistance of each light?

6. A 20-ohm lamp and a 5-ohm lamp are connected in series and placed across a difference in potential of 50 volts. (a) What is the total resistance of the circuit? (b) What current flows in the circuit? (c) What is the voltage drop across each resistor?

7. A 20-ohm lamp and a 5-ohm lamp are connected in parallel and placed across a difference in potential of 50 volts. (a) What is the total resistance of the circuit? (b) What current flows in the circuit? (c) What current flows through each resistor? (d) What is the voltage drop across each resistor?

8. A 16-ohm resistor, a 20-ohm resistor, and an 80-ohm resistor are connected in parallel. A difference in potential of 40 volts is applied to the combination. (a) Compute the total resistance of the parallel circuit. (b) What total current flows in the circuit? (c) What current flows through the 16-ohm resistor?

9. A household circuit contains six 240-ohm lamps (60 watt bulbs) and a 10-ohm heater. The voltage across the circuit is 120 volts. (a) What current flows in the circuit when four lamps are on? (b) What current flows when all six lamps are on? (c) What current flows in the circuit if all six lamps and the heater are operating?

10. Determine the reading of each ammeter and each voltmeter.

Figure 25-11

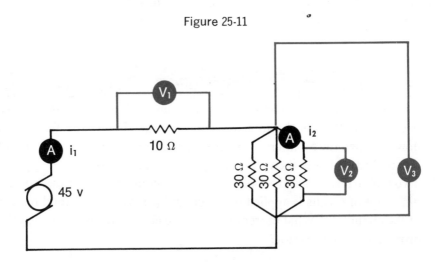

11. Determine the reading of each ammeter and each voltmeter.

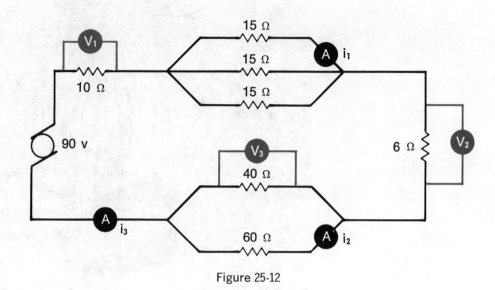

Figure 25-12

12. Determine the power in watts consumed by each resistance shown in Figure 25-11.

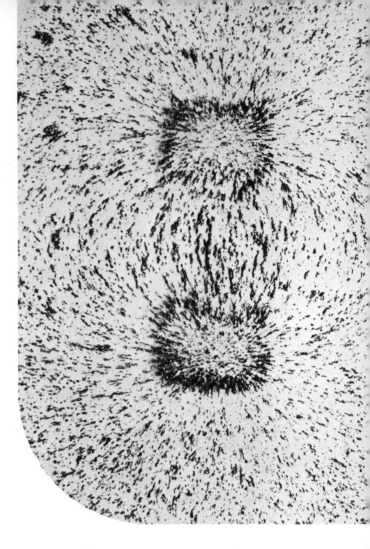

26

The Magnetic Field

Magnetism was studied by the early Greeks who observed the attraction of a rock known as lodestone for iron. Pieces of iron, depending on their arrangement, were found to attract or repel one another. Magnetized iron suspended to allow free rotation was observed to orient itself in a north-south direction, thus resulted the first compass. In the above photograph can you see a pattern in the iron filings located around the two magnetic poles?

26:1 General Properties of Magnets

Many electric measuring devices depend upon the relationship of magnetism to electricity. Before the magnetic effects of electric currents are studied, a knowledge of magnetic fields is necessary. A magnetic field is a region in which a magnetic force is detected. Magnetic force is detected by the behavior of a magnet in the field. Here is a summary of the properties of a magnet.

1. A magnet has polarity. The end of a suspended magnet that points north is the north seeking pole (*N* pole) of the magnet. The opposite end that points south is its south seeking pole (*S* pole). These poles are distinct but not separable.

2. Like magnetic poles repel one another. Unlike magnetic poles attract one another.

3. Iron, cobalt, and nickel are the important magnetic substances. Strong, permanent magnets are made from these metals and alloys of these metals. Permanent magnets retain their magnetism for some time.

4. Iron, cobalt, and nickel are magnetized by induction. When a magnetic substance is close to or touches a magnet, it becomes a magnet also. A soft-iron nail on the end of a bar magnet becomes a temporary magnet. When removed from the strong magnet, the nail quickly loses its magnetic properties.

5. A magnetic compass is a small suspended magnet. The north seeking pole of the compass magnet points north. The magnetic north pole of the earth and the geographic north pole of the earth are not in the same place. A compass points toward the magnetic north pole but not necessarily toward true geographic north.

Figure 26-1.   (a) Magnets attract and repel the poles of other magnets. (b) A magnet induces magnetic properties in certain metals. (c) A suspended magnet may be used as a compass needle. The N pole points to the earth's magnetic north pole.

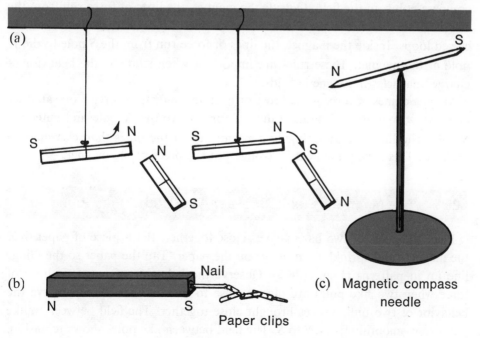

(a)

(b)   Nail   N   S   Paper clips

(c)   Magnetic compass needle

26:2 The Magnetic Fields Around Permanent Magnets

To demonstrate the presence of a magnetic field around a permanent magnet, cover the magnet with a piece of paper. Sprinkle small iron filings onto the paper. The iron filings form lines running from pole to pole (Figure 26-2). These

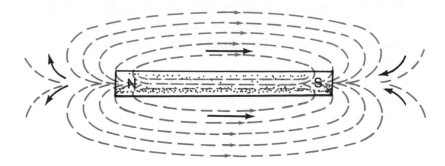

Figure 26-2.   Lines of force extend from the N pole to the S pole outside the magnet and from the S pole to the N Pole inside the magnet.

lines are lines of force or magnetic flux. Lines of force are not actual lines. They are imaginary lines taken by the magnetic flow or flux when passing from pole to pole. *The flux density is the number of lines per unit area.* The intensity of the magnetic field is proportional to the flux density.

The direction of the magnetic lines of force is the direction the N pole of a compass points in the field. Outside the magnet, the lines of force run from the N pole of the magnet to the S pole of the magnet. Lines of force always exist in closed loops. Inside the magnet, the lines of force run from the S pole to the N pole of the magnet. These rules are important when studying the behavior of charged particles in magnetic fields.

Magnetic lines of force never cross or overlap. In fact, they repel one another and follow well-defined paths. Lines of force leave the N pole and enter the S pole. The lines are more highly concentrated at the poles than elsewhere in the field. This is why the field is strongest at the poles of the magnet.

26:3 The Magnetic Fields Between Like and Unlike Poles

Place the poles of two bar magnets close together. Put a piece of paper over the magnets and sprinkle iron filings on the paper. Tap the paper so the filings line up in patterns (Figure 26-3). Observe the behavior of magnetic lines of force when two like poles are placed close to one another. Now observe the behavior of two unlike poles brought close together. The field between unlike poles runs smoothly from N to S. The field between like poles shows repulsion.

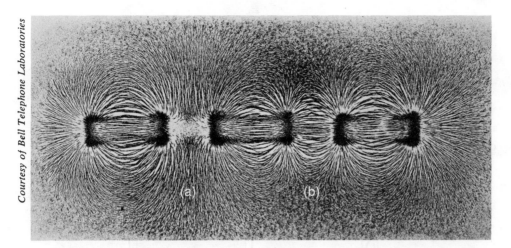

Figure 26-3.　(a) Repulsion of like poles. (b) Attraction of unlike poles.

26:4　Electromagnetism

In 1820, the Danish physicist Hans Christian Oersted (1777–1851) made one of the most important scientific discoveries of all time. Oersted determined that when a current-bearing wire is held near a compass needle, the needle is deflected This discovery opened up the entire field of electromagnetism. Eventually it led to a partial understanding of the nature of light. The discovery of electromagnetism lent impetus to the industrial revolution.

The mere presence of wire does not account for the deflection of a compass needle (a magnet) when it is near a current-bearing wire. Copper wires do not affect magnets. The deflection of the needle is accounted for only in terms of the current flowing through the wire. When an electric current flows in a wire, a magnetic field appears about the wire. *Electric currents produce magnetic fields.*

Figure 26-4. The lead sphere floats between two lead rings that carry electric currents when the temperature is near absolute zero. The repulsion between magnetic fields of the sphere and rings balances the sphere's weight so that it floats.

26:5   The Field About a Current-Bearing Wire

To investigate the magnetic field about a current-bearing wire, place a wire vertically through a piece of cardboard. Pass an electric current through the wire. Sprinkle iron filings on the cardboard around the wire. Tap the cardboard until the filings arrange themselves in concentric circles (circles with a common center) about the wire.

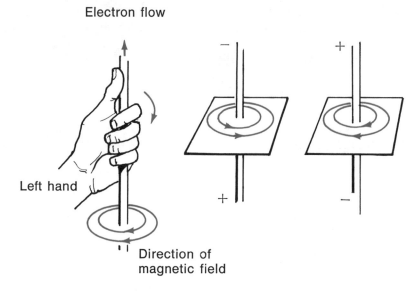

Figure 26-5.   Determining the direction of the magnetic field produced by current in a straight wire conductor.

The circular lines indicate that the lines of force form closed loops. The intensity of the magnetic field about the wire varies directly as the magnitude of the current flowing in the wire.

To find the direction of the magnetic field about the wire, use the left-hand rule. *Grasp the wire with the left hand. Keep the thumb of that hand pointed in the direction of electron flow. The fingers of the hand circle the wire pointing in the direction of the magnetic field.*

26:6   The Magnetic Field Around a Coil

Form a wire into a circular loop. The magnetic field inside the loop is created by the current flowing through the wire. The magnetic field runs in the same direction all around the loop. Apply the left-hand rule around the loop. The fingers always point in the same direction inside and outside the loop.

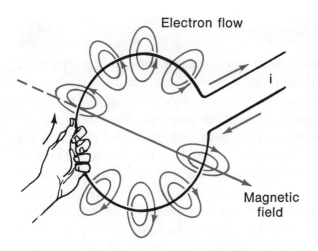

Electron flow

Magnetic field

Figure 26-6. The magnetic field about a circular loop of current-bearing wire. The circular field around the wire reinforces the field in the center of the loop.

Connect several loops of wire to a source of current (Figure 26-7). The coil (or solenoid) formed behaves like a permanent bar magnet. The coil has a north seeking pole and a south seeking pole. It is an electromagnet. Determine the direction of the *N* pole of the electromagnet by a second left-hand rule. *Grasp the coil with the left hand. Curl the fingers around the loops in the same direction as the electrons are flowing. The thumb points toward the N pole of the electromagnet.* The strength of an electromagnet is increased significantly by adding a soft iron core. The iron is influenced by the field inside the coil. The iron core becomes a magnet and adds its intensity to that of the coil.

The intensity of the magnetic field about a current-bearing wire is proportional to the current flowing in the wire. The intensity of the field about an electromagnet also is proportional to the current flowing through the wire. Each loop of wire of a coil has the same field about it as any other loop. The more loops added to an electromagnet, the stronger is the field. The strength of an electromagnet's magnetic field is proportional to the current, the number of turns or loops, and the nature of the core.

Figure 26-7. Finding the polarity of a solenoid by the left hand rule.

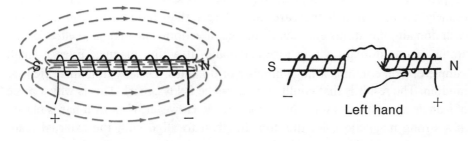

Electron flow　　　　　　　　　　　　　　Electron flow

26:7   Theory of Magnetism

Similarity between the behavior of an electromagnet and that of a permanent bar magnet is too strong to be the result of mere coincidence. In the early years of the nineteenth century, a theory of magnetism was postulated by Andre Ampere (1775-1836). Ampere reasoned that the magnetic effects of an electromagnetic coil are due to the current flowing through its loops. Therefore, the magnetic effects of a bar magnet must be the result of tiny "loops" of current within the bar. At that time, Ampere's reasoning was sound, and in essence, still is correct. The magnetic effect of a magnet is attributed to the electrons as they spin on their axes and move about the nuclei of atoms. Each moving electron constitutes a small electric current that sets up a magnetic field of its own. When a sufficient number of the atoms in a metal bar are oriented in the same way, their magnetic fields superimpose each other. Then the bar takes on the properties of a magnet.

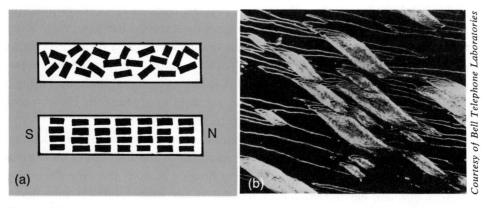

Figure 26-8.   (a) A model of the domain theory in which magnetic properties appear only when domains align. (b) Magnetic domains in iron-nickel-molybdenum alloy.

The atoms in a magnet do not operate independently of the surrounding atoms. Instead, the atoms act in groups or domains. The atoms in domains are coupled as a result of complementary electron spins. These domains are extremely small, although they are much larger than individual atoms. Within each domain, the atoms are aligned in one direction. The magnetic effect of the atoms of one domain acting together makes it a tiny magnet. Even a small sample of iron contains a huge number of domains. Usually domains orient at random. The result is that conflicting magnetic fields cancel. This is why a piece of iron does not always show magnetic effects. However, if an iron bar is placed in a strong magnetic field, the domains tend to align with the external field. Iron, cobalt, nickel, and their alloys often retain this domain alignment after being removed from the external field. Thus, they become permanent magnets.

26:8   Interaction of Magnetic Fields

Ampere conducted further experiments with magnetic fields. He noted that if two parallel wires carry current in the same direction, the wires attract one another. But if two parallel wires carry current in opposite directions, the wires repel one another. These forces of attraction and repulsion which wires exert on one another through magnetic fields result from the electric current flowing through the wires.

The intensity or strength of a magnetic field is given the symbol B. Because the terminology for field intensity was not known in Ampere's day, this is referred to as the induction of the magnetic field. *Induction as used here means field intensity.* Magnetic induction is a vector quantity. The symbol B represents the magnitude of the induction.

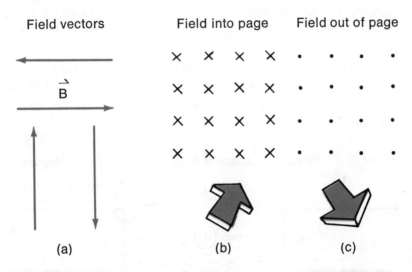

Figure 26-9. (a) Directions of magnetic field vectors are indicated by directional arrows when the field is in the plane of the page. (b) When the field is perpendicular to the plane of the page, crosses indicate the field into the page; (c) dots indicate the field out of the page toward you.

Figure 26-9 (a) shows magnetic field vectors, $\vec{B}$, in several different directions. Figure 26-9 (b) and (c) show magnetic field vectors directed perpendicular to the plane of the page. Those directed into the page are indicated by crosses. Those directed out of the page are indicated by dots. This convention is symbolic of a flight of arrows seen as points approaching the reader head on (dots). The crosses represent tail feathers receding from the reader. This convention is used in three-dimensional representations.

Figure 26-10 illustrates that the direction of the magnetic fields about each of the current-bearing wires agrees with the left-hand rule. Figure 26-10 (a) il-

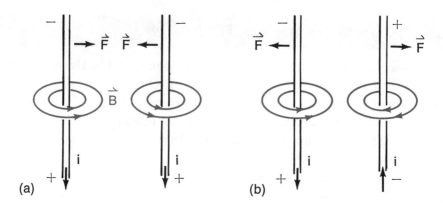

Figure 26-10. Two current bearing conductors (a) attract (b) repel.

lustrates that the fields between the wires are in opposition. Since magnetic fields add vectorially, the field between the wires is at weak strength while the field outside the wires is at normal strength. The wires are forced together, or attract each other.

In Figure 26-10 (b) the opposite situation exists. The fields between the wires act in the same direction. The field between the wires is strengthened. Outside the wires, the fields are at normal strength. Therefore, the wires are forced away from each other by the more intense field between them.

Figure 26-11. Forces of a magnetic field upon a current bearing wire.

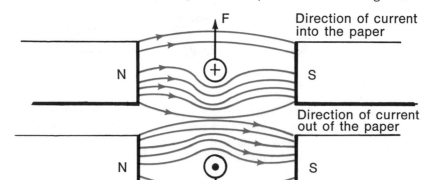

Observe the behavior of a small segment of wire at right angles to an external magnetic field. As a current is sent through the wire, a magnetic field appears about the wire. The two magnetic fields interact. In Figure 26-11 (a) the field due to the current in the wire opposes the field due to the magnets above the wire. The field below the wire is strengthened. The result is a net upward force perpendicular to both the external field and the direction of the current in the wire. In Figure 26-11 (b) the electrons flow in the opposite direction in the wire. Therefore, the field about the wire is opposite to that of Figure 26-11 (a). The wire is forced downward.

26:9   The Direction of the Force

The force on a current-carrying wire in a magnetic field is determined by the interaction between the field about the wire and the external magnetic field. A quicker method to determine the force is to use a third left-hand rule. *Point the fingers of the left hand in the direction of the magnetic field. Point the thumb in the direction of the electron flow in the wire. The palm of the hand then faces in the direction of the force acting on the wire.*

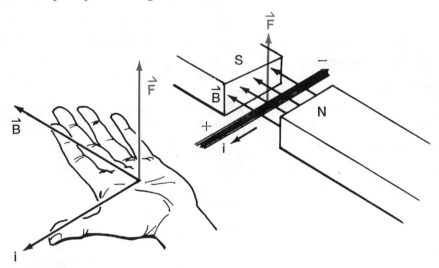

Figure 26-12. The left hand rule shows directions of force, current, and magnetic field.

26:10   Measuring the Force on the Wire

Michael Faraday discovered that when a wire and a magnetic field are at right angles, a force acts on the wire due to the interaction of the fields. The force is proportional to three factors:

(1) the magnetic induction or strength (B) of the field

(2) the electron current (i) in the wire

(3) the length of the wire (l) that lies in the magnetic field.

The force acting on the wire is proportional to the product of i, l, and B. If B is in the proper units,

$$F = Bil$$

To solve this equation for B,

$$B = \frac{F}{il}$$

The strength or induction of a magnetic field is measured in newtons per ampere-meter. That is, the strength of a magnetic field is measured in terms of the interaction force it exerts on the magnetic field produced about a standard length of wire carrying a standard current. This is the same method used to measure gravitational field strengths and electric field strengths. A gravitational field is evaluated by the force the gravitational field produces by interacting with the gravitational field about a standard kilogram mass (nt/kg). Electric field intensity measures the force of interaction of an electric field on a standard unit of charge. Electric field intensity is measured in newtons per coulomb (nt/coul). A magnetic field is evaluated in terms of its interaction with the standard magnetic field about a current-bearing wire. Thus B is expressed as newtons per ampere-meter.

Sample Problem 1

A wire 1 m long carries a current of 5 amp. The wire is at right angles to a uniform magnetic field. The force on the wire is 0.2 nt. What is the magnetic induction (B) of the field?

Solution:

$$B = \frac{F}{il} = \frac{0.2 \text{ nt}}{5 \text{ amp} \times 1 \text{ m}}$$
$$= 0.04 \text{ nt/amp-m}$$

Sample Problem 2

A wire 10 cm long is at right angles to a uniform magnetic field. The field has magnetic induction 0.06 nt/amp-m. The current through the wire is 4 amp. What force acts on the wire?

Solution:

$$F = Bil$$
$$= 0.06 \frac{\text{nt}}{\text{amp-m}} (4 \text{ amp})(0.1 \text{ m})$$
$$= 0.024 \text{ nt}$$

Problems

1. A wire 0.10 m long carrying a current of 2.0 amp is at right angles to a magnetic field. The force on the wire is 0.04 nt. What is the intensity of the magnetic field?

2. A wire 0.5 m long carrying a current of 8 amp is at right angles to a magnetic field of 0.40 nt/amp-m. What force acts on the wire?

3. A wire 75 cm long carrying a current of 6 amp is at right angles to a uniform magnetic field. The force acting on the wire is 0.6 nt. What is the magnetic induction of the field?

4. A magnetic field produces a force of 1.0 nt on a wire. The wire is 25 cm long and carries a current of 5 amp. What is the magnetic induction?

5. A copper wire 40 cm long carries a current of 6 amp and weighs 0.35 nt. Placed in a certain magnetic field, the wire remains suspended in the field. What is the induction of the field?

6. A wire 60 cm long is in a magnetic field of induction 0.4 nt/amp-m. The force acting on the wire is 1.8 nt. What current is in the wire?

7. A wire 0.03 m long carrying a current of 5 amp is at right angles to a magnetic field. The force acting on the wire is 9.0×10^{-3} nt. What is the induction of the magnetic field?

26:11   The Force on a Single Charged Particle

The development of efficient air pumps made it possible to manufacture large glass tubes with good vacuums. Vacuum tubes are equipped with a pair of metal electrodes. (Figure 26-13.) A high voltage is applied across the electrodes. A stream of electrons leaves the negative electrode (cathode) and moves across

Figure 26-13.   Apparatus for showing the effect of a magnetic field on moving electrons.

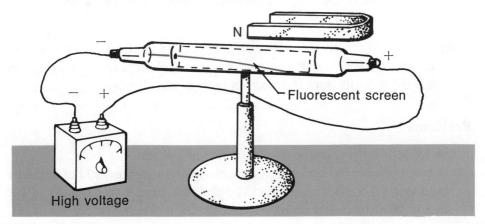

the tube to the positive electrode (anode). By applying a magnetic field to the tube, the beam of electrons is deflected.

The force *Bil* acts on a short wire at right angles to a magnetic field. *B* is the induction of the field in newtons per ampere-meter; *i* is the electron current flowing through the wire; and l is the length of the wire in the field. Substituting coulomb per second for current in amperes,

$$F = Bil$$

$$= B \times \frac{coul}{sec} \times m$$

$$= B \times \frac{q}{sec} \times m$$

Rearrange the sec from *q*/sec to m/sec

$$= B \times q \times \frac{m}{sec}$$

Since m/sec are units of velocity

$$F = Bqv$$

B is the induction of the magnetic field; *q* is the charge on the particle in coulombs; and *v* is the speed of the particle. This equation determines the force exerted on a charged particle as it moves through a magnetic field.

Sample Problem 3

A beam of electrons travels at 3.0×10^6 m/sec through a uniform magnetic field. The induction is 4.0×10^{-2} nt/amp-m. (a) The beam is at right angles to the magnetic field. What force acts on each electron? (b) What force acts on a proton moving at the same speed and in the same direction as the electron in part (a)?

Solution:

(a) $F = Bqv$

   $= (4.0 \times 10^{-2} \text{ nt/amp-m})(1.6 \times 10^{-19} \text{ coul})(3.0 \times 10^6 \text{ m/sec})$

   $= 1.9 \times 10^{-14}$ nt

(b) The force is exactly the same on a proton as an electron. The proton and the electron bear exactly the same charge in coulombs. Because the proton has the opposite sign, it deflects in the opposite direction.

Problems

Use 1.6×10^{-19} *coul as the elementary unit of charge.*

8. A beam of electrons moves perpendicularly to a magnetic field of magnetic induction 6.0×10^{-2} nt/amp-m. The electrons have a speed of 2.5×10^7 m/sec. What force acts on each electron?

9. An electron passes through a magnetic field perpendicularly to the field at a speed of 4.0×10^6 m/sec. The intensity of the magnetic field is 0.5 nt/amp-m. What force acts on the electron?

10. A stream of doubly-ionized particles (missing 2 electrons and so carrying a net charge of 2 elementary charges) moves at a speed of 3.0×10^4 m/sec perpendicularly to a magnetic field of 9.0×10^{-2} nt/amp-m. What force acts on each ion?

11. Triply ionized particles in a beam carry a net positive charge of three elementary charge units. The beam enters a magnetic field of magnetic induction 4.0×10^{-2} nt/amp-m at right angles to the field. The particles have a speed of 9.0×10^6 m/sec. What force acts on each?

26:12   Electric Motors

The current passing through a wire loop in a magnetic field is directed in one side of the loop and out the other side. Apply the third left-hand rule to each side of the loop. One side of the loop is forced down. The other side of the loop is forced up. The loop experiences a torque. Torque is the turning motion caused by a force at right angles to the motion. An electric motor operates on this principle.

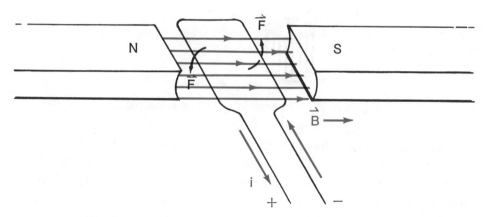

Figure 26-14.   A wire loop conducting a current is placed in a magnetic field. The wire exhibits a torque or turning effect.

A simple loop of wire in a magnetic field experiences a torque but does not rotate more than 180°. In Figure 26-14, the force acting upward on the right side of the loop pushes the loop up. At the same time, the force acting downward on the left side of the loop pushes that side down. The loop turns until it reaches the vertical position. The loop does not continue to turn because the force acting on the right side of the loop still is directed up. It cannot move down through the field. Likewise, the left side of the loop does not move up through the field. The force acting on it still is directed down.

For the loop to rotate 360° in the field, the current running through the loop must reverse just as the loop reaches the vertical position. This maintains the proper forces on the loop and enables it to rotate (Figure 26-15). The split-ring commutator conducts current into the loop by rubbing against the brushes. The split ring is arranged so that just as the loop reaches the vertical position, each half of the commutator changes brushes. Then the current in the loop reverses and the loop rotates.

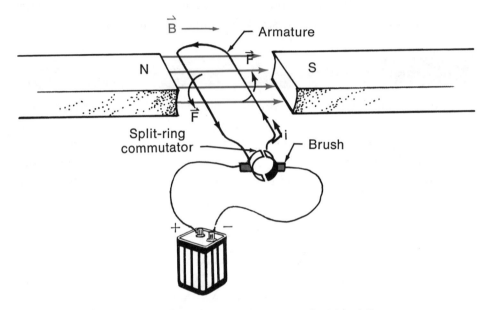

Figure 26-15.   The principle of the electric motor.

In practice, electric motors have several rotating loops. Collectively, they are the armature of the motor. The armature is basically a length of wire placed in a magnetic field. The total force acting on the armature is proportional to the product of Bil. The force acting on the armature can be varied. This is done by changing the magnetic field, by varying the current through the armature or by changing the number of loops in the armature which changes l.

26:13   Electric Meters

The force acting on a wire loop placed in the field of a permanent magnet depends on the strength of the current in the wire. Figure 26-16 illustrates how the force exerted on a loop of wire in a magnetic field is used to measure current in the loop. A small coil of wire is placed in the strong magnetic field of a per-

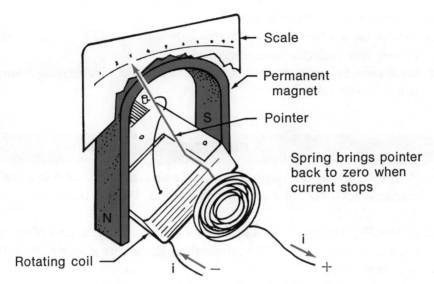

Scale

Permanent magnet

Pointer

Spring brings pointer back to zero when current stops

Rotating coil

Figure 26-16.   Components of an electric meter.

manent magnet. The current to be measured is allowed to flow through the coil. The current creates a magnetic field about the coil. The induction of the field is proportional to the intensity of the current. Therefore, the force acting on the coil is proportional to the magnitude of the current. The coil turns against the restraining action of a small spring. The meter is calibrated by noting how much the coil turns when known currents are sent through it. The meter then is used to measure other unknown currents.

QUESTIONS

1. Define the poles of a magnet.
2. State the law of magnetic attraction and repulsion.
3. Name the three most important magnetic elements.
4. How does a temporary magnet differ from a permanent magnet?
5. Draw a small bar magnet to show the lines of force as they appear about the magnet. Use arrowheads to show the direction of the lines of force.
6. Draw the field between two like magnetic poles. Show the direction of the field.
7. Draw the field between two unlike magnetic poles. Show the direction of the field.
8. Draw the field about a straight current-bearing wire. Show its direction.
9. Explain the left-hand rule to determine the direction of a magnetic field about a straight current-bearing wire.
10. Explain the left-hand rule to determine the polarity of an electromagnet.
11. List three factors that control the strength of an electromagnet.

12. Describe a theory of magnetism.
13. Explain the left-hand rule to determine the direction of force on a current-bearing wire placed in a magnetic field.
14. What three factors control the force that acts on a wire carrying a current in a magnetic field?

PROBLEMS

1. A wire 0.5 m long carrying a current of 8 amp is at right angles to a uniform magnetic field. The force on the wire is 0.4 nt. What is the intensity of the magnetic field?
2. A wire 20 cm long is at right angles to a uniform magnetic field of magnetic induction 0.3 nt/amp-m. The current through the wire is 6 amp. What force acts on the wire?
3. A wire 1.5 m long carrying a current of 10 amp is at right angles to a uniform magnetic field. The force acting on the wire is 0.6 nt. What is the induction of the magnetic field?
4. The current through a wire 0.8 m long is 5 amp. The wire is placed perpendicular to a magnetic field of induction 0.6 nt/amp-m. What force acts on the wire?
5. The force on a wire 0.8 m long placed perpendicularly to a magnetic field of induction 6.0×10^{-2} nt/amp-m is 0.12 nt. What current flows through the wire?
6. The force acting on a wire at right angles to a magnetic field is 3.6 nt. The current flowing through the wire is 7.5 amp. The magnetic field has an induction of 0.8 nt/amp-m. How long is the wire?
7. A stream of electrons travels through a magnetic field of induction 0.6 nt/amp-m at a speed of 4.0×10^6 m/sec. The electrons travel at right angles to the field. What force acts on each of them?
8. Doubly-ionized helium atoms (alpha particles) are traveling perpendicularly through a magnetic field at a speed of 4.0×10^4 m/sec. The induction of the field is 5.0×10^{-2} nt/amp-m. What force acts on each particle?
9. A beta particle (high-speed electron) is traveling at right angles to a magnetic field of induction 0.6 nt/amp-m. It has a speed of 2.5×10^7 m/sec. What force acts on the particle?
10. The mass of an electron is about 9.0×10^{-31} kg. What acceleration does the beta particle in Problem 9 undergo in the direction of the force acting on it?
11. The induction of a magnetic field is 0.3 nt/amp-m. A wire in the field has 4.0×10^{20} free electrons moving through it at a speed of 2.0×10^{-2} m/sec. What total force acts on the wire?

Electromagnetic Induction

A special magnet called an electromagnet can be constructed by causing an electric current to flow through a wire surrounding a soft iron core. This kind of magnet loses its magnetism rapidly when the electric current ceases to flow. What are some uses for electromagnets?

27:1   Faraday's Discovery

Oersted discovered that an electric current flowing through a wire induces a magnetic field. This discovery led Michael Faraday to reason that if an electric current is capable of producing a magnetic field, then a magnetic field should be capable of producing an electric current. By experimenting with magnetic fields and lengths of wire, Faraday discovered the process by which a magnetic field generates an electric current. When a wire is moved through a magnetic field in a direction perpendicular to the direction of the field, an electric current is induced in the wire.

Figure 27-1 shows Faraday's experiments. A wire that is part of a closed circuit is held in a magnetic field. The wire is moved perpendicular to the field. The meter indicates an electric current flowing in the wire. When the wire moves up through the field, the current flows in one direction. When the wire moves down through the field, the current flows in the opposite direction. If the conductor is held stationary in the field or is moved in a direction parallel with the field, no current flows in the circuit. An electric current is generated in a conductor only when the conductor cuts through the lines of force of the magnetic field.

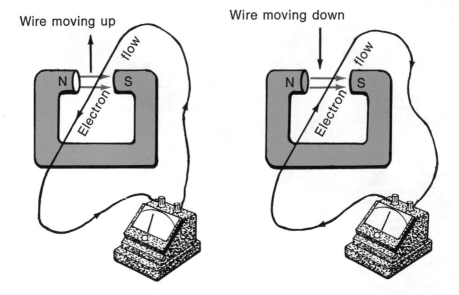

Figure 27-1.   When a wire is moved in a magnetic field, a current flows in the wire. The current flows only while the wire is moving. The faster the wire moves, the greater the current that is induced. The stronger the magnetic field, the greater the current induced in the wire. The direction the electron current flows can be determined by applying the left hand rule (Figure 27-2.)

It is of no consequence whether the conductor moves through the field or the field moves past the conductor. The wire may be held stationary and the magnet moved up and down, or the wire may be moved in the magnetic field. In either case, an electric current is generated in the wire. It is the wire cutting through the magnetic field that generates the current.

Suppose a conductor moves through a magnetic field at an angle to the field. Only that component of the conductor's velocity that is perpendicular to the direction of the field generates a current. Whether the conductor moves perpendicularly to the field or at an angle to the field, the current generated is an induced current. The process of generating a current in this way is *electromagnetic induction*.

27:2   Direction of a Current in a Wire

The force acting on the free electrons in a conductor as it moves through a magnetic field is perpendicular to the direction of the current and the direction of the magnetic field. To determine the direction of the electron current that flows in a conductor moving through a magnetic field, use the left-hand rule described in Chapter 26. Hold the left hand so the thumb points in the direction

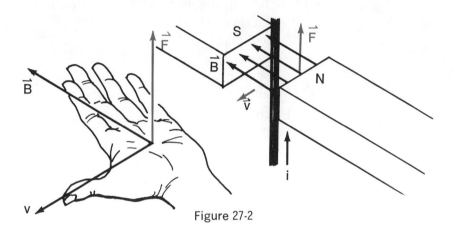

Figure 27-2

of the moving wire and the fingers point in the direction of the magnetic field. The palm of the hand points in the direction the electrons flow in the wire.

27:3   Induced EMF

EMF, meaning electromotive force, is not an accurate term. *EMF is really the energy imparted to each unit of charge by an energy source.* It does not refer to the force acting on the unit of charge.

EMF induced in a wire is measured in volts. Voltage is the work done on a unit charge. The work done to move an electron through a length of wire l in a field is force $\times$ distance, or Fl. The force which acts on each electron is Bqv (Chapter 26, Section 26:11). If e represents the charge on a single electron, Bqv becomes Bev. Therefore, the work done on each electron is Fl, or $Bevl$. The work done per unit charge is W/q. In this case, q is e. The voltage, therefore, is W/e, or Fl/e. By substitution, $Bevl/e$ is Blv.

$$EMF = Blv$$

The EMF (voltage) induced by moving a wire in a magnetic field is the product of three factors. These factors are: the intensity of the field, B; the length of the wire in the field, l; and the speed of the moving wire, v.

Sample Problem 1

A wire 0.2 m long moves perpendicularly through a magnetic field of induction 8.0×10^{-2} nt/amp-m at a speed of 7 m/sec. (a) What EMF is induced in the wire? (b) The wire is a part of a circuit which has a resistance of 0.5 ohms. What current flows in the circuit?

Solution:

(a) $EMF = Blv$

$$= 8.0 \times 10^{-2} \text{ nt/amp-m} \times 0.2 \text{ m} \times 7 \text{ m/sec}$$

$$= 0.11 \frac{\text{(nt)(m)(m)}}{\left(\dfrac{\text{coul-m}}{\text{sec}}\right)\text{(sec)}}$$

$$= 0.11 \frac{\text{nt-m}}{\text{coul}}$$

$$= 0.11 \text{ j/coul}$$

$$= 0.11 \text{ volts}$$

(b) $i = \dfrac{V}{R}$

$$= \frac{0.11 \text{ volts}}{0.5 \text{ ohms}}$$

$$= 0.22 \text{ amp}$$

Problems

1. A wire 0.5 m long cuts straight up through a magnetic field of induction 0.4 nt/amp-m at a speed of 20 m/sec. (a) What EMF is induced in the wire? (b) The wire is part of a circuit of total resistance 6 ohms. What current flows in the circuit?

2. A wire has a total length of 0.6 m perpendicular to a field of magnetic induction 0.5 nt/amp-m. (a) The wire is moved through the field at a speed of 20 m/sec. What EMF is induced in the wire? (b) The wire is part of a circuit of total resistance 15 ohms. What current flows in the circuit?

3. A horseshoe magnet has a uniform magnetic field of 2.0×10^{-2} nt/amp-m. An instructor places a copper wire of total resistance 0.5 ohms across a galvanometer. He holds part of the wire between the poles of the magnet. The length of the wire between the magnetic poles is 10 cm. The instructor quickly moves the wire up through the field at 5 m/sec. What current does the galvanometer indicate?

4. A wire 30 m long moves at 2 m/sec perpendicularly through a magnetic field of induction 1 nt/amp-m. (a) What EMF is induced in the wire? (b) The total resistance of the circuit of which the wire is a part is 15 ohms. What current flows?

5. A wire 16 m long is perpendicular to a magnetic field of induction 0.5 nt/amp-m. The wire is moved through the field at 15 m/sec. (a) What EMF is induced in the wire? (b) The wire is part of a circuit of 20 ohms resistance. What current flows?

27:4   The Electric Generator

The electric generator, invented by Michael Faraday, converts mechanical energy, such as falling water, to electric energy. In essence, an electric generator is a number of wire loops, an armature, in a strong magnetic field. The wire loops are mounted so they rotate freely in the field. As the loops turn, they cut through magnetic lines of force. This induces a current. The more loops in the armature, the longer is the length of the wire in the field and the greater is the induced EMF. Figure 27-3 shows one loop of a generator.

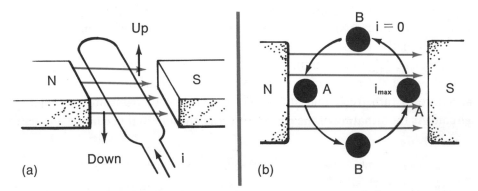

Figure 27-3.   Generation of an alternating current in a wire loop. (a) as the loop rotates. (b)Two positions of the loop in the magnetic field as the loop is viewed in cross section.

Using Figure 27-3 and the left-hand rule, notice that the current induced in the loop moves in opposite directions in each side of the loop. This results in the current flowing in one direction. Only while the loop is in the horizontal position do the two segments cut through the field perpendicularly. In this position, the current is at its maximum value. As the loop moves from the horizontal position to the vertical position, it cuts through the lines of force at an ever increasing angle. Accordingly, the current decreases until the loop reaches the vertical position. In this position, the segments move parallel to the field. The current is zero. As the loop continues to turn, the segment that previously was moving up begins to move down. The segment that previously was moving down begins to move up. The direction of the current in the loop changes. This change in direction takes place each time the loop turns through 180°. Thus, the direction of the current alternates, or is alternating current (ac). The voltage fluctuates smoothly from zero to some maximum value and back to zero during each half-cycle of the loop. Then it reverses direction. The graph of EMF versus time yields the sine curve in Figure 27-4.

Figure 27-4.   Variation of voltage with time as the loop rotates.

27:5   Alternating Current Generator

The armature of a generator contains many loops of wire. The armature is rotated in the field by the energy source at a set number of turns, or rev/sec. Commercially, this frequency usually is 60 hertz. The current changes direction after each half-turn, or alternates 120 times a second.

In Figure 27-5, an alternating current in the armature of a generator is transmitted to the rest of the circuit. The brush-slip-ring arrangement permits the armature to turn freely and still allows the current to pass into the external circuit. As the armature of the generator turns, the alternating current fluctuates

Figure 27-5.   The principle of the alternating current generator.

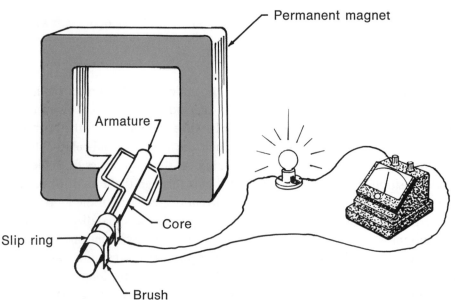

between some maximum value and zero. The light in the circuit does not appear to dim or brighten because the fluctuations are too fast for the eye to detect.

The effective value of an alternating current, is rated by comparing it to a direct current. If an alternating current is applied to a heater, the heat the current generates in one minute can be measured. The steady, direct current needed to generate the same amount of heat in the same time is then calculated. The ac current is then rated equal to the dc current. Such measurements always show that the effective value of an alternating current is its maximum value multiplied by 0.707. Likewise, the effective value of the alternating EMF also is 0.707 × the maximum value. (0.707 is the sine of 45°.)

$$i_{\text{eff}} = 0.707 \, i_{\text{max}}$$
$$V_{\text{eff}} = 0.707 \, V_{\text{max}}$$

Sample Problem 2

An ac generator develops a maximum voltage of 100 volts and delivers a maximum current of 20 amp to an external circuit. (a) What is the effective voltage of the generator? (b) What effective current is delivered to the external circuit? (c) What is the resistance of the external circuit?

Solution:

$$\begin{aligned} \text{(a)} \quad V_{\text{eff}} &= 0.707 \, V_{\text{max}} \\ &= 0.707 \, (100 \text{ volts}) \\ &= 70.7 \text{ volts} \end{aligned}$$

$$\begin{aligned} \text{(b)} \quad i_{\text{eff}} &= 0.707 \, i_{\text{max}} \\ &= 0.707 \, (20 \text{ amp}) \\ &= 14.1 \text{ amp} \end{aligned}$$

$$\begin{aligned} \text{(c)} \quad R &= \frac{V_{\text{eff}}}{i_{\text{eff}}} \\ &= \frac{70.7 \text{ volts}}{14.1 \text{ amp}} \\ &= 5.1 \text{ ohms} \end{aligned}$$

Problems

6. A generator in a power plant develops a maximum voltage of 170 volts. (a) What is the effective voltage? (b) A 60-watt light bulb is placed across the generator. A maximum current of 0.7 amp flows through the bulb. What effective current flows through the bulb?

7. The effective voltage an ac household outlet delivers is 117 volts. (a) What is the maximum voltage across a lamp connected to the outlet? (b) The effective current through the lamp is 5.5 amp. What maximum current flows in the lamp during a complete cycle?

8. An ac generator delivers a maximum voltage of 250 volts. (a) What effective voltage is available to an external circuit? (b) An 88-ohm resistor is placed across the generator. What effective current flows through it? (c) What is the maximum current through the resistor?

9. (a) What is the effective EMF across a circuit connected to a generator that delivers a maximum voltage of 310 volts? (b) What effective current does this generator deliver to the circuit if its resistance is 55 ohms?

10. An ac generator delivers a peak voltage of 425 volts. (a) What is the effective voltage in a circuit placed across the generator? (b) The resistance of the circuit across the generator is 500 ohms. What effective current flows in it?

27:6   EMF of a Generator

A generator consists of metal wire moving in a magnetic field. The magnitude of the EMF of the generator is calculated by $EMF = Blv$. To increase the magnitude of the EMF delivered by any generator: increase the magnitude of the magnetic field about the armature B; turn the armature faster, and so increase v; place more wire (to increase the number of turns) on the armature, and thus increase l.

Figure 27-6. Giant coils of wire are used to produce the magnetic field in this generator.

France Actuelle

27:7   Generators and Motors

Generators and motors are identical in construction. A generator converts mechanical energy into electric energy. A motor converts electric energy into mechanical energy. An electric current sent into an armature turns the armature. The device is a motor. Once the armature is turned, an electric current comes out of it. The device is a generator.

In many practical situations, a motor and generator are used alternately. France has an entire network of electric trains. For example, in France a train use motors to climb a hill. At the top of the hill, the engineer throws a switch and the motors are used as generators. As the train rolls down the hill, generators convert the kinetic energy of the train into electric energy. This electric energy is sent back into the power lines and used by other trains.

27:8 Lenz's Law

As soon as the armature of a generator starts to turn, current flows in its wires. As a result, the generator behaves very much like an electric motor. The motor-effect of a generator, however, is always in exact opposition to the direction in which the armature is turned. If the armature of a hand generator is turned clockwise, the current that flows tends to cause the armature to turn counterclockwise. This makes the armature more difficult to turn.

Lenz's law states that an induced current always acts in such a direction that its magnetic properties oppose the change by which the current is induced.

Lenz's law also applies to motors. As soon as the armature of a motor begins to turn in a magnetic field, it will generate an electric current. However, the generator effect of a motor always generates current in direct opposition to the current that makes its armature turn. This generator-effect of an electric motor is quite noticeable. It is the "back-EMF" of the motor. When the armature of the motor is turning, back-EMF opposes the current put into the motor. So, if the motor is to operate properly, it must have a resistance that accounts for back-EMF. For this reason, a motor's resistance is very low. Therefore, when a motor first is turned on, it draws a large current into the lead lines. This large current can cause a voltage drop across the lead lines. Suppose a second device, such as a light bulb, is in the same circuit when the motor is turned on. The voltage across the light decreases momentarily and it dims. Once the motor is running, back-EMF appears. Then the voltage in the lines returns to normal.

27:9 Self-Induction

Whenever a coil of wire is part of an electric circuit, it produces an effect called self-induction. Consider the coil in Figure 27-7. When the switch is closed, a current begins to flow in the circuit. The current causes a magnetic field to appear about the coil. The field does not reach its full magnitude at once. It grows as the current increases toward its maximum value. As the field moves out, it constitutes a moving magnetic field that cuts through the loops of the coil. This induces an EMF in the coil. By Lenz's law, this induced EMF tends to op-

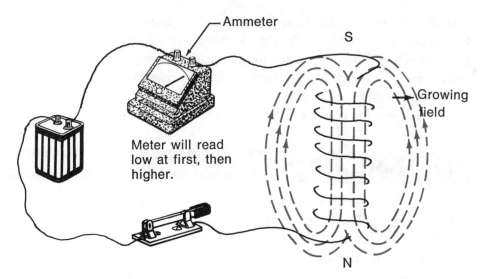

Figure 27-7.   As the direct current steadies, self induction diminishes.

pose the current flowing in the loops. The current is prevented from reaching its maximum value for a short time. In a dc circuit, such as Figure 27-7, the self-inductance of the coil disappears rapidly. This happens because as soon as the current reaches its maximum value, the field becomes stable and does not move. However, if the source of dc current is replaced with an ac source, the field about the coil constantly changes as the current in the circuit increases, decreases, and alternates directions. The self-inductance of the coil presents a formidable opposition to current flow in the circuit.

27:10   Transformers

A transformer has two coils wound around a common core. The introduction of an alternating current into the primary coil of a transformer causes the magnetic field constantly to fluctuate about the coil. The current in the coil constantly fluctuates between zero and its maximum. The magnetic field continually changes in intensity. It changes direction every half cycle. The magnetic field sweeps through the loops of the secondary coil. This induces an EMF in the second coil. The rate of change of magnetic flux is considered the same about both coils. Therefore, the EMF induced in the secondary coil is in the same ratio to the EMF in the primary coil as the number of turns on the secondary is to the number of turns on the primary. This develops from the relationship $EMF = Blv$. The flux passes over both coils in the same time. So v is constant for both. If the secondary coil has more turns on it than the primary coil, it effectively has a greater length, l, than the primary coil. The lengths are in direct proportion to the number of turns on each coil. Thus, the EMF is greater in the

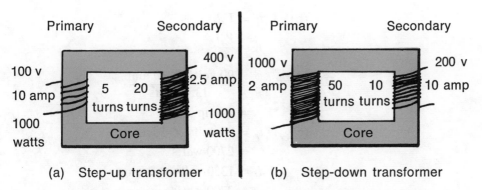

(a) Step-up transformer   (b) Step-down transformer

Figure 27-8. Input and output voltage depend upon the ratio of the number of turns of the primary to the secondary.

secondary coil. If the secondary coil has fewer turns than the primary coil, the EMF induced in it is less in proportion to the ratio of the turns on each coil.

$$\frac{\text{Primary voltage}}{\text{Secondary voltage}} = \frac{\text{Number of turns on primary}}{\text{Number of turns on secondary}}$$

$$\frac{V_p}{V_s} = \frac{N_p}{N_s}$$

A transformer may be a step-up or step-down transformer. This depends upon whether it is used to increase or decrease EMF. In an "ideal" transformer, the power input is equal to the power output. An ideal transformer loses no energy to heat or other effects. This text considers all transformers as ideal. Since many commercial transformers are as high as 99% efficient, this assumption is nearly correct. Since $P = Vi$,

$$V_p i_p = V_s i_s$$

Sample Problem 3

A step-up transformer has 200 turns on its primary coil and 3000 turns on its secondary coil. (a) The primary coil is supplied with an alternating current at 90 volts. What is the voltage in the secondary circuit? (b) The current in the primary circuit is 30 amp. What current flows in the secondary circuit? (c) What is the power in the primary? In the secondary?

Solution:

$$\text{(a)} \quad \frac{V_p}{V_s} = \frac{N_p}{N_s}$$

$$V_s = \frac{V_p N_s}{N_p}$$

$$= \frac{90 \text{ volts} \times 3000}{200}$$

$$= 1350 \text{ volts}$$

(b) $V_p i_p = V_s i_s$

$$i_s = \frac{V_p i_p}{V_s}$$

$$= \frac{90 \text{ volts} \times 30 \text{ amp}}{1350 \text{ volts}}$$

$$= 2 \text{ amp}$$

(c) $V_p i_p = 90 \text{ volts} \times 30 \text{ amp}$

$$= 2700 \text{ watts}$$

$$V_s i_s = 1350 \text{ volts} \times 2 \text{ amp}$$

$$= 2700 \text{ watts}$$

Problems

11. An ideal step-up transformer's primary has 50 turns. Its secondary has 1500 turns. The primary is connected to an ac generator having an EMF of 120 volts. (a) Calculate the EMF of the secondary. (b) Find the current in the secondary circuit if the current in the primary is 90 amp. (c) What power develops in the primary? In the secondary?

12. The secondary of a step-down transformer has 50 turns. The primary has 1500 turns. (a) The EMF of the primary is 3600 volts. What is the EMF of the secondary? (b) The current flowing in the primary is 3 amp. What current flows in the secondary?

13. A step-up transformer has 300 turns on its primary and 90 000 turns on its secondary. (a) The EMF of the generator to which the primary is attached is 60 volts. What is the EMF in the secondary? (b) The current flowing in the primary coil of the transformer is 150 amp. What current flows in the secondary?

14. A step-down transformer has 7500 turns on its primary and 125 turns on its secondary. The voltage across the primary is 7200 volts. (a) What voltage is across the secondary? (b) The current in the primary is 0.6 amp. What current flows in the secondary?

15. A step-up transformer is connected to a generator that delivers 120 volts and 100 amp. (a) The ratio of the turns on the secondary and primary of the transformer is 1000 to 1 respectively. What voltage is in the secondary? (b) What current flows in the secondary? (c) What is the power input of the transformer? (d) What is the power output of the transformer?

16. The primary of a transformer has 150 turns. It is connected to a 120-volt source. Calculate the number of turns on the secondary to supply (a) 600 volts (b) 300 volts (c) 6 volts

QUESTIONS

1. Explain how a wire and a strong magnet generate an electric current.
2. What is the difference between the current generated in a wire when the wire is moved up through a magnetic field and when the wire is moved down through the same field?
3. What causes an electron to move in a wire when it is moved through a magnetic field?
4. What is EMF?
5. Substitute units to show that Blv = volts.
6. Sketch and describe an ac generator.
7. Sketch and describe a dc generator.
8. What kind of current does a dc generator produce?
9. How is the effective value of an ac current determined?
10. What factors determine the EMF of a generator?
11. State Lenz's law.
12. What causes the back-EMF of an electric motor?
13. Why is the self-inductance of a coil an important factor when the coil is in an ac circuit and a minor factor when the coil is in a dc circuit?
14. Upon what does the ratio of the EMF in the primary of a transformer to the EMF in the secondary of the transformer depend?

PROBLEMS

1. A wire segment 30 cm long moves straight up through a magnetic field of intensity 4.0×10^{-2} nt/amp-m at a speed of 15 m/sec. What EMF is induced in the wire?
2. A wire 0.75 m long cuts straight up through a magnetic field of induction 0.3 nt/amp-m at a speed of 16 m/sec. (a) What EMF is induced in the wire? (b) The wire is part of a circuit of total resistance 4.5 ohms. What current flows in the circuit?
3. A wire 20 m long moves at 4 m/sec perpendicularly through a magnetic field of induction 0.5 nt/amp-m. What EMF is induced in the wire?
4. An ac generator develops a maximum voltage of 150 volts. It delivers a maximum current of 30 amp to an external circuit. (a) What is the effective voltage of the generator? (b) What effective current does it deliver to the external circuit?
5. An electric stove is connected to a 220-volt source. (a) What is the maximum voltage across one of the stove's elements when it is operating? (b) The resistance of the operating element is 11 ohms. What effective current flows through it?

6. An ac generator develops a maximum EMF of 565 volts. What effective EMF does the generator deliver to an external circuit?

7. A step-up transformer has 80 turns on its primary coil. It has 1200 turns on its secondary coil. (a) The primary coil is supplied with an alternating current at 120 volts. What voltage is in the secondary coil? (b) The current in the primary coil is 50 amp. What current flows in the secondary circuit? (c) What is the power input and the power output of the transformer?

8. An ideal transformer has 300 turns on its primary coil. It has 9000 turns on its secondary coil. The primary is connected to a 90-volt generator. Calculate (a) the EMF of the secondary (b) the current in the secondary if the current in the primary is 60 amp (c) the power developed in the primary and the secondary.

9. The primary of a transformer has 300 turns. It is connected to a 150-volt source. Calculate the number of turns on the secondary to supply (a) 900 volts (b) 270 volts (c) 12.5 volts (d) 6 volts.

10. In a hydroelectric plant, electric energy is generated at 1200 volts. It is transmitted at 240 000 volts. (a) What is the ratio of the turns on the primary to the turns on the secondary of a transformer connected to one of the generators? (b) One of the plant generators delivers 40 amp to the primary of its transformer. What current flows in the secondary of the transformer?

11. What is the heat loss in a transmission line of total resistance 20 ohms when it carries (a) 40 amp (b) 0.2 amp?

Applications of Electric and Magnetic Fields

Devices employing electric and magnetic fields are used in every phase of life. They are used to study and in some cases control body functions. They facilitate work, transportation and communication. The structure of the atom may be probed by nuclear bombardments, some requiring particle accelerators and sensitive radiation detectors to record resulting radiation. What can radiotelescopes like the one pictured above tell us about outer space?

28:1 Changing Magnetic Fields Generate Changing Electric Fields

When a conductor is in the presence of a changing magnetic field, an induced EMF appears. An induced EMF in a conductor indicates that an electric field has developed. Suppose a wire is connected across the terminals of a dry cell. The electric field between the plates of the cell appears in the wire and pushes electrons through the wire. Electrons also push through a wire when the wire cuts through a magnetic field or the magnetic field passes the wire. Therefore, the changing magnetic field causes an electric field to appear in the wire. A changing magnetic field generates an electric field. Conversely, a changing electric field generates a magnetic field.

In 1864 James Clerk Maxwell showed that conductors are not essential to generate magnetic or electric fields. Maxwell predicted that a magnetic field moving in space generates an electric field moving in space which generates a magnetic field moving in space, and so on. Maxwell also stated that electric and magnetic fields regenerate each other. The fields pass through space at the speed of light in the form of a wave. Maxwell predicted that the magnetic and electric portions of the wave are always at right angles to each other and are both at right angles to the direction of propagation of the wave. Experiments verify this prediction.

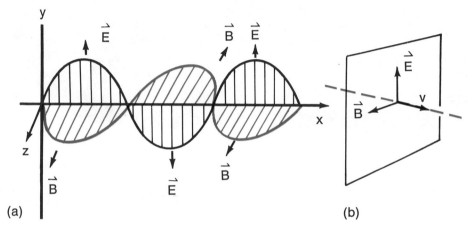

Figure 28-1.   A model of an electromagnetic wave. Note that the electric and magnetic fields are perpendicular to one another and that they are both perpendicular to the direction in which the wave is traveling.

28:2   The Generation of Electromagnetic Waves

The generation of an electrogmagnetic wave requires a changing magnetic field (or electric field). To develop a changing magnetic field, the current in the wire must be constantly changing. A changing electric current implies a changing rate of flow, or the acceleration of the charged particles. An accelerated charged particle generates an electromagnetic pulse which travels off into space.

The relationship between the acceleration of charged particles and the appearance of an electromagnetic wave clears up several issues. Electromagnetic waves travel at the speed of light as Maxwell predicted. This implies that light waves are electromagnetic waves. Since electrons are charged particles, the energy transitions of electrons within the atom are theorized as the origin of the characteristic light waves. This concurs with the idea that electromagnetic waves are due to the acceleration of charged particles. Electrons accelerate as they move from energy level to energy level within the atom. The accelerating electrons generate electromagnetic waves in the visible and nonvisible regions of light.

Maxwell's theory had an important implication. If electrons can oscillate in a wire at a constant frequency, an electromagnetic wave of the same frequency should emanate from the region of the wire. Thus, Maxwell predicted the propagation of radio waves. Maxwell did not live to see his prediction verified by Heinrich Hertz who generated and detected the first radio waves in 1887.

28:3 The Discovery of X Rays

In 1895 in Germany, Wilhelm Roentgen sent electrons through a highly evacuated discharge tube. Roentgen used extremely high voltage across the tube. This accelerated the electrons to very high speeds. The electrons struck the electrode located at the opposite end of the tube. When this happened, Roentgen noted a glow on a phosphorescent screen several feet away. He concluded that some kind of highly penetrating rays were coming from the discharge tube. He found that the rays could pass right through many materials and still excite a fluorescent or phosphorescent screen.

Roentgen called them X rays. Roentgen gave the strange rays this name because he did not know what they were. Now X rays are known to be electromagnetic waves of very high frequency. They are produced by the extremely high deceleration of the electrons as they strike the anode of the tube. The high frequency of X rays indicates that this type of electromagnetic wave is high in energy content. The energy content of an electromagnetic wave is equal to Planck's constant times the frequency of the wave, $E = hf$. Much of the kinetic energy of the high-speed electrons is converted to the energy of the X rays that result when the particles are decelerated at the anode.

Sample Problem 1

Assume an electron starts from rest at one end of a cathode ray tube where the voltage is 10^5 volts. Calculate the speed of the electron when it reaches the other end of the tube. The mass of an electron is 9×10^{-31} kg.

Solution:

100 000 j of work are done on 1 coul of charge to transfer it across 10^5 volts of difference in potential. There are 6.25×10^{18} electrons in 1 coul of charge. Therefore, the work done on a single electron to move it through the potential difference is

$$\frac{100\ 000\ \text{j/coul}}{6.25 \times 10^{18}\ \text{electrons/coul}} = 1.6 \times 10^{-14}\ \text{j/electron}$$

The electron converts this energy to kinetic energy as it travels to the anode.

Therefore, $$KE = \frac{mv^2}{2} = 1.6 \times 10^{-14}\ \text{j}$$

So,
$$v = \sqrt{\frac{2 \times 1.6 \times 10^{-14}\,j}{m}}$$

$$= \sqrt{\frac{3.2 \times 10^{-14}\,j}{9 \times 10^{-31}\,kg}}$$

$$= \sqrt{3.6 \times 10^{16}\,\frac{m^2}{sec^2}}$$

$$= 1.9 \times 10^8 \text{ m/sec*}$$

Sample Problem 2

Assume the energy determined in Sample Problem 1 is roughly correct. (a) Calculate the frequency of the radiation emitted if all the energy of the electron is converted to electromagnetic radiation when it strikes the anode. (b) X rays have frequencies that range between 10^{16} and 10^{21} Hz. Is the radiation calculated in part (a) of this problem of the X ray region?

Solution:

Use Planck's constant (6.6×10^{-34} j/sec) in the relation $E = hf$.

(a) $E = hf$

$$f = \frac{E}{h}$$

$$= \frac{1.6 \times 10^{-14}\,j}{6.6 \times 10^{-34}\,j/sec}$$

$$= 2.4 \times 10^{19} \text{ Hz}$$

(b) Yes, the rays are X radiation.

Problems

1. (a) Calculate the energy given to an electron transferred through a potential difference of 80 000 volts. (b) What energy does each electron give up as it strikes the anode?
2. The electrons in Problem 1 are accelerated across a discharge tube by 80 000 volts. Assume the electrons start from rest. What speed do they attain before reaching the anode?
3. All the energy given up by each electron in Problem 1 is converted to electromagnetic radiation. What is the frequency of the electromagnetic wave emitted at the anode of the discharge tube?
4. An electron falls through a potential difference of 10 000 volts. (a) What energy is given up? (b) The electrons pass through a discharge tube while giving up the energy. What speed do they attain?
5. A proton has a mass of 1.7×10^{-27} kg. What maximum speed does it attain in falling through a potential difference of 100 000 volts?

---

*This figure is not accurate. At these speeds relativistic considerations are necessary to attain accuracy.

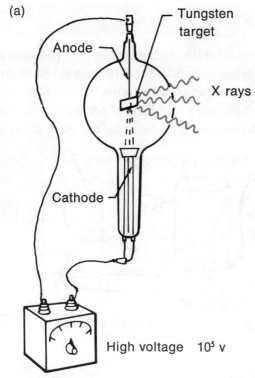

(a)

Tungsten target

Anode

X rays

Cathode

High voltage 10^5 v

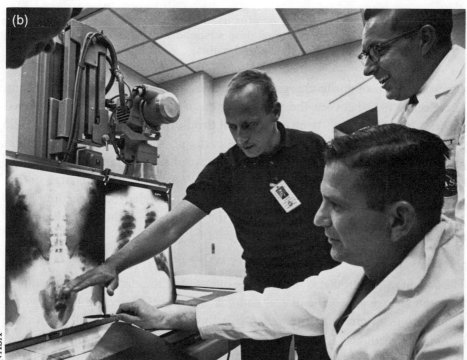

NASA

Figure 28-2.   (a) Apparatus for producing X rays. (b) Negative produced by X rays.

28:4   Millikan's Oil-Drop Experiment

Figure 28-3 shows the method suggested by J. J. Thomson and used by Robert A. Millikan to measure the charge carried by a single electron. Fine oil drops sprayed into the air from an atomizer often bear small charges. The charges are a result of the drops rubbing together and against the air. These drops then fall through the air. A few enter the hole in the top plate of the apparatus. The two

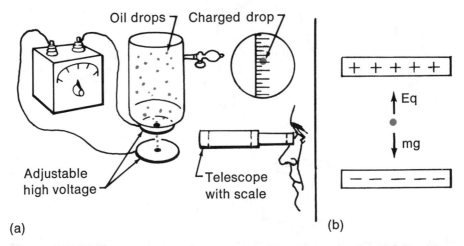

(a)

(b)

Figure 28-3.   (a) Diagram of the apparatus used by Millikan to determine the charge on an electron. (b) Diagram of the oil drop suspended between the two oppositely charged plates.

plates are given opposite charges. This creates an electric field between them. The electric field between the plates and the electric field about the charged particles interact. A negatively-charged oil drop experiences a force toward the positively-charged plate. If the top plate is the positive plate, the oil drop experiences two forces. One force, due to its weight, causes it to fall. Another force, due to the electric field, causes it to move upward. If the charge on the plates is properly adjusted, a charged drop is suspended between the plates. This is because the downward force of the particle's weight and the upward force of the electric field are equal.

$$Eq = mg$$

The weight of the droplet is mg; E is the intensity of the electric field determined from the voltage across the plates; and g is 9.8 m/sec^2. A second measurement is made to determine mg. The weight of a tiny oil drop is too small to measure by ordinary methods. To make this measurement, a "captured" drop is observed and its rate of fall is timed when the electric field is shut off. Because of friction, an oil drop quickly reaches a uniform or "terminal" speed. The speed is related to the mass of the drop in terms of a formula devised by the British physicist, George G. Stokes. This formula is used to calculate the weight of the drop, mg. Since E is known, q is calculated.

Millikan had no way to know whether a drop of oil carried one or several extra charges. The smallest measurement he obtained was always 1.6×10^{-19} coul. Furthermore, all other measurements were exact multiples of this value. In time 1.6×10^{-19} coul became accepted as the charge carried by the electron and the proton.

Sample Problem 3

An oil drop weighs 1.92×10^{-14} nt. It is suspended in an electric field of intensity 4×10^4 nt/coul. (a) What charge is on the oil drop? (b) How many excess electrons does the drop carry if it behaves as a negative particle in the field?

Solution:

$$\text{(a)} \quad mg = Eq$$

$$q = \frac{mg}{E}$$

$$= \frac{1.92 \times 10^{-14} \text{ nt}}{4 \times 10^4 \text{ nt/coul}}$$

$$= 4.8 \times 10^{-19} \text{ coul}$$

$$\text{(b)} \quad \frac{4.8 \times 10^{-19} \text{ coul}}{1.6 \times 10^{-19} \text{ coul/electron}} = 3 \text{ electrons}$$

Problems

6. An oil drop weighs 1.92×10^{-15} nt. It is suspended in an electric field of intensity 6.0×10^3 nt/coul. (a) What charge is on the oil drop? (b) The particle is negative. How many excess electrons does it carry?

7. A positively-charged oil drop weighs 6.4×10^{-13} nt. It becomes suspended between two charged plates when the intensity of the electric field is 4.0×10^6 nt/coul. (a) What charge is on the drop? (b) How many electrons is the drop missing?

8. A negatively-charged oil drop weighs 8.5×10^{-15} nt. The drop is held stationary between two charged plates that produce an electric field of 5.3×10^{-3} nt/coul. (a) What charge is on the drop? (b) How many excess electrons does it carry?

9. During a Millikan experiment, a student records the weight of five different oil drops. He also records the field intensity necessary to hold each drop

stationary. (a) Plot the readings on a graph of W vs E. Plot W vertically.
(b) Determine the slope of the line. What does the slope represent?

W (nt)	E (nt/coul)
1.7×10^{-14}	1.06×10^{5}
5.6×10^{-14}	3.5×10^{5}
9.3×10^{-14}	5.8×10^{5}
2.9×10^{-14}	1.8×10^{5}

28:5   Determining the Mass of the Electron

The British scientist Sir J. J. Thomson (1856–1940) constructed a discharge
tube similar to the one in Figure 28-4. Electrons that leave the cathode of this

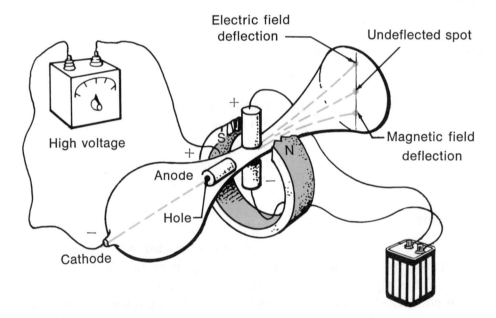

Figure 28-4.   Cathode ray tube designed by J. J. Thomson. With this tube he was
able to determine the charge-to-mass ratio of the electron.

tube accelerate toward the anode. The anode has a small hole through which
some of the high-speed electrons pass. The kinetic energy of the electrons is
enough to send them through the anode and beyond. The second metal plate
beyond the anode guarantees that a straight beam of electrons passes through the
remainder of the tube. Only electrons that align with the holes in both plates
pass on. Farther down the tube a pair of charged plates are arranged to deflect

the negative electrons upward toward the positive plate. The force of the electric field acting on each electron is Ee. E represents the field intensity; e the charge on the electron in coulombs as determined by Millikan. In addition to the electric field, a magnetic field is introduced at right angles to the charged plates. The force of the magnetic field, acting on the electrons Bev, deflects the electrons downward.

When both the electric field and the magnetic field are present, the fields are adjusted until the beam of electrons follows a straight or undeflected path. Then the force on the electrons in the electric field is equal to the force on the electrons in the magnetic field.

$$Bev = Ee$$

$$v = \frac{Ee}{Be}$$

$$v = \frac{E}{B}$$

If the potential difference is removed from the plates, the only force acting on the electrons is due to the magnetic field. This force acts perpendicularly to the direction of motion of the electrons. Therefore, it is a centripetal force which causes the electrons to follow a circular path. When the electric field is absent,

$$Bev = \frac{mv^2}{r}$$

Rearranging,

$$\frac{Br}{v} = \frac{m}{e}$$

Thomson measured the distance between the undeflected spot at the end of the tube and the position of the spot when the electrons are subjected only to the magnetic field. Thomson then calculated the radius, r, of the circular path given to the electrons by the magnetic field. He measured the intensity of the magnetic field B. Then he found the value of v from E/B. Thus, Thomson could evaluate B, r, and v and so calculate Br/v. This gave him the value of m/e. Thomson consistently obtained the value 5.68×10^{-12} kg/coul. Millikan's value of e, 1.6×10^{-19} coul, allows the mass of the electron m to be calculated:

$$\frac{m}{e} = 5.68 \times 10^{-12} \text{ kg/coul}$$

and $\qquad e = 1.6 \times 10^{-19}$ coul

then $\qquad m = (5.68 \times 10^{-12} \text{ kg/coul})(1.6 \times 10^{-19} \text{ coul})$

$$= 9.1 \times 10^{-31} \text{ kg}$$

Mass of the electron $= 9.1 \times 10^{-31}$ kg

These equations apply equally well to a beam of protons sent across a discharge tube in the same way as the electrons. To obtain protons, a small amount of hydrogen gas is placed in the path of high-speed electrons as they travel between an anode and a cathode. The electrons frequently ionize the atoms of hydrogen gas. Since a hydrogen atom consists of a single proton and a single electron, an ionized hydrogen atom is a proton. The protons are drawn into a tube similar to the one used to measure the mass of the electron. The mass of the proton is 1.7×10^{-27} kg.

Sample Problem 4

A beam of electrons travels an undeflected path in a discharge tube. E is 7.0×10^3 nt/coul. B is 3.5×10^{-2} nt/amp-m. What is the speed of the electrons as they cross the tube?

Solution:

$$v = \frac{E}{B}$$
$$= \frac{7.0 \times 10^3 \text{ nt/coul}}{3.5 \times 10^{-2} \text{ nt/amp-m}}$$
$$= 2.0 \times 10^5 \text{ m/sec}$$

Sample Problem 5

An electron of mass 9.1×10^{-31} kg moves with a speed of 2.0×10^5 m/sec across a magnetic field of intensity, $B = 8.0 \times 10^{-4}$ nt/amp-m. What is the radius of the circular path followed by the electrons while in the field?

Solution:

$$\text{Since, } \quad Bev = \frac{mv^2}{r}$$
$$r = \frac{mv}{Be}$$
$$= \frac{(9.0 \times 10^{-31} \text{ kg})(2.0 \times 10^5 \text{ m/sec})}{(8.0 \times 10^{-4} \text{ nt/amp-m})(1.6 \times 10^{-19} \text{ coul})}$$
$$= 1.4 \times 10^{-3} \text{ m}$$

Problems

Assume the direction of all moving charged particles is perpendicular to any field.

10. Protons passing through a magnetic field of 0.6 nt/amp-m are deflected. An electric field of intensity 4.5×10^3 nt/coul is introduced. The protons are brought back to their undeflected path. What is the speed of the traveling protons?

11. A proton moves at a speed of 7.5×10^3 m/sec as it passes through a magnetic field of 0.6 nt/amp-m. Compute the radius of the circular path. The mass of a proton is 1.7×10^{-27} kg. The charge carried by the proton is equal to that of the electron but is positive.

12. Electrons move through a magnetic field of 6.0×10^{-2} nt/amp-m. An electric field of 3.0×10^3 nt/coul prevents the electrons from being deflected. What is the speed of the electrons?

13. Calculate the radius of the circular path the electrons follow in Problem 12 in absence of the electric field. The mass of an electron is 9.0×10^{-31} kg.

14. A proton enters a magnetic field of intensity 6.0×10^{-2} nt/amp-m with a speed of 5.4×10^4 m/sec. What is the radius of the circular path it follows?

15. A proton moves across a magnetic field of intensity 0.36 nt/amp-m. It follows a circular path of radius 0.2 m. What is the speed of the proton?

16. An electron moves across a magnetic field of intensity 4.0×10^{-3} nt/amp-m. It follows a circular path of radius 2.0×10^{-2} m. What is its speed?

Figure 28-5.   A spiral track made by an electron as it is subjected to a magnetic field in a bubble chamber. The radius of curvature is proportional to the momentum of the electron.

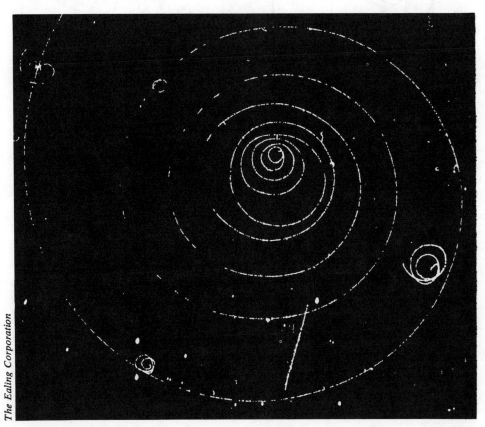

28:6   The Mass Spectrograph

A mass spectrograph measures the masses of atoms. A mass spectrograph is an offspring of the Thomson tube. Electrons leave the cathode at the upper part of the tube and accelerate toward the anode. As the electrons pass through the gaseous sample of an element, they ionize some of the atoms of the gas. These ions are positively charged. They accelerate toward the cathode. The ionized atoms of the gas then pass between the electric field and the magnetic field. The fields adjust until a beam of ions pass the fields undeflected. The speed of the ions is then E/B_1.

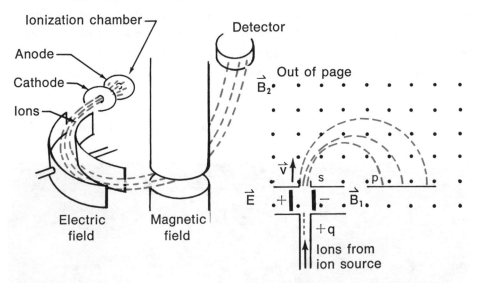

Figure 28-6.   Diagram of a mass spectrograph and its operation. The results are recorded photographically. With this device masses of isotopes can be determined very accurately.

The ions pass through the combined electric and magnetic fields. Then they pass through a slit and enter a second magnetic field B_2. Here the ions, bearing a known charge, follow the arc of a circle of radius r or half the distance from the slit S to the point on the photographic plate P. The charge on the ions is $q = 1e$, $2e$ or $3e$. The charge depends upon whether one, two, or three electrons are lost by the atom during the ionization process. However, the ions that emerge from the slit into the magnetic field B_2 all bear the same charge. This is because the electric field is adjusted for only one of the three possible charges at a time. Ions bearing other charges are deflected. They do not strike the slit. Whether the ions bear one, two, or three elementary charges is indicated by the setting of the electric field needed to offset the magnetic field. Ions with one charge require the strongest field. Those ions with two or three charges utilize a weaker field.

The radius for any ionized atom's circular path can be measured. Using the spectrograph, the known values are B, q, r, and v. From the relation,

$$Bqv = \frac{mv^2}{r}$$

becomes

$$m = \frac{Bqr}{v}$$

Sample Problem 6

These measurements were made in a mass spectrograph for a beam of doubly-ionized neon atoms.

$$B_2 = 5.0 \times 10^{-2} \text{ nt/amp-m}$$

$$q = 2e = 2 \times 1.6 \times 10^{-19} \text{ coul}$$

$$r = 0.053 \text{ m}$$

$$E/B_1 = v = 2.5 \times 10^4 \text{ m/sec}$$

(a) Calculate the mass of a neon atom. (b) One atomic mass unit is equal to 1.7×10^{-27} kg. What is the mass of a neon atom in a.m.u.?

Solution:

(a) $m = \dfrac{Bqr}{v}$

$$= \frac{(5.0 \times 10^{-2} \text{ nt/amp-m})(3.2 \times 10^{-19} \text{ coul})(0.053 \text{ m})}{2.5 \times 10^4 \text{ m/sec}}$$

$$= 3.4 \times 10^{-26} \text{ kg}$$

(b) $\dfrac{3.4 \times 10^{-26} \text{ kg}}{1.7 \times 10^{-27} \text{ kg/a.m.u.}} = 20 \text{ a.m.u.}$

Problems

17. A mass spectrograph gives this data for a beam of doubly-ionized argon atoms:

$$B_2 = 5.0 \times 10^{-2} \text{ nt/amp-m}$$

$$q = 2e = 2 \times 1.6 \times 10^{-19} \text{ coul}$$

$$r = 0.106 \text{ m}$$

$$v = E/B_1 = 2.5 \times 10^4 \text{ m/sec}$$

(a) Determine the mass of an argon atom. (b) Determine its mass in a.m.u.

18. A mass spectrograph gives this data for a beam of singly-ionized oxygen atoms:

$$B_2 = 7.2 \times 10^{-2} \text{ nt/amp-m}$$
$$q = 1.6 \times 10^{-19} \text{ coul}$$
$$r = 0.85 \text{ m}$$
$$v = E/B_2 = 3.6 \times 10^5 \text{ m/sec}$$

(a) Calculate the mass of an oxygen atom. (b) Calculate the mass of an oxygen atom in a.m.u.

19. A mass spectrograph yields this data for a beam of doubly-ionized sodium atoms:

$$B_2 = 8.0 \times 10^{-3} \text{ nt/amp-m}$$
$$q = 2e = 2 \times 1.6 \times 10^{-19} \text{ coul}$$
$$r = 0.77 \text{ m}$$
$$v = 5.0 \times 10^4 \text{ m/sec}$$

(a) Calculate the mass of a sodium atom. (b) Calculate the mass of a sodium atom in a.m.u.

20. A mass spectrograph gives these measurements for a beam of doubly-ionized neon atoms:

$$B_2 = 5.0 \times 10^{-2} \text{ nt/amp-m}$$
$$q = 2e = 2 \times 1.6 \times 10^{-19} \text{ coul}$$
$$r = 0.058 \text{ m}$$
$$v = 2.5 \times 10^4 \text{ m/sec}$$

(a) Calculate the mass of a neon atom. (b) Calculate the mass of a neon atom in a.m.u. (c) Compare this solution with the one given in the sample problem. What accounts for the difference in mass?

QUESTIONS

1. Describe an electromagnetic wave.
2. What always occurs when an electromagnetic wave is generated?
3. Why does an X-ray tube require extremely high voltage?
4. Why does an electron accelerate as it passes from the cathode to the anode of a discharge tube?
5. Substitute units to show that $E/B = \text{m/sec}$.
6. What is the function of a mass spectrograph? What principles are involved in its operation?
7. Describe a method to determine the charge on a particle.

1. The potential difference across the cathode and anode of a discharge tube is 2.5×10^4 volts. What maximum speed does an electron achieve as it travels across the tube? Assume the electron starts from rest.

2. Calculate the speed an electron achieves in falling through a potential difference of 3.2×10^4 volts. Assume the electron starts from rest.

3. What speed does a proton develop as it falls through a potential difference of 3.4×10^4 volts if it starts from rest?

4. The difference in potential between the cathode and anode of a spark plug is 10 000 volts. (a) What energy does an electron give up as it passes between the electrodes? (b) One-fourth of the energy given up by the electron is converted to electromagnetic radiation. What is the frequency of the waves emitted?

5. (a) What energy is added to an electron to transfer it across a difference in potential of 4.0×10^5 volts? (b) The energy is converted to electromagnetic radiation. What is the frequency of the wave emitted?

6. A beam of electrons returns to its undeflected position when a magnetic field of 6.5×10^{-2} nt/amp-m is placed at right angles to the deflecting electric field of 1.3×10^3 nt/coul. What is the speed of an electron passing through the crossed fields?

7. A stream of protons maintains its path without deflection as it passes through a magnetic field of intensity 1.8×10^{-2} nt/amp-m perpendicular to an electric field of intensity 3.6×10^4 nt/coul. (a) What is the speed of the protons? (b) The protons enter a magnetic field of 4.0×10^{-2} nt/amp-m and follow a circular path of 0.53 m. What is the mass of a proton?

8. A stream of singly-ionized lithium atoms does not deflect as it passes through a magnetic field of intensity 1.5×10^{-3} nt/amp-m perpendicular to an electric field of intensity 6.0×10^2 nt/coul. (a) What is the speed of the lithium atoms as they pass through the crossed fields? (b) The lithium atoms move into a magnetic field of intensity 0.18 nt/amp-m. They follow a circular path of radius 0.165 m. What is the mass of a lithium atom? (c) What is the mass of an atom in a.m.u.?

9. An oil drop weighs 9.6×10^{-15} nt. It is suspended in an electric field of intensity 2×10^4 nt/coul. (a) What is the charge on the oil drop? (b) How many excess electrons does it carry?

10. A positively-charged oil drop weighs 9.6×10^{-13} nt. It becomes suspended in an electric field of intensity 6.0×10^6 nt/coul. (a) What is the charge on the oil drop? (b) How many electrons does it lack?

29

The Quantum Theory

The quantum theory was an attempt to explain how light can behave both as a wave and as a particle. Scientists became concerned with demonstrating that small particles like electrons could exhibit wave properties, and that waves like light could exhibit the properties of particles. Arthur H. Compton, above, actually demonstrated the particle nature of waves in 1922. Why was this a giant step forward in learning more about the structure of the atom?

29:1 The Dual Nature of Light

During our study of light it was shown that light follows the rules of wave behavior. We will now examine the photoelectric effect and the Compton effect both of which can only be accounted for by assuming that light is emitted and absorbed in discrete bundles of energy called *quanta* or *photons*. Hence we are forced to recognize the particle nature of as well as the wave nature of electromagnetic radiation. A model for light must therefore be a dual model capable of accounting for both its wave aspects and its particle aspects.

29:2   The Photoelectric Effect

The photoelectric effect is studied by the use of a photocell circuit (Figure 29-1). Two electrodes, one coated with zinc, are sealed in an evacuated tube

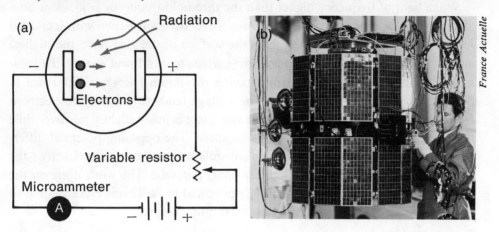

Figure 29-1. (a) Diagram of a photocell circuit in which a quartz tube is used. (b) This solar battery, which provides electricity for a satellite and is mounted externally, is composed of special light-sensitive crystals.

made of quartz. A difference in potential is placed across the electrodes. A variable resistor is included in the circuit so the difference in potential can be varied.

When light is absent, no current flows in the circuit. This is indicated by the sensitive microammeter. When light of the proper frequency falls on the zinc electrode, a current immediately flows in the circuit. Light causes electrons to leave the zinc plate and travel to the opposite positive plate. This completes the circuit. The electrons ejected from the metal plate by the light are photoelectrons. The term means that light causes the electrons to leave the plate. There is no difference between photoelectrons and any other electrons.

If light of different frequencies falls on the zinc plate, it is found that incident light of a certain minimum frequency is needed to eject electrons from the plate. This minimum frequency varies with the metal or other substance used. It is the threshold frequency (f_o) of that metal. Light of any frequency below the threshold frequency does not eject electrons from the metal, no matter how intense is the light. On the other hand, light of the threshold frequency or higher causes electrons to leave the metal immediately, even if the light is extremely faint. According to the wave theory of light, this should not be the case. More intense light means more energy along the wave fronts. This should cause more electrons to leave the plate. Since this does not happen when intense light of less than threshold frequency is used, it is logical to assume that light consists of particles. In this view threshold frequency is readily explained. Photons of frequencies below the threshold frequency do not have enough energy to provide even the more easily removed surface electrons with the energy to escape the metal.

When light of frequency higher than the threshold frequency is incident on a zinc plate in an evacuated tube, electrons travel across the tube with increased kinetic energy. Electrons ejected from the surface of the zinc have the highest energy. Electrons ejected from below the surface have a lower energy. To measure the kinetic energy of electrons having maximum energy, a difference in potential is placed across the tube. The voltage tends to prevent the electrons from leaving the zinc plate. That is, the zinc plate is made slightly positive while the second metal plate is made slightly negative. The opposing potential difference is increased until no electrons have sufficient energy to travel across the tube. This potential difference is the *stopping potential*. The work done on the most energetic electrons by the stopping potential is V_e. This is exactly equal to the kinetic energy of electrons having maximum energy.

Sample Problem 1

The stopping potential to prevent electrons from flowing across a photoelectric cell is 4.0 volts. What maximum kinetic energy is given to the electrons by the incident light?

Solution:

$$KE_{max} = V_e$$
$$= 4\,\text{j/coul} \times 1.6 \times 10^{-19}\,\text{coul}$$
$$= 6.4 \times 10^{-19}\,\text{j}$$

Figure 29-2.   Graph of kinetic energy of ejected electrons versus frequency of incident radiation.

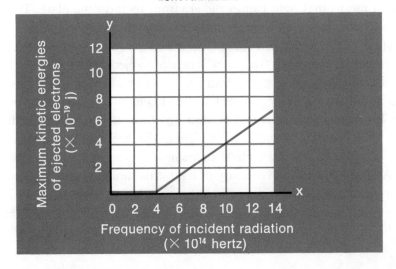

Figure 29-2 plots the maximum kinetic energies of the electrons ejected from a metal versus the frequencies of the incident radiations. The result is a straight line graph. All metals yield similar graphs having exactly the same slopes. The graphs differ only in the point of origin which varies with the threshold frequency of the metal. The slope of the line is the rise divided by the run or $\Delta y/\Delta x$. The slope of the line is Planck's constant h.

$$h = \frac{\Delta y}{\Delta x} = \frac{\text{Maximum kinetic energies of ejected electrons}}{\text{Frequency of incident radiations}} = 6.6 \times 10^{-34} \text{ j-sec}$$

This is the source of Planck's constant.

The threshold frequency times Planck's constant (hf_o) is the energy needed to free the surface electrons from the metal. This is the work function of the metal. Therefore, the maximum kinetic energy of an electron ejected from the metal is equal to the frequency of the incident photons times Planck's constant, less the work function. This is the photoelectric equation.

$$KE_{max} = hf - hf_o$$

Sample Problem 2

The threshold frequency of sodium is 5.6×10^{14} Hz. (a) What is the work function of sodium? (b) Sodium is illuminated by radiation of frequency 8.6×10^{14} Hz. What is the maximum kinetic energy of the ejected electrons?

Solution:

(a)   Work $= hf_o$

        $= 6.6 \times 10^{-34}$ j-sec $\times 5.6 \times 10^{14}$ Hz

        $= 3.7 \times 10^{-19}$ j

(b) $KE_{max} = hf - hf_o$

        $= (6.6 \times 10^{-34}$ j-sec $\times 8.6 \times 10^{14}$ Hz$) - 3.7 \times 10^{-19}$ j

        $= 2.0 \times 10^{-19}$ j

Problems

1. The stopping potential to prevent electron flow through a photocell is 3.2 volts. Calculate the maximum kinetic energy of the photoelectrons within the cell.

2. The stopping potential to stop electron flow through a photoelectric cell is 5.7 volts. Calculate the maximum kinetic energy of the photoelectrons within the cell.

3. The threshold frequency of zinc is 9.7×10^{14} Hz. (a) What is the photoelectric work function of zinc? (b) Zinc used in a photoelectric cell is irradiated by radiation of frequency 4.5×10^{15} Hz. What is the maximum kinetic energy of the photoelectrons within the cell?

4. The threshold frequency of calcium is 6.5×10^{14} Hz. (a) What is the photo-electric work function of calcium? (b) An electron-volt (ev) is needed to transfer one electron through a potential difference of one volt. This is 1.6×10^{-19} j. What is the work function of calcium in electron-volts?

5. The work function of chromium is 4.6 ev. What is the threshold frequency of chromium?

6. The work function of potassium is 2.2 ev. (a) What is the work function of potassium in joules? (b) What is the threshold frequency of potassium?

29:3   The Quantum Theory of Light

To account for the dual nature of light, the quantum theory of light assumes that light, along with all other electromagnetic radiations, consists of streams of photons. Each photon is characterized in space by a probability wave. The wave determines the position of the photon along the wave at any given time. Accordingly, it is more probable for a photon to be located where the amplitude of the probability wave is high. The probability wave also accounts for interference and diffraction phenomena.

The existence of photons escaped notice for many years because of their extremely small size. Each electromagnetic wave contains a tremendous number of these tiny particles. Photons acting together make the granular nature of the wave highly elusive. Photons are noticeable only when they interact with other extremely small particles, such as electrons.

The quantum theory is not easy to visualize, but the fundamental behavior of light still requires this description. No good reason exists for the fundamental behavior of either light or matter to correspond to observable effects.

29:4   The Compton Effect

In 1922, Arthur Compton experimented with X rays directed at a carbon block. He observed two phenomena. (1) The X rays that emerged from the block often deflected from their original paths. (2) When the deflected rays were sent through a grating and their wavelengths measured, the wavelengths of the emergent rays were longer than the wavelengths of the incident X rays. This indicated that the frequency of the emergent rays was less than the frequency of the incident X rays. Since the energy content of an electromagnetic wave is equal to hf and h is a constant, a decrease in frequency meant that the energy content of the emergent waves was less. Compton also noticed that electrons were ejected from the carbon block as a result of the X ray bombardment. He concluded that collisions were taking place between the X rays and the electrons. In addition, the X rays were giving up energy to the electrons.

(a)

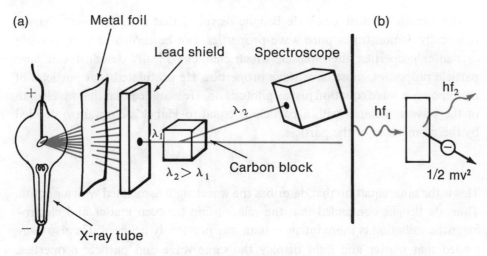

Metal foil

Lead shield   Spectroscope

λ_2

λ_1

$\lambda_2 > \lambda_1$ Carbon block

X-ray tube

(b)

hf_2

hf_1

$1/2\ mv^2$

Figure 29-3.   Diagram of apparatus used by Compton to study the nature of photons.

Compton then measured the kinetic energy of the ejected electrons. The energy of the incident X ray photons is hf_1. The energy of the emergent X rays is hf_2. Compton calculated the difference between hf_1 and hf_2. He found that the energy gained by an ejected electron $\frac{1}{2}\ mv^2$ agreed with the difference in the energy content of the incident and emergent rays. The laws of conservation of energy and conservation of momentum also were upheld. Compton was led to a startling conclusion. Electromagnetic radiation has particle properties and mass!

29:5   The Heisenberg Uncertainty Principle

Werner Heisenberg pointed out one effect of the interaction between photons and atomic size particles. The interaction makes it impossible to measure the exact position and momentum of an atomic particle at the same time. This is true because photons are used to observe atomic particles. Yet the photons interact with the particles in the manner observed by Compton. The result is a change in the position of the particles and the momentum of the particles. Thus, the very act of observing the particles precludes the exact measurement of position and momentum simultaneously.

29:6   Matter Waves

Compton's investigations showed that the momentum (mv) of a photon is described by the equation $mv = \frac{h}{\lambda}$ where h is Planck's constant and λ is the wavelength of the photon. This means that λ would be expressed, $\lambda = \frac{h}{mv}$.

The French scientist Louis de Broglie reasoned that if light, which characteristically demonstrates pure wave properties, can be shown to have particle or matter properties, then matter, which characteristically demonstrates pure particle properties, must have wave properties. He postulated that particles of matter obey a wave equation just as photons do. He assumed that the wavelength of the wave associated with a particle is equal to Planck's constant h divided by the momentum of the particle.

$$\lambda = \frac{h}{mv}$$

This is the same equation that describes the wavelength associated with a photon. Thus, de Broglie contended that the relationship between matter and electromagnetic radiation is more intrinsic than was previously believed. He also contended that matter and light display the same wave and particle properties.

The wave properties of matter had never been observed. Thus, de Broglie's concept of matter waves met with considerable skepticism. However, in 1927 G. L. Thomson, son of J. J. Thomson, used a beam of electrons and a small crystal and succeeded in diffracting electrons. The spacing of the atoms in the crystalline lattice acted as a diffraction grating for the electrons. Since diffraction is a wave phenomenon, Thomson demonstrated the wave nature of matter.

De Broglie's equation for the wavelength of matter waves explains why the wave nature of large particles is not observable. Consider the de Broglie wavelength of a baseball of approximate mass 0.25 kg when it leaves a bat with a speed of 20 m/sec.

$$\lambda = \frac{h}{mv}$$
$$= \frac{6.6 \times 10^{-34} \text{ j-sec}}{0.25 \text{ kg} \times 20 \text{ m/sec}}$$
$$= 1.3 \times 10^{-34} \text{ m}$$

This wavelength is far too small to be observable. On the other hand, calculate the de Broglie wavelength of one of Thomson's electrons moving with a typical speed of 10^6 m/sec,

$$\lambda = \frac{h}{mv}$$
$$= \frac{6.6 \times 10^{-34} \text{ j-sec}}{9.1 \times 10^{-31} \text{ kg} \times 10^6 \text{ m/sec}}$$
$$= 7.3 \times 10^{-10} \text{ m}$$

This wavelength approximates the distance between the atoms in a crystal. It makes the wavelength suitable for diffraction and interference effects if a crystal is used as a grating. Thus, the wavelengths of very small particles of matter are readily observable.

Problems

7. What de Broglie wavelength is associated with a proton moving with a speed of 10^6 m/sec? The mass of a proton is 1.67×10^{-27} kg.

8. Calculate the de Broglie wavelength of a ping-pong ball of mass 0.015 kg moving at a speed of 3 m/sec.

9. What is the de Broglie wavelength of a 75-kg boy running at a speed of 10 m/sec?

10. Calculate the de Broglie wavelength of a neutron traveling at a speed of 10^3 m/sec. The mass of a neutron is 1.67×10^{-27} kg.

11. Determine the de Broglie wavelength of a ship of mass 2×10^6 kg that has a speed of 8 m/sec.

12. The earth has a mass of 6.0×10^{24} kg and an average speed of 2.7×10^4 m/sec. Determine the de Broglie wavelength of the earth.

QUESTIONS

1. The removal of an electron from nickel requires more energy than the removal of an electron from potassium. Which metal has the highest work function? Which metal has the highest threshold frequency?

2. How does the photoelectric effect indicate the particle nature of light?

3. What is the constant of proportionality between the energy possessed by a photon and the frequency of the photon?

4. Which has higher energy, photons of long wavelength or photons of short wavelength?

5. Express h/mv in fundamental units. Show that the expression yields length.

6. Why is it difficult to detect the particle nature of light?

7. Explain the Heisenberg uncertainty principle.

8. Which particle is more likely to have a detectable de Broglie wavelength associated with it, a high-speed electron or a speeding bullet? Use the de Broglie equation to explain your choice.

PROBLEMS

1. The stopping potential to prevent electron flow through a photocell is 5.2 volts. What is the maximum kinetic energy of the photoelectrons within the cell?

2. To prevent electron flow in a photocell, a stopping potential of 3.8 volts is used. What is the maximum kinetic energy of the photoelectrons within the cell?

3. The threshold frequency of tin is 1.1×10^{15} Hz. (a) What is the work function of tin? (b) Radiation of frequency 1.8×10^{15} Hz falls on tin. What is the maximum kinetic energy of the ejected electrons?

4. The work function of iron is 7.5×10^{-19} j. (a) What is the threshold frequency of iron? (b) Iron is irradiated with radiation of frequency 6.2×10^{15} Hz. What is the kinetic energy of the ejected electrons?

5. The threshold frequency of magnesium is 9.0×10^{14} Hz. (a) What is the work function of magnesium? (b) Radiation of frequency 2.0×10^{15} Hz falls on magnesium. What kinetic energy is possessed by the ejected electrons?

6. Determine the de Broglie wavelength of a deuteron of mass 3.3×10^{-27} kg that moves with a speed of 2.5×10^4 m/sec.

7. A spacecraft is fired and reaches a speed of 1.2×10^3 m/sec. The mass of the spacecraft is 2.0×10^3 kg. What de Broglie wavelength is associated with it?

8. A proton of mass 1.67×10^{-27} kg moves in a particle accelerator at a speed of 2×10^8 m/sec. What is its de Broglie wavelength?

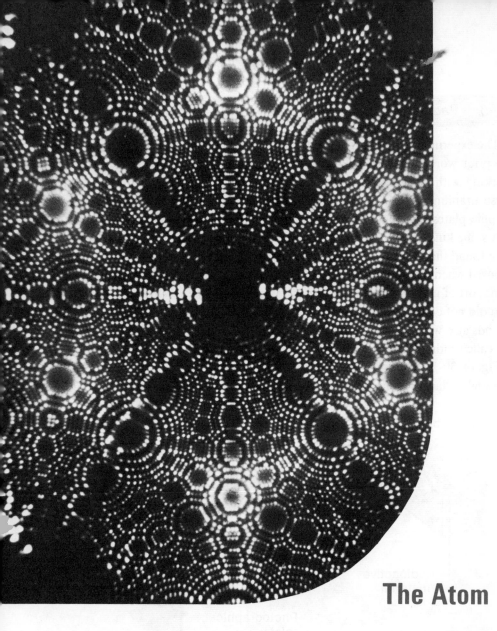

The Atom

The atom has long been a puzzle to man. Even now scientists are not able to view an individual atom. However, using a field ion emission microscope scientists have studied some crystal patterns like that of tungsten in the photograph above. Theorizing that all substances are made up of the same fundamental particles how can you account for great differences in their chemical activity, solubility, crystal structure, color, conductivity and numerous other properties?

Once the electron and the proton were identified, these two particles were assumed to be among the major particles that make up atoms. Both J. J. Thomson and Sir Ernest Rutherford (1871–1937) attempted to determine just how the fundamental particles arrange themselves to form atoms. Rutherford's work met with considerable success.

30:1 Radioactivity

The experiments Rutherford performed to probe the atom were based upon the prior work of Henri Becquerel, a French physicist. In 1896 Becquerel was working with compounds of the element uranium. He discovered that when these uranium compounds were kept some distance from unexposed photographic plates, the plates became fogged or partially exposed. This suggested that some kind of radiation was passing through the plate coverings. Becquerel even found that unexposed plates shielded by several thicknesses of lead became exposed when they were near the uranium. At first he thought he had discovered some sort of invisible rays similar to X rays. Soon it was revealed that the radiation did not consist of X rays. Several materials other than uranium or its compounds also were capable of emitting these rays. Collectively, all these materials are called radioactive materials.

Figure 30-1 illustrates the method Rutherford used to study radioactive materials. Placing a small amount of a radioactive substance at the bottom of

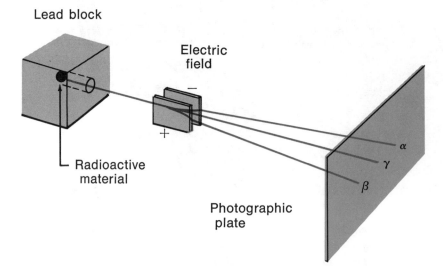

Figure 30-1. Rutherford's apparatus for studying radioactive substances. Note the directions in which the radiations emitted are deflected on passing through an electric field.

a hole drilled in a lead block, he confined the emission to a small beam coming from the hole. Emissions that left the radioactive substance in any direction other than straight through the hole were absorbed by the lead. He then caused the emergent radiation to pass through a strong electric field and to fall on a photographic plate. When the plate was developed, three distinct spots were found on the plate. The spots indicated three distinct types of radiation. These were named alpha, beta, and gamma rays after the first three letters of the Greek alphabet. A study was made of the behavior of these rays in electric and magnetic fields. It was found that *alpha particles are doubly-ionized helium nuclei*, beta rays are high-speed electrons, and gamma rays are photons of very high frequency.*

30:2 Discovery of the Nucleus

To explore the nuclei of atoms, Rutherford's research team of Geiger and Marsden directed alpha rays at very thin sheets of metal. They placed a small fluorescent screen in front of a movable telescope and observed the alpha particles as they passed through the foil. As an alpha particle passed through the foil

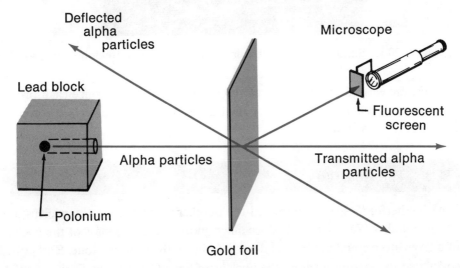

Figure 30-2. Bombardment of gold foil with alpha particles.

and struck the fluorescent screen in front of the telescope, a small flash of light, a scintillation, was observed on the screen. The scintillation was the result of the excitation of the fluorescent material on the screen by the alpha particle.

Rutherford's team found that most of the particles passed straight through the foil. Since the foil was at least several hundreds of atoms thick, this indicated that atoms are mostly empty space. A few alpha particles deflected as they passed through the foil. A few particles even rebounded from the foil.

After observing the angles through which the particles were deflected, Rutherford's team came to this conclusion: most of the mass of the atom is located in a very small core or nucleus.

---

*The helium atom has two electrons. An alpha particle is the helium atom with a deficit of two electrons. The alpha particle thus has a $+2$ charge, or is "doubly-ionized."

Going further, Rutherford's team measured the velocity of the alpha particles as they approached the foil. Since they knew the charge and the mass of the alpha particles, they could apply Coulomb's law and Newton's laws of motion. In a brilliant series of experiments and analysis of results, they determined the

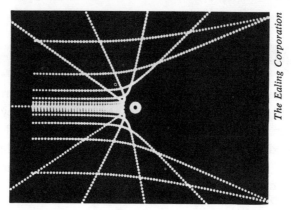

The Ealing Corporation

Figure 30-3.   Simulation of bombardment of a nucleus with alpha particles.

total charge carried by the nuclei of several different atoms. Since each proton carries one elementary charge, they then determined the number of protons in the nucleus of each atom.

30:3   The Neutron

As Rutherford's team determined the number of protons in the nucleus, the atomic number (Z), another fact became rapidly clear. The mass of the nucleus of a given atom could not be explained in terms of the protons alone. Rutherford postulated the existence within the nucleus of a neutral particle. Such a particle could bear no net charge. Rutherford called this particle a neutron. In 1932, James Chadwick demonstrated the existence of the neutron. The neutron has a mass roughly equal to the mass of the proton. This is approximately one atomic mass unit. The mass of the protons in an atom plus the mass of the neutrons in the atom account for the mass of the nucleus. Therefore, the approximate mass of a nucleus in atomic mass units is the number of protons plus the number of neutrons within that nucleus. The mass of the nucleus is taken to be the mass of the atom since the electrons outside the nucleus are of negligible mass.

30:4   Planetary Model of the Atom

Rutherford knew that ordinarily most materials bear no net charge. He postulated that each atom, unless it had been ionized, contains as many electrons as protons. Because electrons often are ejected from the atom, he further postulated that the electrons were located outside the nucleus. Figure 30-4 shows the planetary model of the atom as put forth after Rutherford's work.

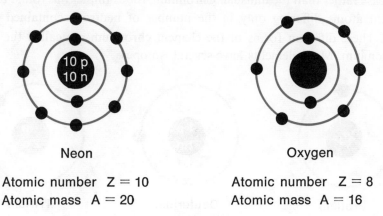

Neon

Oxygen

Atomic number Z = 10

Atomic number Z = 8

Atomic mass A = 20

Atomic mass A = 16

Figure 30-4. Planetary models of a neon atom and an oxygen atom. How does this model differ from more recent models?

30:5   Isotopes

For some time, scientists all over the world were puzzled by the fact that the masses of the atoms of most of the elements, measured in atomic mass units, were not exactly whole numbers. If, as was postulated, the nucleus is made up of protons and neutrons each of which bears a mass of approximately 1 a.m.u. (atomic mass units), then the total mass of any atom should be near a whole number. However, most measurements revealed that the masses of atoms are not whole numbers. For example, careful measurements of the mass of the boron atom consistently yield 10.8 a.m.u.

The problem presented by decimal values for the mass of the atoms was solved with the innovation of the mass spectrometer (Chapter 28). The mass spectrometer showed that an element has atoms of different masses. For example, neon has atoms of two different masses. Using a pure sample of neon, it was found that not one, but two spots appeared on the screen of the spectrometer. Careful measurements showed that the two spots represented neon atoms of different mass. One neon atom has a mass of about 20 a.m.u. The second neon atom has a mass of about 21 a.m.u. All neon atoms have ten protons in their nuclei. This means that one "kind" of neon has ten neutrons in its nucleus while the other has eleven neutrons in its nucleus. Thus, neon is a mixture of neon atoms which have different numbers of neutrons in their nuclei. When the mass of neon was determined prior to the invention of the mass spectrometer, the result always had given the average mass of the two kinds of neon, 20.183 a.m.u. Hence, while the mass of any individual atom of neon is close to a whole number, the mass of any given sample of neon is not.

Further investigation revealed that the situation described for neon was the usual case rather than the unusual. Chromium, for example, was found to have 4 different atoms differing only in the number of neutrons contained in their nuclei. These different forms of the element chromium are called the *isotopes* of chromium. Most elements have several isotopes.

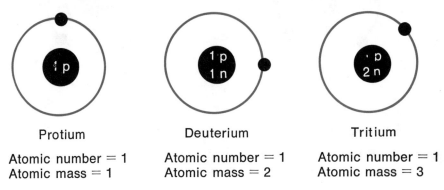

Protium	Deuterium	Tritium
Atomic number $= 1$	Atomic number $= 1$	Atomic number $= 1$
Atomic mass $= 1$	Atomic mass $= 2$	Atomic mass $= 3$

Figure 30-5. Hydrogen's three known isotopes.

Sample Problem 1

An isotope of iron has an atomic mass of 56 a.m.u. If the atomic number of iron is 26, how many neutrons are in the nucleus of an atom of this iron isotope?

Solution:

Since the mass of the atom is 56 a.m.u. and the atom contains 26 protons, the number of neutrons must be $56 - 26$, or 30.

A special method is used to express the isotopes of the elements. A small subscript for the atomic number is written to the lower left of the symbol of that element. A small superscript is written to the upper left of the symbol for the atomic mass. This takes the form $_Z^A E$. To illustrate, for oxygen of atomic number 8 and atomic mass 16, the form is $_8^{16}O$. For neon of atomic mass 20 and atomic number 10, the form is $_{10}^{20}Ne$.

Problems

1. An isotope of oxygen has an atomic mass of 15 a.m.u. If the atomic number of oxygen is 8, how many neutrons are in the nuclei of this isotope?
2. Three isotopes of uranium have atomic masses of 234, 235, and 238. How many neutrons are in the nuclei of each of these isotopes if the atomic number of uranium is 92?
3. How many neutrons are in an atom of the isotope of mercury $_{80}^{200}Hg$?

4. Write the symbolic expression for the three isotopes of hydrogen in Figure 30-5.

5. Under proper circumstances, the nucleus of the isotope $^{238}_{92}U$ absorbs an extra neutron. (a) Write the symbolic expression for this new isotope of uranium. (b) How many neutrons are in the nuclei of each of these isotopes?

6. Shortly after $^{238}_{92}U$ absorbs the neutron described in Problem 5, an electron is ejected from the nucleus. What is the new nucleus formed?

30:6   The Bohr Model of the Atom

The planetary model of the atom which pictured the electrons circling the nuclei of atoms was severely criticized. It has been established that whenever a charged particle is accelerated, energy is emitted in the form of electromagnetic radiation. If an electron follows a circular path, it undergoes continuous acceleration and it should continuously emit radiation. This would cause the electron to suffer a constant energy loss with the result that it would spiral down into the nucleus of the atom. In short, on the basis of the planetary model, atoms should not exist at all.

Another objection to the planetary model was that it failed to account for the quantum nature of electromagnetic radiations. The photoelectric effect clearly demonstrated that each photon of light carries a definite quantity of energy. What is more, the spectrum of each element, as seen in a spectroscope, is always the same. This indicates that the radiation emitted by any given element is always the same. Maxwell had shown that electromagnetic radiation is the result of the accelerations of charged particles. Assuming that atoms emit radia-

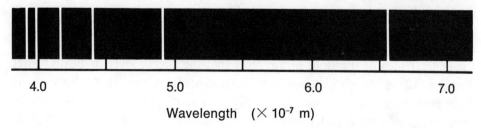

4.0   5.0   6.0   7.0

Wavelength   ($\times$ 10^{-7} m)

Figure 30-6. Line spectrum of hydrogen. The lines correspond to definite electron transitions within the atom.

tion as their electrons accelerate, the electrons within an atom must undergo some very definite transitions. Rutherford made no provision for this in his atomic model. If the electrons could orbit anywhere about the nucleus, then all wavelengths of radiation, at least within a set range, should be observable from any sample of an element. The elements should, under these circumstances, emit a continuous spectrum. Since this does not happen, a new model of the atom was needed.

The Danish physicist Niels Bohr (1885–1962) extended Rutherford's model of the atom. He presented two bold theories. (1) Bohr asserted that electrons can move about the nucleus of an atom without radiating energy, and (2) he introduced the idea of the energy states of the atom, suggesting the positive nucleus and the orbiting negative electrons endow the atom with energy. The energy state of an atom can be changed when it absorbs or emits radiation. Although orbits no longer are considered to exist, a mental picture is possible of electrons circling about the nuclei of atoms in certain allowed orbits. Figure 30-7 illustrates

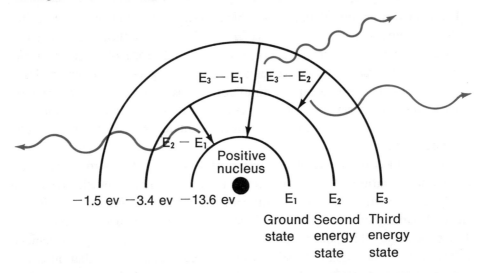

Figure 30-7. Bohr model of an atom. A definite amount of energy is released when each electron moves from a higher to a lower energy level. The energy released in each transition corresponds to a definite line in the characteristic spectrum of an element.

the general idea of the Bohr atom. Note that the energy levels indicate higher energy as the electron's distance from the nucleus increases. This is because the force between an electron and the nucleus is one of attraction. Work must be done on the electron in order to move it away from the nucleus. The system gains energy when the electron moves from an inner to an outer orbit. Thus, the energy content of an electron at E_2 is greater than the energy content of an electron at E_1. A base level ($PE = 0$) is chosen at an infinite distance from the nucleus. Since an electron loses energy as it approaches the nucleus, the energy states must be expressed in negative values.

According to Bohr, the atom emits no radiation as long as the electrons occupy their allowed orbital paths. However, if the atom absorbs energy, an electron can move to a higher energy level. In this way, the atom increases its potential energy. Usually, the atom returns immediately to its normal energy state as the electron returns to its normal level. During the down-transition, a photon of energy is released. By the law of conservation of energy, the energy content of the photon (hf) is equal to the energy difference represented by the electron transition, that is $hf = E_{initial} - E_{final}$. Thus, Bohr directly relates the energy changes within the atom to Einstein's photoelectric equation for the energy of a photon. The photon's energy is the energy released by an atom as its energy content decreases during the transition of an electron from a higher to a lower energy level.

30:7 Bohr's Equations

Section 30:6 treats Bohr's picture of the atom qualitatively. That is, a description is given of how the atom could be arranged so that the discrete spectrum of the atoms and the energy of photons can be accounted for. If this was all that Bohr had contributed, his concept of the atom might have seemed contrived and would have been largely ignored. But Bohr did much more than this. Using Coulomb's law to define the force of attraction between the electron and the positive nucleus, Bohr then applied Newton's conditions for angular momentum and centripetal force. He added one or two brilliant hypotheses and derived several equations. He determined an equation for the radius of the hydrogen orbits; an equation for the energy content of the allowed orbits; and an equation that predicted, in precise agreement with experimental evidence, the frequencies and wavelengths of the hydrogen spectrum. This type of mathematical evidence lends strong credence to theory. Bohr's model of the atom was generally accepted.

The derivations of the Bohr equations are straightforward and easily understood by anyone familiar with elementary algebra and Newtonian mechanics. The derivations are omitted here, but the equations and their applications are presented. Note that these equations apply only to the hydrogen atom.

THE RADII OF HYDROGEN ORBITS

$$r = \frac{n^2 h^2}{4\pi^2 K m e^2}$$

Here n represents whole number values for the orbits beginning with 1 for the innermost orbital level. K is the constant 9.0×10^9 nt-m²/coul² used in Coulomb's law, h is Planck's constant, m is the mass of the electron and e is the charge in coulombs.

Sample Problem 2

Calculate the radius of the innermost orbital level of the hydrogen atom.

Solution:

$n = 1$

$K = 9.0 \times 10^9$ nt-m²/coul² $m = 9.1 \times 10^{-31}$ kg

$e = 1.6 \times 10^{-19}$ coul

$h = 6.6 \times 10^{-34}$ j-sec $r = \dfrac{n^2 h^2}{4\pi^2 K m e^2}$

$$r = \frac{(1)^2 (6.6 \times 10^{-34} \text{ j-sec})^2}{(4)(9.86)(9.0 \times 10^9 \text{ nt-m}^2/\text{coul}^2)(9.1 \times 10^{-31} \text{ kg})(1.6 \times 10^{-19} \text{ coul})^2}$$

$r = 5.3 \times 10^{-11}$ m

ORBITAL ENERGY OF ELECTRONS IN THE HYDROGEN ATOM

$$E = \frac{-2\pi^2 K^2 m e^4}{n^2 h^2}$$

Here K, m, e, and h are the same constants used in the equation for the radii of the hydrogen orbits. The constants are combined to give a simplified version of the equation. Hence,

$$E = \frac{-2.17 \times 10^{-18}}{n^2} \text{ j}$$

Since an electron-volt (ev) is equal to 1.60×10^{-19} j the above equation may be written as,

$$E = \frac{-13.6 \text{ ev}}{n^2}$$

Sample Problem 3

(a) Determine the energy associated with the innermost orbit of the hydrogen atom ($n = 1$). (b) Determine the energy associated with the second orbit of the hydrogen atom. (c) What energy does an incoming photon possess to raise an electron from the first to the second allowed orbit of the hydrogen atom?

Solution:

$$\text{(a)} \quad E = \frac{-13.6 \text{ ev}}{n^2}$$

$$= \frac{-13.6 \text{ ev}}{1^2}$$

$$= -13.6 \text{ ev}$$

$$\text{(b)} \quad E = \frac{-13.6 \text{ ev}}{n^2}$$

$$= \frac{-13.6 \text{ ev}}{2^2}$$

$$= -3.4 \text{ ev}$$

(c) Since $hf = E_f - E_i$

$$hf = -13.6 \text{ ev} - (-3.4 \text{ ev})$$

$$= -10.2 \text{ ev}$$

FREQUENCY AND WAVELENGTH OF EMITTED PHOTONS

Since $hf = E_f - E_i$

$$f = \frac{E_f - E_i}{h}$$

Also since $c = f\lambda$

$$\lambda = \frac{c}{f}$$

Sample Problem 4

An electron drops from the second energy level to the first energy level within an excited hydrogen atom. (a) Determine the energy of the photon emitted. (b) Calculate the frequency of the photon emitted. (c) Calculate the wavelength of the photon emitted.

Solution:

(a) From Sample Problem 3 (c), the energy of the photon hf equals $E_2 - E_1 = 10.2$ ev.

(b) Since $hf = 10.2$ ev

$$f = \frac{10.2 \text{ ev}}{h}$$

$$= \frac{10.2 \text{ ev } (1.6 \times 10^{-19} \text{ j/ev})}{6.6 \times 10^{-34} \text{ j-sec}}$$

$$= 2.5 \times 10^{15} \text{ Hz}$$

(c) $\lambda = \dfrac{c}{f}$

$$= \frac{3.0 \times 10^8 \text{ m/sec}}{2.5 \times 10^{15} \text{ Hz}}$$

$$= 1.2 \times 10^{-7} \text{ m}$$

Problems

7. Sample Problem 2 shows how to calculate the radius of the innermost orbit of the hydrogen atom. Notice that all factors in the formula are constants with the exception of n^2. Use the solution to the sample problem to determine the radius of the second, third, and fourth allowable energy levels within the hydrogen atom.

8. Calculate the energy associated with the second, third, and fourth energy levels within the hydrogen atom.

9. Calculate the energy difference between E_3 and E_2. Do the same between E_4 and E_3 within the hydrogen atom.

10. Determine the frequency and wavelength of the photon emitted when an electron drops from E_3 to E_2 within an excited hydrogen atom.

11. Determine the frequency and wavelength of the photon emitted when an electron drops from E_4 to E_3 within an excited hydrogen atom.

12. What is the difference between the energy associated with the energy level E_4 and E_1 of the hydrogen atom?

13. Determine the frequency and wavelength of the photon emitted when an electron drops from E_4 to E_1 within an excited hydrogen atom.

30:8   Success of Bohr's Model of the Atom

Although Bohr's work was successful only when dealing with the hydrogen atom, it did broaden the general knowledge of atomic structure. For example, the Bohr model explained the absorption spectra of the atoms. Atoms tend to absorb radiation of the same frequency that they emit. When light is sent through hydrogen gas, the dark absorption lines appear for photons of energy $E_2 - E_1$, $E_3 - E_2$. This verifies Bohr's predictions. Also the minimum energy content needed by incident photons to ionize hydrogen atoms is just 13.6 ev. This is as calculated by Bohr.

30:9   Present Model of the Atom

The atom consists of a positively charged nucleus which contains all of the atoms's protons and neutrons. Electrons surround the nucleus. They are equal in number to the number of protons in the nucleus. *The electrons no longer are considered to occupy specific orbits.* Instead, the electrons are thought of as forming an electron cloud. The cloud exists only in specific energy arrangements, and has a definite total energy content. The difference between these allowed energy contents accounts for the discrete energy content of the photons emitted by the atom. Thus, the transition that leads to the formation of a photon is due to the change in energy content undergone *by the atom.*

QUESTIONS

1. Describe Rutherford's method for analyzing radioactive materials.
2. Name and identify the three types of radiation emitted by naturally radioactive materials.
3. Describe the neutron. What is its mass?
4. Upon what does the mass of a nucleus depend?
5. What are isotopes?
6. What criticism was leveled at the original planetary model of the atom?

7. What two basic postulates did Niels Bohr make in order to extend Rutherford's model of the atom?

8. How does the Bohr model of the atom account for the emission of radiation?

9. What major difference exists between the present-day model of the atom and Bohr's model of the atom?

PROBLEMS

1. An isotope of magnesium has an atomic mass of 24 a.m.u. If the atomic number of magnesium is 12, how many neutrons does the nucleus of this isotope contain?

2. An isotope of nitrogen has an atomic mass of 15 a.m.u. If the atomic number of nitrogen is 7, how many neutrons does the nucleus of this isotope contain?

3. List the number of neutrons an atom contains in each of these isotopes.
   (a) $^{112}_{48}$Cd (b) $^{209}_{83}$Bi (c) $^{208}_{83}$Bi (d) $^{80}_{35}$Br (e) $^{1}_{1}$H (f) $^{40}_{18}$Ar (g) $^{132}_{54}$Xe

4. Calculate the radius of the allowed energy levels E_5 and E_6 of the hydrogen atom.

5. What energy is associated with the hydrogen atom energy levels E_5 and E_6?

6. What energy is associated with the hydrogen energy levels E_2, E_3, and E_4?

7. Calculate these values for the hydrogen atom. (a) $E_6 - E_5$ (b) $E_6 - E_3$
   (c) $E_4 - E_2$ (d) $E_5 - E_2$ (e) $E_5 - E_3$

8. Use Problem 7 solutions to determine the frequencies of the photons emitted when the hydrogen atom passes through the energy differences.

9. Use Problem 8 solutions to determine the wavelengths of the photons having the frequencies listed.

10. A photon of energy 16 ev enters a hydrogen atom whose election is in the ground state. The photon ejects an electron from the atom. What is the kinetic energy in ev of the electron?

Use Figure 30-8 to solve Problems 11 through 14. The left side of the diagram gives the energy level for mercury in electron-volts. The right side gives the energy required to raise the atom from the ground state to each energy level.

11. An electron is accelerated by a potential difference of 7.7 volts. (a) What energy does the electron possess in electron volts? (b) The electron strikes a mercury atom in its ground state. To which energy level is the mercury atom raised?

12. A mercury atom is in the excited state when its energy level is 6.67 ev above the ground state. A photon of energy 2.15 ev strikes the mercury atom and is absorbed by it. To which energy level is the atom raised?

13. A mercury atom drops from 8.81 ev above its ground state to 6.67 ev above its ground state. What is the energy of the photon emitted by the mercury atom?

14. In Problem 13, calculate the photon's (a) frequency (b) wavelength.

Figure 30-8.   Ionization energy table for a mercury atom.

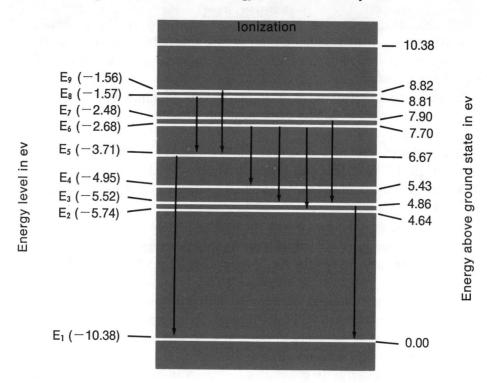

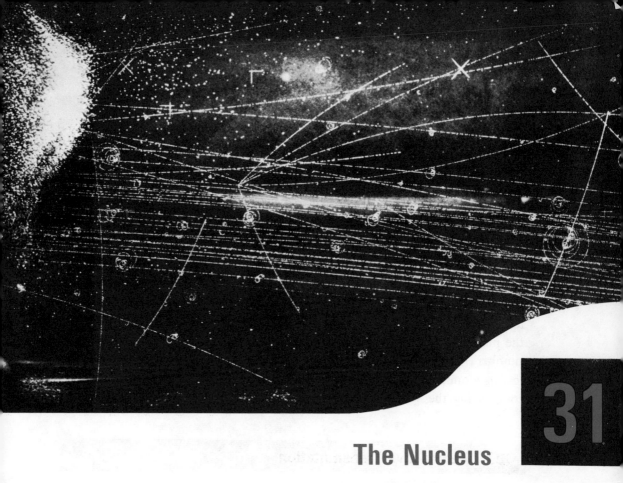

The Nucleus

The nucleus of an atom still presents something of a mystery. New particles are constantly being discovered. What you see in the above photograph is not a proton or an antiproton, but rather a change in the composition of the photographic film brought about by the energy released when these two particles were annihilated on contact. Why do nuclear reactions release much larger quantities of energy than chemical reactions?

31:1   Early Discoveries

Becquerel discovered the radioactive properties of uranium. The search by Pierre and Marie Curie for other radioactive elements resulted in the discovery of polonium and radium. Other investigations led to the discovery of the radioactive properties of thorium and actinium. Rutherford added the discovery of radon, the radioactive noble gas, to his impressive list of achievements.

The nuclei of naturally radioactive elements are unstable. An unstable nucleus emits radiation in the form of alpha, beta, and gamma rays. Thus, the nucleus undergoes a gradual change until it becomes stable. The radioactive element uranium, for example, undergoes fourteen separate transformations before becoming the stable isotope of lead $^{206}_{82}Pb$. *The change in the identity of a radioactive element is nuclear transmutation.*

413

31:2 Atomic Number and Mass Number

The identity of the element to which a nucleus belongs depends only upon the number of protons in the nucleus. As studied in Section 30:3, this is the atomic number (Z) of the nucleus.

In Chapter 30, the number of neutrons in the nucleus of an atom was determined by subtracting the number of protons from the atomic mass of the nucleus. This works only when the atomic mass of the element or the isotope of any given element is stated in terms of a whole number. Strictly speaking, the atomic mass unit is $\frac{1}{12}$ of the mass of an atom of $^{12}_{6}C$. Precise atomic mass measurements do not yield whole numbers. However, the numbers come close to being whole numbers. They are the mass numbers of isotopes. For example, the mass of a helium isotope in atomic mass units is 4.00260 a.m.u. Its mass number is 4. Recall that the number of neutrons in a nucleus is its mass number less its atomic number. In future sections, we will refer to the superscripts accompanying the symbols of the elements more correctly as mass numbers.

31:3 Radioactive Transmutation

An alpha particle is a helium nucleus, $^{4}_{2}He$, which contains two protons and two neutrons. If the nucleus of a uranium atom, $^{238}_{92}U$, emits an alpha particle, it must lose two protons and two neutrons or a total of four units of mass from its nucleus. Since the atomic number, the number of protons in the nucleus, determines the identity of the element, the atom of uranium changes its identity. It is no longer uranium. After the loss of two protons, the nucleus has an atomic number $Z = 90$. This is thorium. Its mass number is $238 - 4$, or 234. Thus, the isotope of thorium, $^{234}_{90}Th$, is formed. One element has been transmuted, or changed, into another element.

A radioactive atom undergoes beta decay by emitting an electron from the nucleus. The nucleus is changed correspondingly by an increase of one positive charge. Thus the atomic number of the element is raised by one. The mass of an electron is considered insignificant. This means that the atomic mass of a nucleus is not changed by the emission of a beta particle. However, the increase in the atomic number by one brings about a change in the identity of the nucleus. This results in a transmutation. For example, after a uranium atom becomes thorium, the newly formed thorium atom emits a beta particle. By emitting an electron (beta particle), the thorium atom gains a positive charge. Thus, $^{234}_{90}Th$ gains a proton in its nucleus. However, it undergoes no change in mass and becomes protactinium, $^{234}_{91}Pa$.

The emission of a beta particle by the disintegration of a neutron is accompanied by the emission of a second particle from the neutron, an antineutrino. The antineutrino bears no charge and is of negligible mass. It is difficult to detect. Hence, the existence of the antineutrino was postulated long before it was actually detected.

When a gamma ray is emitted by a nucleus, no transmutation takes place. This is because a gamma ray is a quantum of energy and bears no net charge. The emission of a gamma ray is the means by which a nucleus rids itself of excess energy as it rearranges itself during decay.

31:4   Nuclear Equations

Nuclear reactions are expressed in equation form. Using nuclear equations facilitates the calculation of atomic number and mass number in a transformation. For example, here is how to write the nuclear reaction for the transmutation of uranium to thorium due to the emission of an alpha particle:

$$^{238}_{92}U \longrightarrow ^{204}_{90}Th + ^{4}_{2}He$$

$$Uranium \longrightarrow Thorium + Alpha\ Particle$$

Since no nuclear particles are destroyed during the transmutation process, the sum of the superscripts on the right side of the equation must equal the sum of the superscripts on the left side of the equation. Thus, the superscripts on the right total 238 and equal the superscript on the left of 238. Charge is also conserved, so the total of the subscripts on the right equals the total of the subscripts on the left.

A beta particle is represented by the symbol $_{-1}^{0}e$. This indicates that the electron bears a negative charge of one and an atomic mass number of zero. The equation for the transmutation of a radioactive substance by the emission of a beta particle is written:

$$^{234}_{90}Th \longrightarrow ^{234}_{91}Pa + ^{0}_{-1}e$$

$$Thorium \longrightarrow Protactinium + Beta\ Particle$$

The sum of the superscripts on the right side of the equation equals the sum of the superscripts on the left side of the equation. Also, the sum of the subscripts on the right side of the equation equals the sum of the subscripts on the left side of the equation.

Sample Problem 1

Write the equation for the transmutation of radioactive radium $^{226}_{88}Ra$ into the element radon $^{222}_{86}Rn$ by the emission of an alpha particle.

Solution:
$$^{226}_{88}Ra \longrightarrow ^{222}_{86}Rn + ^{4}_{2}He$$

Sample Problem 2

Write the equation for the transmutation of radioactive lead $^{209}_{82}$Pb into the element bismuth $^{209}_{83}$Bi by the emission of a beta particle.

Solution:

$$^{209}_{82}\text{Pb} \longrightarrow ^{209}_{83}\text{Bi} + ^{0}_{-1}e$$

Problems

1. Write the nuclear equation for the transmutation of radioactive uranium $^{234}_{92}$U into thorium $^{230}_{90}$Th by the emission of an alpha particle.
2. Write the nuclear equation for the transmutation of radioactive thorium $^{230}_{90}$Th into radioactive radium $^{226}_{88}$Ra by the emission of an alpha particle.
3. Write the equation for the transmutation of radioactive radium $^{226}_{88}$Ra into radioactive radon $^{222}_{86}$Rn by the emission of an alpha particle.
4. Radioactive lead $^{214}_{82}$Pb can change to radioactive bismuth $^{214}_{83}$Bi by the emission of a beta particle. Write the equation for this transmutation.
5. A nucleus of radioactive bismuth $^{214}_{83}$Bi emits a beta particle. Use the Appendix C-1 to determine the element formed. Write the equation.
6. A nucleus of radioactive polonium $^{210}_{84}$Po emits an alpha particle. Use Appendix C-1 to determine the element formed. Write the equation to represent the transformation.

31:5   Nuclear Bombardment

One important method to study the nuclei of atoms is to bombard them with smaller particles such as alpha particles or neutrons. When such particles strike the nucleus of an atom, the nucleus disintegrates. Much is learned by studying the rays and particles emitted as the nucleus breaks down.

When a sample of an element emits radiation after nuclear bombardment, the sample is artificially radioactive. Nuclear bombardment also results in the transmutation of elements. This can create new elements with atomic numbers higher than that of uranium (92). These elements are transuranium elements.

31:6   The Cyclotron

In 1930, the cyclotron was developed by E. O. Lawrence. The cyclotron is a device to accelerate protons and deuterons (the nuclei of "heavy hydrogen" — the hydrogen isotope $^{2}_{1}$H) to extremely high velocities. This gives them sufficient energy to enter the nuclei of atoms. A cyclotron consists of two hollow half-cylinders. They are called "dees" because of their D-shapes. The dees are enclosed in an evacuated chamber and placed between the poles of a powerful electromagnet. The dees are also connected to a source of high frequency (10^7 Hz) alternating voltage of at least 50 000 volts. This changes the charge on each dee during each half-cycle.

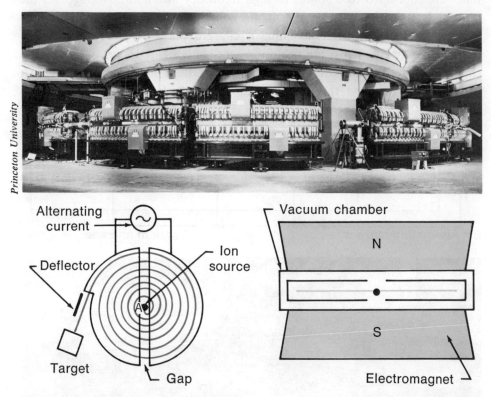

Figure 31-1. Magnet ring of the Princeton-Pen accelerator. Included is a diagram of the internal structure of the cyclotron.

Figure 31-1 illustrates how the cyclotron works. A proton is introduced at A. Protons are obtained by using singly-ionized hydrogen atoms ${}_1^1\text{H}$. When the proton enters at A, it moves slowly at first. The strong magnetic field causes its path to be circular. Soon it reaches the gap between the two dees. The applied voltage across the dees is synchronized so that the dee the proton is leaving is charged positively. The opposite dee is charged negatively. Hence the proton is accelerated across the 50 000-volt difference of potential. The increased velocity causes the proton to follow a circular path of larger radius since the electromagnetic field is kept constant. Each time the proton crosses the gap between the dees, its velocity increases. Therefore, the radius of its circular path also increases. The proton is brought to an extremely high velocity. When directed at a target, the particles bombard the nuclei of various elements. The transformations that result are then studied.

31:7   Linear Accelerators

A linear accelerator consists of a long series of hollow evacuated tubes. The tubes are connected to a source of high frequency alternating voltage. As the protons leave each tube, the alternating voltage is arranged so that the tube from which the proton is emanating is charged positively. The next tube is charged negatively. Thus, the proton is accelerated as it leaves one tube and enters another. The total energy imparted to the proton depends upon the length of the accelerator and the difference in potential placed across the tubes.

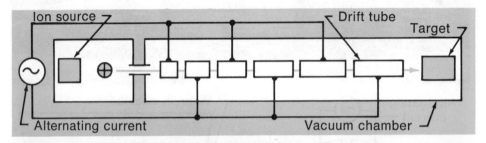

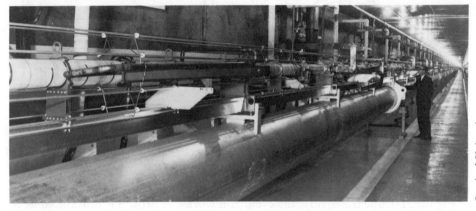

Figure 31-2.   Linear accelerator at Stanford University. The internal structure of this acceleration is diagramed above.

31:8   Particle Detectors

Photographic plates become "fogged" or exposed when alpha particles, beta particles, or gamma rays fall upon them. This makes photographic plates useful as a means of detecting the presence of these rays. However, many other devices detect the charged particles and gamma rays emitted by radioactive atoms. Most of these devices employ the principle that a high-speed particle removes electrons from atoms. The high-speed particles ionize the matter upon which they are incident or through which they pass. For example, a fluorescent substance fluoresces when exposed to certain types of radiation. Then it is a radiation detector.

The Geiger-Muller tube employs an avalanche effect (Figure 31-3). The tube contains a gas at low pressure (0.1 atm). At one end of the tube is a very thin "window." Charged particles or gamma rays pass through the window. Inside the tube is a metal cylinder negatively charged. A rigid wire positively charged runs down the center of this cylinder. The voltage across the wire and cylinder is kept just below the point where a spontaneous discharge might occur.

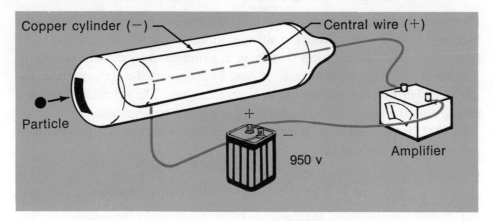

Figure 31-3. A diagram of a Geiger counter.

When a charged particle enters the tube, it ionizes a gas particle located between the metal cylinder and the wire. It does this by ejecting an electron from the gas atom. Immediately, the electron is accelerated toward the positive wire by the potential difference. The ionized gas particle is accelerated toward the metal cylinder. As these particles move, they strike other particles. This produces more ions. These ions, in turn, move toward the negatively-charged cylinder and ionize even more atoms in their path. Thus, an avalanche of charged particles is created and the tube discharges. This discharge can be amplified sufficiently to cause an audible signal (a click) or to operate a counter, or both. To operate the tube continuously, a temporary drop in voltage is placed across the tube to "quench" the discharge. This is done electronically as an automatic reaction to the discharge. The tube must then wait for a new particle before a new avalanche can begin.

The Wilson cloud chamber creates an area that is supersaturated with water vapor. When ions travel through the chamber, the water vapor tends to condense upon the ions. This leaves visible trails of water particles, or fog, behind. The bubble chamber operates on a similar principle but is much more sensitive than the cloud chamber. Particles, such as neutrinos, that cannot be detected in a cloud chamber can be detected in a bubble chamber.

31:9   Artificial Transmutation

The first deliberate artificial transmutation of one element into another was achieved by Lord Rutherford. Rutherford bombarded pure nitrogen gas with alpha particles. Oxygen gas appeared in the once pure sample of nitrogen. This reaction is written:

$$^{14}_{7}N + {}^{4}_{2}He \longrightarrow {}^{17}_{8}O + {}^{1}_{1}H$$

Nitrogen + Alpha Particle⟶Oxygen + Proton

Here an alpha particle strikes the nitrogen nucleus and is absorbed. During the process it ejects a proton from the nitrogen atom. The proton is represented by the symbol $^{1}_{1}H$. This indicates that it is a hydrogen nucleus with an atomic number of one and a mass number of one. By absorbing the alpha particle, the nitrogen nucleus gains one proton to become oxygen. The net addition of one proton and two neutrons increases the mass number to seventeen.

In 1932, James Chadwick bombarded beryllium nuclei with alpha particles and made this observation:

$$^{9}_{4}Be + {}^{4}_{2}He \longrightarrow {}^{12}_{6}C + {}^{1}_{0}n$$

Beryllium + Alpha Particle⟶Carbon + Neutron

This reaction confirmed the existence of the neutron. As the equation shows, an alpha particle is captured by the beryllium nucleus and a neutron is ejected. In this way, the nucleus gains two protons raising its atomic number from 4 to 6. It now becomes a carbon nucleus. The ejected neutrons, in turn, make excellent particles for bombarding the nuclei of other elements. This is because they bear no net charge. Unlike protons, neutrons are not subjected to a repulsive force as they approach the positively-charged nucleus of an atom.

31:10   Artificial Radioactivity

After bombarding otherwise stable nuclei with neutrons, alpha particles, beta particles and accelerated protons, these once stable nuclei often display a lack of stability. The now unstable nuclei emit radiation until they achieve stability. Thus, the once stable nuclei have been made artificially radioactive. Artificially radioactive substances, like naturally radioactive substances, can emit alpha and beta particles. However, artificially radioactive substances also can emit a particle called a *positron*. A positron is a positive electron which has the same mass as an electron but bears a positive charge rather than a negative charge. Its symbol is $^{0}_{+1}e$. A positron is the result of the conversion of a proton into a neutron accompanied by the emission of a *neutrino*. Just as a neutron can produce a proton by emitting a negative electron and an antineutrino, a proton can produce a neutron by emitting a positive electron and a neutrino.

When a proton produces a neutron by the emission of a positive electron, the atomic number (Z) of the nucleus containing the proton decreases by one. Hence transmutation takes place. For example, artificially radioactive phosphorus decays into stable silicon by the emission of a positron.

$$^{30}_{15}P \longrightarrow ^{30}_{14}Si + ^{0}_{+1}e$$

$$\text{Phosphorus} \longrightarrow \text{Silicon} + \text{Positron}$$

Problems

7. Use Table C-1 of the Appendix to complete the equations for these transmutations.

    (a) $^{14}_{6}C \longrightarrow ? + ^{0}_{-1}e$ (b) $^{55}_{24}Cr \longrightarrow ? + ^{0}_{-1}e$

8. Write the nuclear equation for the transmutation of radioactive uranium $^{238}_{92}U$ into thorium $^{234}_{90}Th$ by the emission of an alpha particle.

9. Write the nuclear equation for the transmutation of radioactive radium $^{226}_{88}Ra$ by alpha decay.

10. Radioactive polonium $^{214}_{84}Po$ decays by alpha emission and becomes lead. Write the equation for this transmutation.

11. Write the nuclear equations for the beta decay of (a) $^{210}_{82}Pb$ (b) $^{210}_{83}Bi$ (c) $^{234}_{90}Th$ (d) $^{239}_{93}Np$

12. When bombarded by protons ($^{1}_{1}H$) lithium absorbs a proton and then ejects two alpha particles. Write the nuclear equation for this reaction.

13. Complete the equations for these transmutations:

    (a) $^{30}_{15}P \longrightarrow ? + ^{0}_{+1}e$

    (b) $^{238}_{92}U \longrightarrow ? + ^{0}_{+1}e$

14. The unstable radioactive nuclei indicated in each equation disintegrate by emitting a positron. Complete each equation.

    (a) $^{21}_{11}Na \longrightarrow ? + ^{0}_{+1}e$

    (b) $^{49}_{24}Cr \longrightarrow ? + ^{0}_{+1}e$

15. Each of the nuclei is capable of absorbing an alpha particle. Complete the equation assuming that no secondary particles are emitted by the nucleus that absorbs the alpha particle.

    (a) $^{14}_{7}N + ^{4}_{2}He \longrightarrow ?$

    (b) $^{27}_{13}Al + ^{4}_{2}He \longrightarrow ?$

16. In each reaction, a neutron is absorbed by a nucleus which then emits a proton. Complete the equations.

    (a) $^{65}_{29}Cu + ^{1}_{0}n \longrightarrow ? + ^{1}_{1}H$

    (b) $^{14}_{7}N + ^{1}_{0}n \longrightarrow ? + ^{1}_{1}H$

31:11 Half-Life

The time required for half of the atoms in any given quantity of a radioactive element to disintegrate is the half-life of that element. The half-life of a pure radioactive sample is unique to that particular radioactive substance. For example, the half-life of radium 226 is 1600 years. This means that in 1600 years, half of a given quantity of radium 226 will disintegrate into another substance. Another 1600 years is required for half of the remaining radium 226 to disintegrate, leaving just one-quarter of the original amount.

The half-lives of radioactive materials differ radically. One isotope of uranium has a half-life of 4.5 billion years. An isotope of radioactive lead has a half-life of less than one-thousandth of a second.

Figure 31-4. Half-life graph for $^{238}_{93}$Np. The half-life of this isotope is 2 days. What does the shape of the graph indicate?

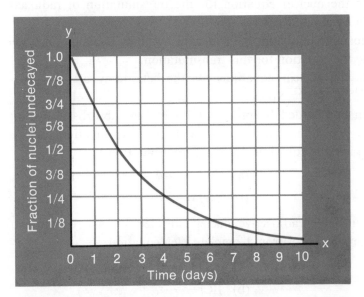

31:12 Binding Force Within the Nucleus

The negative electrons that move about the positively-charged nucleus of an atom are held in place by a force of electric attraction. The nucleus, however, contains positively-charged protons and neutral neutrons. The protons are in extremely close proximity. Normally, the strong electric repulsive force between the protons would cause the nucleus to fly apart. Since this does not happen, an even stronger force must exist within the nucleus to hold it together. This force is the nuclear binding force. The nuclear binding force exists only when the nucleons are very close together. That is, when they are in a nucleus. To develop the binding force, mass is converted into energy. The lost mass equals the binding energy. The energy lost in providing the nuclear binding force within the nucleus is in keeping with the equation $E = mc^2$. For example, the helium nucleus $_2^4$He consists of two protons and 2 neutrons. The mass of a proton is 1.007825 a.m.u. The mass of a neutron is 1.008665 a.m.u. Accordingly, the mass of a helium nucleus should be equal to the sum of the masses of 2 protons and 2 neutrons, or 4.032980 a.m.u. However, careful measurements show the mass of a helium nucleus to be only 4.00260 a.m.u. Thus, when a helium atom is formed, 4.032980 − 4.00260, or 0.03038 a.m.u. is missing. Hence, the mass of the helium nucleus is less than the mass of its constituent parts. This difference is the mass defect (MD) of the nucleus.

The mass represented by the mass defect of a nucleus is converted into energy in the form of radiation. It is in keeping with the equation $E = mc^2$. Before a nucleus can be separated into its constituent parts, the same amount of energy must be restored to it. For example, before a helium nucleus can be separated into 2 protons and 2 neutrons, energy in the amount 0.03038 a.m.u. $\times c^2$ must be added to it.

31:13   Calculating Binding Energy

The mass defect of a nucleus provides its binding energy. It follows that the binding energy of any nucleus can be calculated if its mass and the number of protons and neutrons it contains are known. First, find the mass defect. Then use $E = mc^2$ to determine the energy equivalent of the mass defect.

Mass defects are determined in a.m.u. If the energy equivalent of one atomic mass unit is found, this quantity can be multiplied by any mass defect. This is a quick way to convert mass defects to binding energies. An atomic mass unit is equivalent to 1.66×10^{-27} kg. The energy equivalent of one a.m.u. is:

$$E = mc^2$$

$$= (1.66 \times 10^{-27} \text{ kg})(3.0 \times 10^8 \text{ m/sec})^2$$

$$= 14.9 \times 10^{-11} \text{ j}$$

Recall that an electron-volt is 1.6×10^{-19} j. This value for the energy equivalent of one atomic mass unit can be expressed as

$$\frac{14.9 \times 1^{-11} \text{ j}}{1.6 \times 10^{-19} \text{ j/ev}}$$

or

$$9.31 \times 10^8 \text{ ev}$$

It is customary to express mass-energy equivalents as millions of electron-volts (Mev)

$$1 \text{ a.m.u.} = 931 \text{ Mev}$$

Sample Problem 3

(a) The mass of a proton is 1.007825 a.m.u. The mass of a neutron is 1.008665 a.m.u. The mass of a helium nucleus ($^4_2$He) is 4.00260 a.m.u. What is the nuclear mass defect of the helium nucleus? (b) What is the binding energy of the helium nucleus?

Solution:

(a) As indicated by the superscript and subscript in the symbol for helium, its nucleus contains 2 protons and 2 neutrons. To compute its mass defect:

$$2 \text{ protons} = 2 \times 1.007825 \text{ a.m.u.} = 2.015650 \text{ a.m.u.}$$
$$2 \text{ neutrons} = 2 \times 1.008665 \text{ a.m.u.} = \underline{2.017330 \text{ a.m.u.}}$$
$$\text{Total} = 4.032980 \text{ a.m.u.}$$

$$\text{Mass of helium nucleus} = \underline{4.00260 \text{ a.m.u.}}$$
$$\text{Mass defect} = 0.03038 \text{ a.m.u.}$$

(b) Since 1 a.m.u. is equivalent to 931 Mev, the binding energy of the helium nucleus is,

$$0.03038 \text{ a.m.u.} \times 931 \text{ Mev/a.m.u.} = 28.3 \text{ Mev}$$

Problems

Use the values: mass of a proton 1.007825 a.m.u., mass of a neutron 1.008665 a.m.u., and 1 a.m.u. = 931 Mev.

17. The isotope carbon 12 ($^{12}_6$C) has a nuclear mass of 12.0000 a.m.u. (a) Calculate its mass defect. (b) Calculate its binding energy in Mev.
18. The isotope of hydrogen that contains 1 proton and 1 neutron is deuterium. The mass of its nucleus is 2.0140 a.m.u. (a) What is its mass defect? (b) What is the binding energy of deuterium in Mev?
19. The isotope of nitrogen $^{15}_7$N has seven protons and eight neutrons. Its nucleus has a mass of 15.00011 a.m.u. (a) Calculate the mass defect of this nucleus. (b) Calculate the binding energy of the nucleus.

31:14 Nuclear Particles

Although neutrons and protons are the major nuclear particles, many other particles can be produced from the nucleus. Many of these particles have been discovered as a result of bombardment and detection techniques. Some of the particles appear to be constituent parts of protons and neutrons, while others seem to be created at the moment the bombarding particle strikes the nucleus. The particles are classified according to mass as follows:

Leptons — from the lightest to 210 times the electron mass

Mesons — from 210 times the electron mass to the mass of the proton

Hyperons — from the mass of the proton (which is a hyperon) up

The discovery and identification of the neutron as the second major nuclear particle led the Japanese physicist Hideki Yukawa to theorize about the force needed to hold the nucleus together. Yukawa thought the nuclear binding force was the result of a particle of "middle mass," or mesons. The mesons could pass back and forth between the neutrons and the protons. Yukawa predicted the mass of the meson to be about 300 times the mass of the electron. Eventually, not only one, but two definite types of mesons were discovered. These were pi (π) mesons and K mesons (kaons).

Pi mesons have a mass of about 273 times the mass of the electron. They suit the purposes of Yukawa's theory. Actually, there are three pi mesons: one with a single positive charge (π^+), one with a single negative charge (π^-), and a neutral meson (π^0). When a proton emits a π^+ meson, it becomes a neutron. When a neutron absorbs a π^+ meson, it becomes a proton. Similarly, when a neutron emits a π^- meson, the neutron becomes a proton. If a proton absorbs the π^- meson, the proton becomes a neutron. Passing mesons back and forth between neutrons and protons holds the nucleus together.

The Ealing Corporation

Figure 31-5. A photograph of tracks of hyperons in a bubble chamber.

The discovery of mesons explained nuclear binding forces. However, the origin of the beta particles was still in question. The beta particle is an electron which emanates from the nucleus. For some time physicists thought the nucleus contained electrons. The nuclear electrons seemed to explain how the nucleus is held together. However, many reasons soon made it clear that electrons as such do not exist in the nucleus. First, mesons satisfactorily explained the nuclear binding force. Second, matter waves associated with electrons did not fit the diameter of the nucleus. Studies finally showed that beta particles are created by the transformation of a nuclear neutron into a nuclear proton. During the transformation, beta particles receive energy and leave the nucleus at high speed. One fact still puzzled the physicists. All the beta particles did not leave their respective nuclei with the same amount of energy. This contradicted the law of conservation of energy. The contradiction led to the prediction of yet another particle to share energy with the beta particle during the transformation of a neutron into a proton. The new particle would have almost zero mass and bear no charge. The predicted particle was the neutrino, or little neutron. The small mass and lack of charge made the neutrino an exceptionally difficult particle to detect. Eventually experiments demonstrated that neutrinos do exist. Today neutrinos and antineutrinos are accepted particles.

The bombardment of nuclei with high speed (therefore, high energy) protons and electrons led to the identification of many other particles. Seemingly, every particle has an antiparticle. The proton has the antiproton; the neutron has the antineutron; the electron has the positron, and so on. A particle and an antiparticle are annihilated when they meet. The annihilation is accompanied by the emission of gamma radiation. The radiation carries away the momentum and energy of the particles.

31:15 Nuclear Fission

During fission, a nucleus is split into two or more nearly equal fragments. Whenever this occurs, the mass of the fragments is less than the mass of the original nucleus. The mass difference is converted into energy in the form of radiation and in keeping with $E = mc^2$. There are many examples of nuclear fission. The most well-known is the fission of an isotope of uranium, $^{235}_{92}U$. A ^{235}U nucleus splits when struck by a neutron of proper speed. The split sometimes forms the elements barium and krypton. The reaction is:

$$^{235}_{92}U + ^{1}_{0}n \longrightarrow ^{92}_{36}Kr + ^{141}_{56}Ba + 2\,^{1}_{0}n + 200\ \text{Mev}$$

The splitting of a ^{235}U nucleus is accompanied by the liberation of free neutrons. These neutrons can move on to split other ^{235}U nuclei. If the sample of ^{235}U is of sufficient mass, or critical mass, the free neutrons created when one atom splits have a high probability of striking the nuclei of other ^{235}U atoms.

Then a chain reaction occurs. If the sample is less than critical mass, the free neutrons have a high probability of escaping the sample without splitting other nuclei. Then a chain reaction is highly improbable. To make a nuclear fission bomb, two samples of less than critical mass are kept apart until just before the bomb strikes its target. The two samples then are forced together. A chain reaction occurs and liberates huge amounts of energy.

Fermi, Bohr, Teller, and the many other scientists who helped to produce the first nuclear bomb encountered one principal difficulty. Only a minute quantity of ^{235}U is found in any sample of uranium. Uranium consists predominantly of the isotope ^{238}U. The problem was to separate the ^{235}U, which could sustain a chain reaction, from the ^{238}U which could not under the same conditions. This is not a simple matter since the mass difference is slight, and the chemical properties of both isotopes are identical.

Figure 31-6. Enrico Fermi, famous Italian-born physicist and Nobel prize winner, directed the first controlled fission chain reaction at the University of Chicago, December 2, 1942.

Figure 31-7. A model of a nuclear fission chain reaction of ^{235}U.

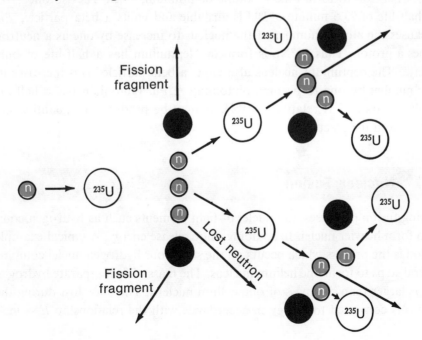

31:16 The Nuclear Reactor

One type of nuclear reactor consists of uranium rods surrounded by graphite (carbon) blocks. Between the graphite blocks are cadmium rods which may be lifted or lowered. When the proper amount of uranium is in the reactor, a chain reaction is regulated by the presence of the cadmium rods. The rods are good absorbers of free neutrons. As the cadmium rods are lifted out of or lowered into the reactor, the rate at which the chain reaction occurs is controlled. The graphite blocks slow down the free neutrons. ^{235}U nuclei are more susceptible to splitting when struck by slower moving neutrons.

The energy released by the fission of uranium inside the reactor usually is converted to electric energy. This is done by surrounding the reactor with water. The water is heated by the reaction and made to operate steam turbines.

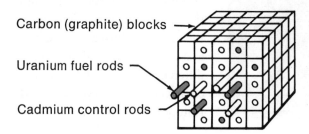

Carbon (graphite) blocks

Uranium fuel rods

Cadmium control rods

Figure 31-8. Diagram of a nuclear pile reactor indicating graphite block moderators, the cadmium control rods and the ^{235}U fuel cylinders.

The uranium used in a nuclear reactor contains ^{235}U and ^{238}U. The reactor also can create the elements neptunium and plutonium. The ^{238}U nucleus can absorb a neutron to form a new isotope of uranium, ^{239}U. The isotope ^{239}U has a half-life of 23.5 minutes. ^{239}U is unstable and emits a beta particle, $_{-1}^{0}e$. This causes the atomic number of the nucleus to increase by one as a neutron becomes a proton. Thus, $_{93}^{239}Np$ is formed. Neptunium has a half-life of only 2.35 days. The neptunium nucleus also emits a beta particle. This increases its atomic number by one to become plutonium $_{94}^{239}Pu$. Plutonium has a half-life of 24 400 years and is relatively stable. It may be produced in quantity and collected from the reactor.

31:17 Nuclear Fusion

During fusion processes, the nuclei of light elements such as hydrogen combine to form heavier nuclei. In so doing, they release energy. A typical example of fusion is the process which occurs on the sun. Four hydrogen nuclei combine in several steps to form one helium nucleus. The mass of four separate hydrogen nuclei is larger than the mass of one helium nucleus. The mass lost during the reactions is converted to energy in accordance with the relationship $E = mc^2$.

Nuclear fusion only takes place when temperatures are extremely high. Fusion reactions are called *thermonuclear reactions.* The temperatures in the interior of the sun are suitable for the fusion of hydrogen. This reaction provides the sun with its ability to release radiation. On earth, a suitable temperature for the fusion of hydrogen to form helium is attained only during the explosion of a nuclear fission bomb. By attaching a quantity of hydrogen to the bomb, the fusion of hydrogen is added to the fission of the plutonium. This increases the power of the bomb greatly. Bombs, however, only serve to discredit mankind. Scientists of the world are directing much effort toward controlling the fusion process. Controlled fusion would give the world an almost limitless source of energy. Its attainment, however, presents difficult problems. At present, no container can hold the reaction due to the high temperatures involved. Still, promising methods of controlling fusion are under study.

QUESTIONS

1. What is transmutation?
2. What determines to which element an atom belongs?
3. What happens to the atomic number and atomic mass of an atom that ejects an alpha particle?
4. What happens to the atomic number and atomic mass of an atom that ejects a beta particle?
5. Distinguish between natural and artificial radioactivity.
6. Describe the change that takes place within a nucleus when it emits a positron.
7. What change takes place in a nucleus when it emits a gamma ray?
8. Describe the construction and operation of the cyclotron.
9. Write the symbol of the (a) proton (b) electron (c) positron (d) neutron (e) alpha particle.
10. What is the "half-life" of a radioactive element?
11. What is the mass defect of a nucleus? What does it account for?
12. A uranium atom splits. Compare the total mass of the fragments with the mass of the original atom.

PROBLEMS

1. The unstable $^{55}_{24}Cr$ nucleus emits a beta particle. Write a nuclear equation to show the element formed and the complete reaction.
2. The aluminum nucleus $^{25}_{13}Al$ when bombarded by alpha particles absorbs an alpha particle and then emits a neutron. Write a nuclear equation to show the result of this transmutation.

3. When the boron nucleus $^{10}_5B$ is subjected to neutron bombardment, it absorbs a neutron and then emits an alpha particle. (a) What element results other than helium (the alpha particle)? (b) Write the nuclear equation for this reaction.

4. The first fusion reaction produced by man involved the use of deuterons (heavy hydrogen ^2_1H). During this reaction, two deuterons combine to form the helium isotope ^3_2He. What other particle is produced by this reaction?

5. On the sun four ordinary hydrogen atoms (^1_1H) combine to form the isotope of helium ^4_2He. The reaction is $4\ ^1_1H \longrightarrow ^4_2He + 2\underline{\ ?\ }$. What particle is missing from this equation?

6. If the mercury isotope $^{200}_{80}Hg$ is bombarded with deuterons (^2_1H) the mercury nucleus absorbs the deuteron and then emits an alpha particle. (a) What element is formed by this reaction? (b) Write the nuclear equation for the reaction.

7. An isotope of nitrogen $^{14}_7N$ has seven protons and 7 neutrons in its nucleus. Its nuclear mass is approximately 14.00307 a.m.u. (a) Calculate the mass defect of the nucleus. (b) What is the binding energy of this nucleus?

8. Assume that each nucleon shares the binding energy of the nucleus equally. Calculate the energy needed to eject a neutron from the nucleus of the isotope $^{14}_7N$.

9. The isotope carbon 13 ($^{13}_6C$) has a nuclear mass of approximately 13.00335 a.m.u. (a) What is the mass defect of this isotope? (b) What is the binding energy of its nucleus?

10. An isotope of oxygen ($^{16}_8O$) has a nuclear mass of about 15.99491. (a) What is the mass defect of this isotope? (b) What is the binding energy of its nucleus?

APPENDICES

ANSWERS

APPENDIX A

Trigonometric Functions

A.1. Relationship of Function to Angle Supplements

$$\sin x = \sin(180° - x)$$
$$\cos x = -\cos(180° - x)$$
$$\tan x = -\tan(180° - x)$$

A:2. Signs and Limits of Value Assumed by Functions

Quadrants

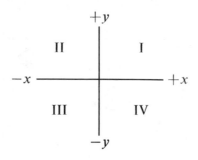

Table A-1.

Signs and Limits of Functions

Function	Quadrant I		Quadrant II		Quadrant III		Quadrant IV	
	Sign	Value	Sign	Value	Sign	Value	Sign	Value
sin	+	0 to 1	+	1 to 0	−	0 to 1	−	1 to 0
cos	+	1 to 0	−	0 to 1	−	1 to 0	+	0 to 1
tan	+	0 to ∞	−	∞ to 0	+	0 to ∞	−	∞ to 0

A:3. Table A-2

Natural Trigonometric Functions

Angle	sin	cos	tan	Angle	sin	cos	tan
0°	.0000	1.0000	.0000	45°	.7071	.7071	1.0000
1°	.0175	.9998	.0175	46°	.7193	.6947	1.0355
2°	.0349	.9994	.0349	47°	.7314	.6820	1.0724
3°	.0523	.9986	.0524	48°	.7431	.6691	1.1106
4°	.0698	.9976	.0699	49°	.7547	.6561	1.1504
5°	.0872	.9962	.0875	50°	.7660	.6428	1.1918
6°	.1045	.9945	.1051	51°	.7771	.6293	1.2349
7°	.1219	.9925	.1228	52°	.7880	.6157	1.2799
8°	.1392	.9903	.1405	53°	.7986	.6018	1.3270
9°	.1564	.9877	.1584	54°	.8090	.5878	1.3764
10°	.1736	.9848	.1763	55°	.8192	.5736	1.4281
11°	.1908	.9816	.1944	56°	.8290	.5592	1.4826
12°	.2079	.9781	.2126	57°	.8387	.5446	1.5399
13°	.2250	.9744	.2309	58°	.8480	.5299	1.6003
14°	.2419	.9703	.2493	59°	.8572	.5150	1.6643
15°	.2588	.9659	.2679	60°	.8660	.5000	1.7321
16°	.2756	.9613	.2867	61°	.8746	.4848	1.8040
17°	.2924	.9563	.3057	62°	.8829	.4695	1.8807
18°	.3090	.9511	.3249	63°	.8910	.4540	1.9626
19°	.3256	.9455	.3443	64°	.8988	.4384	2.0503
20°	.3420	.9397	.3640	65°	.9063	.4226	2.1445
21°	.3584	.9336	.3839	66°	.9135	.4067	2.2460
22°	.3746	.9272	.4040	67°	.9205	.3907	2.3559
23°	.3907	.9205	.4245	68°	.9272	.3746	2.4751
24°	.4067	.9135	.4452	69°	.9336	.3584	2.6051
25°	.4226	.9063	.4663	70°	.9397	.3420	2.7475
26°	.4384	.8988	.4877	71°	.9455	.3256	2.9042
27°	.4540	.8910	.5095	72°	.9511	.3090	3.0777
28°	.4695	.8829	.5317	73°	.9563	.2924	3.2709
29°	.4848	.8746	.5543	74°	.9613	.2756	3.4874
30°	.5000	.8660	.5774	75°	.9659	.2588	3.7321
31°	.5150	.8572	.6009	76°	.9703	.2419	4.0108
32°	.5299	.8480	.6249	77°	.9744	.2250	4.3315
33°	.5446	.8387	.6494	78°	.9781	.2079	4.7046
34°	.5592	.8290	.6745	79°	.9816	.1908	5.1446
35°	.5736	.8192	.7002	80°	.9848	.1736	5.6713
36°	.5878	.8090	.7265	81°	.9877	.1564	6.3138
37°	.6018	.7986	.7536	82°	.9903	.1392	7.1154
38°	.6157	.7880	.7813	83°	.9925	.1219	8.1443
39°	.6293	.7771	.8098	84°	.9945	.1045	9.5144
40°	.6428	.7660	.8391	85°	.9962	.0872	11.4301
41°	.6561	.7547	.8693	86°	.9976	.0698	14.3007
42°	.6691	.7431	.9004	87°	.9986	.0523	19.0811
43°	.6820	.7314	.9325	88°	.9994	.0349	28.6363
44°	.6947	.7193	.9657	89°	.9998	.0175	57.2900
45°	.7071	.7071	1.0000	90°	1.0000	.0000	∞

APPENDIX B

Factor Label Method of Unit Conversion

B:1. The Factor Label Method

In problem solving not only numbers but also labels must be considered. Measurements can be added or subtracted only if they are expressed in like units. However, multiplication and division of measurements with unlike labels can be performed providing the labels are carried appropriately. The factor label method of unit conversion enables you not only to arrive at the correct answer, but also to double check the correctness of your mathematical reasoning.

Sample Problem 1

$$35 \text{ cm} + 15 \text{ in.} = ?$$

Solution:

Before these quantities can be added, they must be expressed in similar units. Inches must be converted to centimeters, or centimeters must be converted to inches.

Use 2.54 cm = 1 in.

Converting inches to centimeters:

$$35.0 \text{ cm} + \frac{15.0 \text{ in.}}{} \left| \frac{2.54 \text{ cm}}{1 \text{ in.}} \right. =$$

$$35.0 \text{ cm} + 38.1 \text{ cm} = 73.1 \text{ cm}$$

Converting centimeters to inches:

$$\frac{1 \text{ in.}}{2.54 \text{ cm}} \left| \frac{35.0 \text{ cm}}{} \right. + 15.0 \text{ in.} =$$

$$13.8 \text{ in.} + 15.0 \text{ in.} = 28.8 \text{ in.}$$

In the first solution, the inch labels canceled. In the second solution the centimeter labels canceled. Both solutions involved multiplication by a ratio equal to 1:

$$\frac{1 \text{ in.}}{2.54 \text{ cm}} = 1 \quad \text{and} \quad \frac{2.54 \text{ cm}}{1 \text{ in.}} = 1$$

Whenever a quantity is multiplied by 1, the value is unchanged. This method of converting one unit to an equivalent unit by multiplying by ratios or factors equal to one is called the factor label method of unit conversion.

More than one conversion to an equivalent unit may be required in a given problem. These conversions can be done simultaneously by using the necessary number of ratios, all equalling one.

Sample Problem 2

$$\text{Convert} \quad 60 \text{ mi/hr to m/sec}$$

Solution:

Convert miles to meters and hours to seconds.

$$1 \text{ hr} = 3600 \text{ sec}$$
$$1 \text{ km} = 0.62 \text{ mi}$$

$$\frac{60 \text{ mi}}{1 \text{ hr}} \left| \frac{1 \text{ km}}{0.62 \text{ mi}} \right| \frac{1000 \text{ m}}{1 \text{ km}} \left| \frac{1 \text{ hr}}{3600 \text{ sec}} \right. =$$

$$\frac{(60)(1000 \text{ m})}{(0.62)(3600 \text{ sec})} = 26.8 \text{ m/sec} = 27 \text{ m/sec}$$

APPENDIX C

C:1. Table C-1

International Atomic Weights

Element	Symbol	Atomic number	Atomic weight	Element	Symbol	Atomic number	Atomic weight
Actinium	Ac	89	227*	Mercury	Hg	80	200.59
Aluminum	Al	13	26.9815	Molybdenum	Mo	42	95.94
Americium	Am	95	243*	Neodymium	Nd	60	144.24
Antimony	Sb	51	121.75	Neon	Ne	10	20.179
Argon	Ar	18	39.948	Neptunium	Np	93	237.0482*
Arsenic	As	33	74.9216	Nickel	Ni	28	58.71
Astatine	At	85	210*	Niobium	Nb	41	92.9064
Barium	Ba	56	137.34	Nitrogen	N	7	14.0067
Berkelium	Bk	97	247*	Nobelium	No	102	253*
Beryllium	Be	4	9.01218	Osmium	Os	76	190.2
Bismuth	Bi	83	208.9806	Oxygen	O	8	15.9994
Boron	B	5	10.81	Palladium	Pd	46	106.4
Bromine	Br	35	79.904	Phosphorus	P	15	30.9738
Cadmium	Cd	48	112.40	Platinum	Pt	78	195.09
Calcium	Ca	20	40.08	Plutonium	Pu	94	244*
Californium	Cf	98	251*	Polonium	Po	84	209*
Carbon	C	6	12.011	Potassium	K	19	39.102
Cerium	Ce	58	140.12	Praseodymium	Pr	59	140.9077
Cesium	Cs	55	132.9055	Promethium	Pm	61	145*
Chlorine	Cl	17	35.453	Protactinium	Pa	91	231.0359*
Chromium	Cr	24	51.996	Radium	Ra	88	226.0254
Cobalt	Co	27	58.9332	Radon	Rn	86	222*
Copper	Cu	29	63.546	Rhenium	Re	75	186.2
Curium	Cm	96	247*	Rhodium	Rh	45	102.9055
Dysprosium	Dy	66	162.50	Rubidium	Rb	37	85.4678
Einsteinium	Es	99	254*	Ruthenium	Ru	44	101.07
Erbium	Er	68	167.26	Samarium	Sm	62	150.4
Europium	Eu	63	151.96	Scandium	Sc	21	44.9559
Fermium	Fm	100	253*	Selenium	Se	34	78.96
Fluorine	F	9	18.9984	Silicon	Si	14	28.086
Francium	Fr	87	223*	Silver	Ag	47	107.868
Gadolinium	Gd	64	157.25	Sodium	Na	11	22.9898
Gallium	Ga	31	69.72	Strontium	Sr	38	87.62
Germanium	Ge	32	72.59	Sulfur	S	16	32.06
Gold	Au	79	196.9665	Tantalum	Ta	73	180.9479
Hafnium	Hf	72	178.49	Technetium	Tc	43	98.9062*
Helium	He	2	4.00260	Tellurium	Te	52	127.60
Holmium	Ho	67	164.9303	Terbium	Tb	65	158.9254
Hydrogen	H	1	1.0080	Thallium	Tl	81	204.37
Indium	In	49	114.82	Thorium	Th	90	232.0381
Iodine	I	53	126.9045	Thulium	Tm	69	168.9342
Iridium	Ir	77	192.22	Tin	Sn	50	118.69
Iron	Fe	26	55.847	Titanium	Ti	22	47.90
Krypton	Kr	36	83.80	Tungsten	W	74	183.85
Lanthanum	La	57	138.9055	Uranium	U	92	238.029
Lead	Pb	82	207.2	Vanadium	V	23	50.9414
Lawrencium	Lw	103	257*	Xenon	Xe	54	131.30
Lithium	Li	3	6.941	Ytterbium	Yb	70	173.04
Lutetium	Lu	71	174.97	Yttrium	Y	39	88.9059
Magnesium	Mg	12	24.305	Zinc	Zn	30	65.37
Manganese	Mn	25	54.9380	Zirconium	Zr	40	.91.22
Mendelevium	Md	101	256*	Element 104†		104	257*

*The mass number of the isotope with the longest known half-life.
†Element 104 has not been accepted by IUPAC at the time of this printing.

APPENDIX D

Physical Constants and Conversion Factors

D:1. Physical Constants

Avogadro's number: $N_O = 6.02 \times 10^{23}$

Speed of light in vacuum: $c = 2.99793 \times 10^8$ m/sec $= 186\ 272$ mi/sec

Gravitational constant: $G = 6.670 \times 10^{-11}$ m³/kg-sec²
$$G = 3.41 \times 10^{-8}\ \text{ft}^3/\text{slug-sec}^2$$

Universal gas constant: $R = 8.31$ j/mole-K°

Planck's constant: $h = 6.626 \times 10^{-34}$ j-sec $= 4.136 \times 10^{-15}$ ev-sec

Constant in Coulomb's law: $K = 2.306 \times 10^{-28}$ nt-m²/unit charge²
$$K = 8.988 \times 10^9\ \text{nt-m}^2/\text{coul}^2$$

Acceleration due to gravity at sea level, lat. 45°: $g = 9.806$ m/sec²
$$g = 32.17\ \text{ft}/\text{sec}^2$$

Absolute zero of temperature: $0°\text{K} = -273°\text{C}$

Charge of electron: $e = -1.602 \times 10^{-19}$ coul

Mass of electron: $m_e = 9.109 \times 10^{-31}$ kg

Mass of proton: $m_p = 1.672 \times 10^{-27}$ kg

Mean wavelength of sodium light: 5.893×10^{-7} m

Standard atmospheric pressure: 1 atm $= 1.013 \times 10^5$ nt/m² $= 14.7$ lb/in²

D:2. Conversion Factors

1 atomic mass unit $= 1.66 \times 10^{-27}$ kg

1 electron volt $= 1.602 \times 10^{-19}$ j

1 joule $= 1$ nt-m

1 joule $= 1$ volt-coulomb

1 calorie $= 4.184$ j

1 lb $= 4.448$ nt

1 coulomb $= 6.242 \times 10^{18}$ elementary charge units

APPENDIX E

Useful Equations

Quadratic equation: A quadratic equation may be reduced to the form

$$ax^2 + bx + c = 0$$

then
$$x = \frac{-b \pm \sqrt{b^2 - 4ac}}{2a}$$

Remember that the sign immediately preceding the coefficient is carried with the coefficient in solving for the two values of x.

Circumference of a circle: $C = 2\pi r$ or $C = \pi d$

Area of a circle: $A = \pi r^2$

Volume of a cylinder: $V = \pi r^2 h$

Surface area of a sphere: $A = 4\pi r^2$

Volume of a sphere: $V = \dfrac{4 \pi r^3}{3}$

ANSWERS

ANSWERS TO ODD NUMBERED PROBLEMS
(Answers are given to slide rule accuracy.)

Chapter 1: Fundamental Mathematics

1. (a) 2×4, (b) $\dfrac{8}{2}$

3. (a) $2s/a$, (b) $2s/t^2$, (c) at^2/s

5. (a) fs, (b) $mv^2/2$, (c) mc^2

7. (a) $v^2/2a$, (b) $\dfrac{v^2}{2s}$, (c) $\sqrt{2as}$

9. (a) 5.8×10^{-4}, (b) 4.5×10^{-7},
   (c) 3.6×10^{-3}, (d) 4×10^{-3}

11. (a) 7.3×10^{-3}, (b) 8.7×10^{-4},
    (c) 3.2×10^{-3}, (d) 1.66×10^{-19}

13. (a) 8×10^{-7}, (b) 7×10^{-3},
    (c) 3.96×10^{-19}, (d) 9.8×10^{-12}

15. (a) 2×10^{-8}, (b) 1.9×10^{-12},
    (c) 3.0×10^{-9}

17. (a) 5.4×10^{-7}, (b) 6.2×10^{-3},
    (c) 3.2×10^{-14}

19. (a) 8×10^{12}, (b) 6×10^{10},
    (c) 3×10^5, (d) 3×10^{-11},
    (e) 6.25×10^9

21. (a) 2×10^4, (b) 2×10^{12},
    (c) 3×10^8, (d) 3×10^1

23. (a) $30°$, (b) $80°$, (c) $45°$, (d) $45°$,
    (e) $45°$, (f) $20°$, (g) $64°$

25. (a) Should agree with b.
    (b) opp $= 7.7$ cm, adj $= 9.2$ cm

27. 20 cm

29. (a) Should agree with b.
    (b) 7.55 cm

31. $66°$

33. side $a =$ side $b = 17.4$ cm

Chapter end problems

1. (a) W/f, (b) s/k, (c) F/m, (d) f/q,
   (e) ym

3. (a) 6.5×10^5, (b) 5×10^6,
   (c) 2.2×10^4, (d) 2.26×10^2,
   (e) 4.5×10^3

5. (a) 9×10^8, (b) 5.8×10^4,
   (c) 9.5×10^{16}, (d) 5.6×10^8,
   (e) 1.0×10^6

7. (a) 6×10^8, (b) 2.4×10^{11},
   (c) 7.9×10^{32}, (d) 5.7×10^{23},
   (e) 6.25×10^9

9. (a) $4.9°$, (b) $31°$, (c) $18°$, (d) $11°$,
   (e) $39°$, (f) $75°$, (g) $20°$, (h) $45°$,
   (i) $72°$

11. adj $= 7.1$ cm, hyp $= 11$ cm

13. (a) 45, (b) 216, (c) 864, (d) 10 560,
    (e) 1560, (f) 672, (g) 30.8, (h) 2280,
    (i) 62.6, (j) 1680

15. (a) 2.12, (b) 20, (c) 25, (d) 51.8,
    (e) 2.97

Chapter 2: Measurement

1. (a) 4, (b) 3, (c) 2, (d) 4, (e) 2, (f) 3

3. 26.3 cm

5. 71.7 kg

7. 2.5 g

9. 48.2 oz

11. (a) 150 in.^{2}, (b) 39.0 cm, (c) 876 m^2

Chapter end problems

1. (a) 3, (b) 4, (c) 1, (d) 1, (e) 5

3. 34.7 ft

5. 46.00 cm^2

7. (a) 1.7 cm^2, (b) 21 m^2, (c) 188 in.^{2},
   (d) 12.0 cm^3

9. 240 m^3

11. (a) 682 g, (b) 6.3 cm^3

13. (a) A straight line with slope,
    (b) The acceleration of the mass is
    directly proportional to the applied
    force.

Chapter 3: Motion in a Straight Line

1. (a) 58 mi/hr, (b) 85 ft/sec

3. (a) 2.4×10^4 mi/hr,
   (b) 3.5×10^4 ft/sec

5. 1.5×10^8 km

7. (a) 1.8×10^3 ft/sec,
   (b) 1.2×10^3 mi/hr

9. -2 ft/sec²

11. 14.4 ft/sec²

13. -32 ft/sec², ∴ deceleration = 32 ft/sec²

15. 60 ft/sec

17. (a) 66 ft/sec, (b) 45 mi/hr

19. 730 ft

21. (a) 200 m/sec, (b) 1750 m

23. (a) 40 sec, (b) 3.5×10^3 ft

25. (a) -8.0 ft/sec², ∴ deceleration = 8.0 ft/sec², (b) 490 ft

27. 16 m/sec²

29. 32 ft/sec²

31. 88 ft/sec

33. deceleration = 8 m/sec²

35. 49 m/sec

37. 78.4 m

39. (a) 25.3 ft/sec, (b) 253 ft/sec

41. 64 ft/sec

Chapter end problems

1. 6 m/sec²

3. 2×10^5 m/sec²

5. -40 ft/sec², ∴ deceleration = 40 ft/sec²

7. 24 ft/sec

9. 924 ft

11. 225 ft

13. 2×10^5 m/sec²

15. 71 m/sec

17. (a) 900 ft, (b) 7.5 sec

19. 144 ft or 44 m

Chapter 4: Graphical Analysis of Motion

1. (a)

t (sec)	s (m)
0	0
1	50
2	100
3	150
4	200
...	...
20	1000

(b) Straight line with slope,
(c) Should give 50 m/sec,
(d) Horizontal straight line, (e) 150 m

3. (a) 10 ft/sec, (b) 0 ft/sec, (c) 10 ft/sec, (d) 20 ft/sec

5.

t (sec)	v (ft/sec)
0	0
10	10
20	10
30	10
40	10
50	0
60	0
70	0
80	-10
90	-10
100	-20

7. (a) Straight line with slope,

(b) $\dfrac{\Delta y}{\Delta x} = 40$ ft/sec,

(c) Horizontal straight line. The area under the line is vt and thus represents total distance traveled during a given time interval.
(d) 40 ft. The distance traveled during one second.

Chapter end problems

1. (a) Student diagram, (b) 8 m, (c) 32 m, (d) 110 m, (e) 4 m/sec² (acceleration), (f) 0 (constant speed, i.e. no acceleration)

3. (a) 6 m/sec², (b) 0 m/sec², (c) -2 m/sec², (d) -4 m/sec²

5. Between A and B the moving body was undergoing acceleration.
Between B and C the speed of the body was constant.
Between C and D the body was decelerating.
Between D and E the body was at rest.
Between E and F the body accelerated in the opposite direction $(-a)$.
Between F and G the body had constant speed.
Between G and H the body was decelerating.

7. (a)

t (sec)	s (ft)
1	16
2	64
3	144
4	256
5	400

(b) parabola, (c) Should turn out to be about 64 ft/sec and 128 ft/sec.

9. (a) Constant speed, (b) speed
11. (a) Uniform acceleration, (b) the acceleration, (c) distance
13. (a) A parabola, (b) speed, (c) indicates higher speed

Chapter 5: Vectors

1. 112 mi/hr, 27° west of north
3. (a) 18.4 m/sec, (b) 8.5 sec, (c) 76.5 m
5. 80 km, 43° east of north
7. (a) 120 nt, (b) 115 nt, (c) 104 nt, (d) 85 nt, (e) 0 nt
9. $\theta = 24°$. The angle with the horizontal is 66°.
11. 112 lb, 27° east of north
13. (a) 8.8 m/sec, 25° downstream, (b) 5 sec, (c) 19 m
15. (a) 20 nt, (b) 19 nt, (c) 14 nt, (d) 10 nt, (e) 0 nt
17. (a) 100 lb, 37° east of north (b) 100 lb, 37° west of south
19. 100 lb, 8° south of east

21. 40 lb
23. (a) 250 mi/hr, (b) 433 mi/hr
25. (a) 35 nt, (b) 54 nt, (c) 61 nt
27. 41 lb

Chapter end problems

1. 35 lb east
3. (a) $v = 9$ m/sec, (b) 30 sec, (c) 120 m
5. 273 lb
7. 193 mi N, 230 mi E
9. (a) $F_h = 10$ lb, $F_v = 17$ lb, (b) $F_h = 17$ lb, $F_v = 10$ lb
11. (a) 3.1 mi/hr, (b) 6.7 mi/hr
13. 17 lb/wire

Chapter 6: Dynamics

1. 2.5 m/sec²
3. 0.5 slug
5. (a) 4 m/sec², (b) 2 m/sec², (c) 1 m/sec², (d) 0.5 m/sec², (e) 0.2 m/sec²
7. 9.8 nt
9. 8800 lb
11. 3 slugs
13. 10 kg
15. 640 lb
17. 9800 nt
19. 9.8 m/sec²
21. (a) 3 slugs, (b) 4 ft/sec²
23. 4 ft/sec²
25. (a) 0.25 slug, (b) 4 lb, (c) 16 ft/sec²

27. (a) 50 slugs, (b) 16 ft/sec², (c) 160 ft/sec

Chapter end problems

1. 5 m/sec²
3. (a) 320 lb, (b) 704 lb, (c) 8 lb, (d) 24 lb, (e) 137 nt, (f) 4.21 nt, (g) 6.86 nt
5. 20 lb
7. (a) 1000 kg, (b) 13 800 nt
9. 10 ft/sec²
11. 4.9 m/sec²
13. The meteoroid just touches the spaceship.

Chapter 7: Momentum and its Conservation

1. (a) 50 slugs, (b) 2000 slug-ft/sec, (c) 20 sec
3. 250 lb
5. (a) 5500 nt-sec, (b) 92 nt

7. (a) 2.0×10^4 nt-sec, (b) 300 nt
9. 16 cm/sec in same direction
11. 6.7 ft/sec
13. 42 cm/sec

15. 1600 ft/sec
17. 7.5 m/sec
19. 50 m/sec
21. (a) Student diagram,
  (b) $v_A = v_B = 2.8$ m/sec
23. (a) Student diagram,
  (b) $v_1 = 5$ m/sec, $v_2 = 8.6$ m/sec

Chapter end problems

1. 100 nt-sec
3. (a) 8800 slug-ft/sec, (b) 293 lb
5. (a) 32 000 kg-m/sec, (b) 40 sec
7. -6 m/sec

Chapter 8: Motion in Two Dimensions

1. 200 m
3. 600 m
5. 47 m
7. 20 m
9. (a) $v_v = 110$ ft/sec, $v_h = 64$ ft/sec,
  (b) 6.8 sec, (c) 435 ft
11. (a) $v_v = 495$ m/sec, $v_h = 495$ m/sec,
  (b) 101 sec, (c) 50 000 ft
13. 237 lb
15. 20 m/sec²
17. (a) 1.18×10^4 nt, (b) 19.8 m/sec²
19. 2.6×10^4 ft/sec = 5 mi/sec =
  18 000 mi/hr
21. 1.1 sec

23. 1.4 sec
25. 32 ft/sec²

Chapter end problems

1. 79 ft
3. (a) 20 sec, (b) 4000 ft
5. 21.2 ft/sec
7. 5.87×10^4 ft
9. (a) 158 ft/sec², (b) 79 lb
11. 6.28 sec
13. 4.4 sec

Chapter 9: Law of Gravitation

1. 8.0×10^{-8} nt
3. 42.6 lb
5. 1.9×10^{20} nt
7. 1.02×10^{-47} nt

Chapter end problems

1. 0.667 nt
3. 6.82×10^{-6} lb

Chapter 10: Work and Power

1. 3.2×10^4 j
3. 1920 ft-lb
5. 7.5×10^3 ft-lb
7. (a) 9.0×10^3 ft-lb, (b) 5.4×10^4 ft-lb
9. 2.9×10^3 j
11. 3.5×10^3 ft-lb
13. (a) 433 lb, (b) 86 600 ft-lb
15. (a) 2000 watts, (b) 2 kw
17. (a) 196 nt, (b) 58 800 j,
  (c) 238 800 j, (d) 133 watts,
  (e) 0.133 kw

19. 62.5 hp

Chapter end problems

1. 900 j
3. (a) 9800 nt-m, (b) 9800 j
5. (a) 9000 j, (b) 450 watts
7. 4.0 hp
9. (a) 33 000 ft-lb,
  (b) 2200 ft-lb/sec, (c) 4.0 hp
11. (a) 1600 nt, (b) 17 600 j,
  (c) 2200 watts

Chapter 11: Energy and its Conservation

1. 19 600 j
3. (a) 2250 ft-lb, (b) 2250 ft-lb

5. (a) 720 ft-lb, (b) 432 ft-lb
7. (a) 96 800 ft-lb, (b) 387 200 ft-lb

9. 144 ft-lb

11. 2.8×10^{-14} j

13. 1170 j

15. 640 ft-lb

17. 20 ft

19. 15.5 m/sec

21. (a) 27.8 ft/sec, (b) 770 ft-lb

23. (a) yes, (b) 2000 j, 1000 j, no,
   (c) yes, (d) yes

25. (a) 4.0×10^6 kg-m/sec,
   (b) 4.0×10^6 kg-m/sec,
   (c) KE (before) = 1.6×10^7 j,
      KE (after) = 8.0×10^6 j
   (d) Note that while momentum was
   conserved during the collision the

kinetic energy was not. This energy
was converted to heat and sound
during the collision.

Chapter end problems

1. (a) 4900 j, (b) 4900 j, (c) 4900 j

3. 675 000 j

5. (a) 880 ft, (b) 540 lb, (c) 88 000 ft-lb,
   (d) 387 200 ft-lb, (e) 43.2 hp

7. (a) 19 600 j, (b) 19 600 j, (c) 44 m/sec

9. 9×10^{16} j

11. 3.3×10^{-16} kg

13. (a) E, (b) B, (c) E

Chapter 12: Measurement of Heat

1. 313° K

3. 546° K

5. −73° C

7. (a) 373° K, (b) 173° K, (c) 573°K,
   (d) 293° K, (e) 250° K

9. 335 cal

11. 21 000 cal or 21 kcal

13. 62.5 Btu

15. 137.5 kcal

17. 63° C

19. 23° C

21. 55° F

23. 27 000 cal

25. 1.2×10^5 cal

27. 37 200 cal

29. 1.6×10^6 cal

Chapter end problems

1. (a) 323° K, (b) 423° K, (c) 73° K,
   (d) 573° K

3. 7000 Btu

5. 1111 C°

7. (a) 252 cal, (b) 0.252 kcal

9. 38° C

11. 7400 cal

13. 35.6° C

Chapter 13: Heat as Energy

1. 4.7×10^2 cal

3. 0.24 cal

5. 0.71 C°

7. (a) 7140 cal, (b) 30 000 j, (c) 612 l

Chapter end problems

1. *See text.*

3. 124 Btu

5. 4500 j or 1070 cal

7. (a) 2658 j or 633 cal
   (b) 1.44 C°

Chapter 14: Kinetic Theory and the Structure of Matter

See text.

Chapter 15: The Structure of Matter

1. (a) 0.5 l of oxygen with 1.0 l of
   nitrogen forms 1.0 l of N_2O. (b) 12 l,
   with 2 l of oxygen left over.

3. 10 hydrogen, 5 oxygen

5. (a) 3.3×10^{-24} g/molecule,
   (b) 1.6×10^{-24} g/atom

7. 222 g/mole

Chapter end problems

1. (a) 98, (b) 36.5, (c) 64, (d) 80
3. (a) 44 g, (b) 4.5×10^{23} molecules
5. 3.2×10^{-7} cm
7. 2×10^{-21} g

9. The length of one side of the oleic acid molecule as used in Problem 6 is the long side. Thus the value for the volume of the molecule is too great. This makes the mass of a single molecule in Problem 7 too great and subsequently the number of molecules in Problem 8 too small.

Chapter 16: The Gas Laws

1. 30 m³
3. 5.0 l
5. 0.67 ft³
7. (a) 253 mm Hg, (b) 4.9 lb/in.²
9. 58 m³
11. 666° K or 393° C
13. 2 atm
15. 200 ft³
17. 0.17 m³/mole

19. 6.5×10^4 nt/m²

Chapter end problems

1. (a) 0.5 atm, (b) 2 atm, (c) 5 atm
3. (a) 200 m³, (b) 68° K or −205° C
5. 333° C
7. 2.33 m³
9. 500 cm³
11. 228 m³
13. 1.13×10^7 nt/m²

Chapter 17: Waves and the Transfer of Energy

1. 1100 ft/sec
3. 28.8 cm/sec
5. (a) 1.5×10^9 Hz, (b) 6.7×10^{-10} sec
7. (a) 0.66 m, (b) 2×10^{-3} sec
9. It is attached to the wall.
11. (a) At A the pulse will be partially transmitted and partially reflected. The reflected pulse will be inverted. (b) At B the pulse will be almost totally reflected. The reflected pulse will be inverted.
13. (a) Boundary A is the boundary of a more rigid medium.

(b) Boundary B is the boundary of a less rigid medium.
(c) Boundary C is the boundary of a less rigid medium.
(d) Boundary D is the boundary of a more rigid medium.

Chapter end problems

1. 22 ft or 6.6 m
3. (a) 5000 ft/sec, (b) 1×10^{-3} sec, (c) 1×10^{-3} sec
5. 3.0×10^8 m/sec
7. 5.0×10^9 Hz
9. (a) 1×10^{24} Hz, (b) 3.0×10^{-16} m

Chapter 18: The Nature of Light

1. 1.6×10^{-3} sec
3. 186 000 mi/sec
5. By starting the mirror rotating from rest and increasing its rate of revolution to the first rate that gives the brightest reflected spot.
7. $\dfrac{1}{9}$
9. 450 cp
11. 125 cp

Chapter end problems

1. 3×10^5 km/sec or 3×10^8 m/sec
3. 8 min. 20 sec.
5. (a) 5.8×10^{12} mi/yr, (b) 2.3×10^{13} mi
7. $\dfrac{1}{4}$
9. 36 cp
11. 2.4×10^{26} cp
13. 6.6×10^{-26} j
15. The gamma ray

Chapter 19: Reflection and Refraction

1. Student diagrams
3. 22°
5. (a) 17°, (b) diamond
7. (a) 19°, (b) alternate interior angles theorem predicts 19°, (c) 30°, (d) away from the normal
9. (a) 1.21, (b) 24°
11. (a) 2.2×10^8 m/sec, (b) 2.05×10^8 m/sec, (c) 2.0×10^8 m/sec
13. 1.52

Chapter end problems

1. 108°
3. Student diagram
5. Student diagrams
7. 26°
9. 45°
11. (a) 30°, (b) 30°, (c) 26°
13. 1.2×10^8 m/sec or 7.7×10^4 mi/sec
15. (a) 1.33, (b) 1.16, (c) 0.872

Chapter 20: Mirrors and Lenses

1. $d_i = 15$ cm, $S_i = 1$ cm
3. (a) Student diagram, (b) 15 cm, (c) 4.5 cm
5. (a) 4 cm, (b) 4 cm, (c) 1 cm
7. 24 in.
9. -15 cm
11. -8.6 cm
13. -16.7 in.
15. 15 cm
17. (a) Student diagram, (b) $d_i = 15$ cm, $S_i = 4.5$ cm
19. (a) Student diagram, (b) $d_i = 4$ cm, $S_i = 1$ cm

21. 40 in.
23. (a) -6 in., (b) 3 in.
25. (a) 25 cm, (b) -60 cm, (c) virtual, (d) inverted

Chapter end problems

1. (a) Student diagram, (b) 13 cm
3. (a) 30 cm, (b) 1.8 cm
5. -7.2 in.
7. -5.96 cm
9. (a) Student diagram, (b) 13.3 cm, (c) 1.0 cm
11. (a) 420 cm, (b) $S_i = 20 \times S_o$

Chapter 21: Diffraction of Light

1. 4.2×10^{-5} cm
3. 5.4×10^{-5} cm
5. 3.6×10^{-5} cm
7. 5.6×10^{14} Hz or 5.6×10^{11} kHz
9. 4.2×10^{-5} cm
11. 5.5×10^{-5} cm
13. 5.9×10^{-5} cm

Chapter end problems

1. 4.5×10^{-5} cm
3. 2×10^{-3} cm

5. 4×10^{-4} cm
7. 6.5×10^{14} Hz or 6.5×10^{11} kHz
9. 12.5 cm
11. (a) 4.8×10^{-5} cm, (b) The distance between the central bright band and the first-order dark bands (in millimeters) is numerically the same as the wavelengths (in 10^{-5} cm).
13. The two people sitting 20 ft to the right and left of the center of the row will hear no sound.

Chapter 22: The Origin of Light

See text.

Chapter 23:   Static Electricity

1. 1.3 nt

3. -4.4×10^3 nt

5. -3.0×10^{-6} coul

7. 4×10^3 m/sec^2

9. 12.5 nt

11. 1 nt/coul

Chapter end problems

1. -10 nt

3. -90 nt

5. -9×10^{-8} nt

7. (a) 9.8×10^{-3} nt,
(b) 5.7×10^{-3} nt,
(c) 2.4×10^{-8} coul

9. (a) 4 nt/coul, (b) toward

11. 5×10^{-5} coul

Chapter 24:   Electric Currents

1. 400 volts

3. 25 000 nt/coul

5. 125 volts

7. 7.5 j

9. (a) 5500 j, (b) 1100 j/sec,
(c) 1100 watts, (d) 1.1 kw

11. 180 watts

13. 144 watts

15. 36 000 j

17. 3 amp

19. (a) 240 ohms, (b) 60 watts

21. 15 ohms

23. (a) Student diagram (b) 1.5 amp

25. (a) Student diagram (b) 28 volts

27. (a) 2 amp, (b) 36 000 j, (c) 8570 cal

29. (a) 9×10^5 j, (b) 2.1×10^5 cal

Chapter end problems

1. 120 volts

3. 100 volts

5. (a) 1800 j, (b) 30 j/sec, (c) 30 watts

7. 9 j

9. (a) 60 j/sec, (b) 18 000 j

11. 1.5 amp

13. 80 ohms

15. 1.7 amp

17. (a) 30 amp, (b)1.1×10^6 j, (c)2.6×10^5 cal

19. (a) 108 000 j, (b) 6430 cal

Chapter 25:   Series and Parallel Circuits

1. (a) 60 ohms, (b) 2 amp

3. (a) 240 ohms, (b) 24 ohms

5. (a) 1.5 amp, (b) 20 ohms

7. (a) 50 ohms, (b) 2 amp,
(c) $V_1 = 40$ volts, $V_2 = 60$ volts,
(d) 100 volts

9. (a) 12 ohms, (b) 1 amp,
(c) $V_1 = 3$ volts, $V_2 = 5$ volts,
$V_3 = 4$ volts, (d) 12 volts

11. (a) 10 ohms, (b) $V_1 = V_2 = 6$ volts

13. (a) 5 ohms, (b) 6 amp, (c) 2 amp

15. (a) 20 ohms, (b) 6 amp,
(c) R_1, 1 amp; R_2, 2 amp;
R_3, 3 amp

17. (a) 2 amp, (b) 1 amp, (c) 3 amp,
(d) 50 ohms,   (e) 3 amp, which agrees

19. (a) 5 ohms, (b) 15 ohms, (c) 3 amp,
(d) 30 volts, (e) 15 volts, (f) 1 amp

21. $i_1 = 3$ amp, $i_2 = 1.5$ amp,
$i_3 = 1.5$ amp, $i_4 = 1.8$ amp,
$i_5 = 1.2$ amp; $V_1 = 15$ volts,
$V_2 = 36$ volts, $V_3 = 9$ volts

Chapter end problems

1. (a) 12 ohms, (b) 1 amp, (c) 1 amp,
(d) $V_1 = 5$ volts, $V_2 = 7$ volts

3. 10 ohms

5. 16 ohms

7. (a) 4 ohms, (b) 12.5 amp,
(c) $i_1 = 2.5$ amp, $i_2 = 10$ amp,
(d) 50 volts

9. (a) 2 amp, (b) 3 amp, (c) 15 amp

11. $i_1 = 0.67$ amp, $i_2 = 0.8$ amp,
$i_3 = 2.0$ amp; $V_1 = 20$ volts,
$V_2 = 12$ volts, $V_3 = 48$ volts

Chapter 26: The Magnetic Field

1. 0.2 nt/amp-m
3. 0.13 nt/amp-m
5. 0.15 nt/amp-m
7. 6×10^{-2} nt/amp-m
9. 3.2×10^{-13} nt
11. 1.7×10^{-13} nt

Chapter end problems

1. 0.1 nt/amp-m
3. 0.04 nt/amp-m
5. 2.5 amp
7. 3.8×10^{-13} nt
9. 2.4×10^{-12} nt
11. 0.38 nt

Chapter 27: Electromagnetic Induction

1. (a) 4 volts, (b) 0.67 amp
3. 0.02 amp
5. (a) 120 volts, (b) 6 amp
7. (a) 165 volts, (b) 7.8 amp
9. (a) 220 volts, (b) 4 amp
11. (a) 3600 volts, (b) 3 amp,
  (c) $V_p i_p = V_s i_s = 10\ 800$ watts
13. (a) 18 000 volts, (b) 0.5 amp
15. (a) 120 000 volts, (b) 0.1 amp,
  (c) 12 000 watts, (d) 12 000 watts

Chapter end problems

1. 0.18 volts
3. 40 volts
5. (a) 310 volts, (b) 20 amp
7. (a) 1800 volts, (b) 3.3 amp,
  (c) $V_p i_p = V_s i_s = 6000$ watts
9. (a) 1800, (b) 540, (c) 25, (d) 12
11. (a) 7.6×10^3cal, (b) 0.19 cal

Chapter 28: Applications of Electric and Magnetic Fields

1. (a) 1.3×10^{-14} j/electron,
  (b) 1.3×10^{-14} j
3. 2.0×10^{19} Hz
5. 4.4×10^6 m/sec
7. (a) 1.6×10^{-19} coul, (b) one
9. (a) Student diagram,
  (b) 1.6×10^{-19} coul. The slope
represents electronic charge.
11. 1.3×10^{-4} m
13. 4.7×10^{-6} m
15. 6.8×10^6 m/sec

17. (a) 6.8×10^{-26} kg,
  (b) 40 a.m.u.
19. (a) 3.94×10^{-26} kg,
  (b) 23.0 a.m.u.

Chapter end problems

1. 9.4×10^7 m/sec
3. 2.5×10^6 m/sec
5. (a) 6.4×10^{-14} j, (b) 1×10^{20} Hz
7. (a) 2×10^6 m/sec, (b) 1.7×10^{-27} kg
9. (a) 4.8×10^{-19} coul, (b) 3 electrons

Chapter 29: The Quantum Theory

1. 5.1×10^{-19} j
3. (a) 6.4×10^{-19} j, (b) 2.3×10^{-18} j
5. 1.1×10^{15} Hz
7. 4×10^{-13} m
9. 8.8×10^{-37} m
11. 4×10^{-41} m

Chapter end problems

1. 8.3×10^{-19} j
3. (a) 7.3×10^{-19} j, (b) 4.6×10^{-19} j
5. (a) 6×10^{-19} j, (b) 7×10^{-19} j
7. 2.8×10^{-40} m

Chapter 30: The Atom

1. 7

3. 120

5. (a) $^{239}_{92}U$, (b) $^{238}_{92}U$ contains 146 neutrons, $^{239}_{92}U$ contains 147 neutrons.

7. $r_2 = 2.1 \times 10^{-10}$ m,
$r_3 = 4.8 \times 10^{-10}$ m,
$r_4 = 8.5 \times 10^{-10}$ m

9. $E_3 - E_2 = 1.5$ ev, $E_4 - E_3 = 0.65$ ev

11. $f = 1.6 \times 10^{14}$ Hz,
$\lambda = 1.9 \times 10^{-6}$ m

13. $f = 3.1 \times 10^{15}$ Hz,
$\lambda = 1 \times 10^{-7}$ m

Chapter end problems

1. 12

3. (a) 64, (b) 126, (c) 125, (d) 45,
(e) 0, (f) 22, (g) 78

5. $E_5 = -0.54$ ev, $E_6 = -0.38$ ev

7. (a) 0.16 ev, (b) 1.12 ev, (c) 2.55 ev,
(d) 2.86 ev, (e) 0.96 ev

9. (a) 7.5×10^{-6} m, (b) 1.1×10^{-6} m,
(c) 5×10^{-7} m, (d) 4.3×10^{-7} m,
(e) 1.3×10^{-6} m

11. (a) 7.7 ev, (b) E_6

13. 2.14 ev

Chapter 31: The Nucleus

1. $^{234}_{92}U \rightarrow ^{230}_{90}Th + ^{4}_{2}He$

3. $^{226}_{88}Ra \rightarrow ^{222}_{86}Rn + ^{4}_{2}He$

5. $^{214}_{83}Bi \rightarrow ^{214}_{84}Po + ^{0}_{-1}e$

7. (a) $^{14}_{6}C \rightarrow ^{14}_{7}N + ^{0}_{-1}e$
(b) $^{55}_{24}Cr \rightarrow ^{55}_{25}Mn + ^{0}_{-1}e$

9. $^{226}_{88}Ra \rightarrow ^{222}_{86}Rn + ^{4}_{2}He$

11. (a) $^{210}_{82}Pb \rightarrow ^{210}_{83}Bi + ^{0}_{-1}e$
(b) $^{210}_{83}Bi \rightarrow ^{210}_{84}Po + ^{0}_{-1}e$
(c) $^{234}_{90}Th \rightarrow ^{234}_{91}Pa + ^{0}_{-1}e$
(d) $^{239}_{93}Np \rightarrow ^{239}_{94}Pu + ^{0}_{-1}e$

13. (a) $^{30}_{15}P \rightarrow ^{30}_{14}Si + ^{0}_{+1}e$
(b) $^{238}_{92}U \rightarrow ^{238}_{91}Pa + ^{0}_{+1}e$

15. (a) $^{14}_{7}N + ^{4}_{2}He \rightarrow ^{18}_{9}F$
(b) $^{27}_{13}Al + ^{4}_{2}He \rightarrow ^{31}_{15}P$

17. (a) 0.098 940 a.m.u., (b) 92.1 Mev

19. (a) 0.123 985 a.m.u., (b) 115.4 Mev

Chapter end problems

1. $^{55}_{24}Cr \rightarrow ^{55}_{25}Mn + ^{0}_{-1}e$

3. (a) Lithium,
(b) $^{10}_{5}B + ^{1}_{0}n \rightarrow ^{7}_{3}Li + ^{4}_{2}He$

5. Positrons ($^{0}_{+1}e$)

7. (a) 0.112 360 a.m.u. (b) 104.5 Mev

9. (a) 0.104 255 a.m.u., (b) 97.1 Mev

INDEX

INDEX

Aberration, chromatic, 266; correcting, 256; in mirrors, 253; spherical, 253

Absolute zero, 138, 180

Absorption spectrum, 244–246, 286, 287, 288; *illus.*, 245, 287

Acceleration, 26, 68, 69, 100; centripetal, 96, 97; determined by slope, 45; distance traveled during, 32–36; distance-time graph, 43–45; and electromagnetic waves, 282, 283, 376, 377; of gravity, 36, 37, 72; of lunar gravity, 108; speed-time graph, 43–45; time graph, 47; uniform, 29–35, 47; unit of, 29; *illus.*, 33, 95

Accelerator, linear, 418; particle, 416–418; *illus.*, particle, 417, 418

Accuracy, of measurement, 17; *illus.*, 18

Achromatic lens, 266; *illus.*, 266

Alpha, particle, 413, 414, 418, 420; ray, 400, 401

Alternating current, 365–367; effective value of, 367; and induction, 370; *illus.*, 362, 365, 366

Alternating current generator, 316, 365–369; used as motor, 368, 369; *illus.*, 365, 358

Ammeter, 320, 340, 358, 359; *illus.*, 340

Ampere, 317

Ampere, Andre, 350, 351

Amplitude, 100; and energy, 192, 193; of wave, 192, 193, 197, 198, 199; *illus.*, wave reflection, 194, 195; work performed by waves, 192

Analyzer (light), 223; polarizer, 223; spectral, 243, 405

Andromeda, *illus.*, 105

Aneroid barometer, 175; *illus.*, 175

Angle, critical, 239; function of, 5–7, 56–58, 115; of incidence, 200, 201; of polarization, 224; of reflection, 200, 201; *illus.*, reflection of light, 218

Annihilation, of atomic particle, 426

Antielectron, 420, 426

Antineutrino, 415, 420, 426

Antineutron, 426

Antinodal line, 272

Antiparticle, 426

Antiproton, 426

Apollo lens, *illus.*, 266

Area, 14, 26; distance determination, 43, 45; speed determination, 47

Armature, 365, 366

A nospheres (Atm), 175

Atmospheric pressure, 175, 176; unit of, 175

Atmospheric refraction, 241

Atom, 168, 299, 376, 406, 410, 422; beta decay of, 414, 415; Bohr model of, 405–407, 410; bombardment of, 416; electron excitation, 283–291; energy transition in, 410; ionization of, 387; isotope, 403, 404, 427; and magnetism, 350; mass of, 169, 386, 403, 404; nucleus of, 292, 293, 401, 402; planetary model, 402, 403, 405; present model of, 410; structure, 292, 293; wave model, 287; *illus.*, Bohr model, 406; electron excitation, 283, 284; planetary model, 403; spectrograph, 386; spectrum, 286, 287, 293; *table*, ionization energy, 412

Atom smasher, 416–418; *illus.*, 417, 418

Atomic binding force, 422–426

Atomic mass unit, 169

Atomic number, 402, 414

Atomic particle, 426; alpha, 400, 401, 414; annihilation of, 426; antineutrino, 415, 420, 426; antineutron, 426; antiproton, 426; beta, 400, 415, 416, 426; electron, 225, 285, 294, 302, 303, 375, 376, 377, 394, 400, 401, 403, 422, 426; hyperon, 425; lepton, 425; meson, 425; 426; neutrino, 419, 420, 426; neutron, 292, 402, 403, 415, 420, 421, 423, 424; pi meson, 425; positron, 420, 426; photon, 225, 226, 289, 390, 394, 396, 407, 410; proton, 292, 293, 294, 302, 303, 402, 403, 414, 420, 423, 424, 425; *illus.*, bubble chamber track, 385

Atomic structure, 292, 293

Avogadro, Amadeo, 168–170

Avogadro's number, 170, 182, 303; *illus.*, 168

Barometer, 175; *illus.*, 175

Base level, of energy, 121

Battery, 302, 316; *illus.*, 301

Beam balance, *illus.*, 75

Becquerel, Henri, 400, 413

Beryllium, 420

Beta, 415, 426; decay, 414, 415; particle, 413, 415, 416, 418, 420, 428; ray, 400, 401

Binding force, 422–426

Bohr model, 405–407, 410; *illus.*, 406

Bohr, Niels, 225, 406, 407, 427

Boiling point, 162; of water, 146; *illus.*, 162

Bomb, hydrogen, 429; nuclear fission, 427, 429; nuclear fusion, 428, 429

Boron, mass of, 403

Boundary, 221, 222, 231, 232; critical angle, 239; effect of waves, 194–199, 200–204; *illus.*, 202, 203, 204; wave reflection, 187, 194, 195

Boyle's law, 176–178; *illus.*, 177

Brahe, Tycho, 104, 106

British thermal unit (Btu), 141

Broglie, Louis de, 396

Brown, Robert, 157

Brownian movement, *illus.*, 157

Bubble chamber, 419; *illus.*, 425

Bumper sticker, 285

Cadmium, 428

Caloric, 135, 136

Calorie, 141, 154

Candle, 216

Carbon, mass standard, 169, 414

Cavendish, Henry, 108, 109; *illus.*, 109

Celsius, *illus.*, scale comparison, 138

Cell, electric, 302, 311, 320

Center of curvature, lens, 262; mirror, 252; *illus.*, 256

Centripetal, acceleration, 96, 97; force, 95–97, 106; *illus.*, 95

Chadwick, James, 402, 420

Chain reaction, 427

Change of state, 145, 160–162

3 4 5 6 7 8 9 10 11 12 13 14 15-80 79 78 77 76 75 74